Problem-Solving Geography

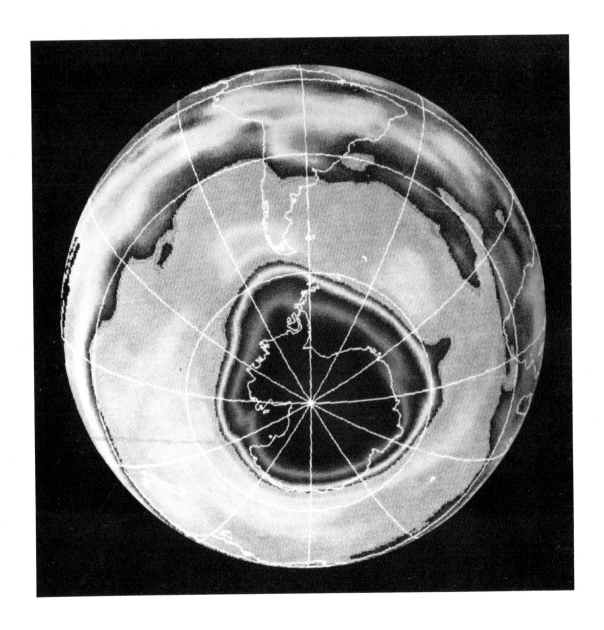

The photo is of the ozone hole over Antarctica (NASA/GSFC/Science Photo Library).

Problem-Solving Geography

Analysis in a Changing World

Norman Law
*Director, QA Research and formerly Head of Geography at
Waingel's Copse School, Woodley, Reading*

David Smith
*Curriculum Co-ordinator,
Ranelagh School, Bracknell*

Stanley Thornes (Publishers) Ltd

Published in 1993 by:
Stanley Thornes (Publishers) Ltd
Old Station Drive
Leckhampton
CHELTENHAM GL53 0DN
England

ISBN 0 7487 1355 7
A catalogue record for this book is available from the British Library.

Typeset by Tech-Set, Gateshead, Tyne & Wear
Printed and bound in Hong Kong.

Acknowledgements

The authors would like to thank the following for their invaluable assistance in the preparation of this book:

Natalie Rowlands for preparing the typescript; Stephen Hays for comments and source material, especially for Chapter 6; Keith Quine for checking the manuscript; Claire Usher for her mental map; our family and friends for their tolerance.

The authors and publishers wish to thank the following for permission to use copyright material.

American Society of Civil Engineers for Fig. 2.3 from M. O. Hayer et al, 'Sensitivity ranking of energy-port shorelines' in *Proceedings of Ports '80*, Norfolk, Virginia, 697–707;
Basil Blackwell Ltd for Figs 4.23, 4.24, 4.25, 4.26 and 4.27 from Moulaert, Chikhaom & Djellal, 'Locational Behaviour of French High-Tech Consultancy Firms', *International Journal of Urban and Regional Research*, Vol. 15, No. 1, 1991;
British Nuclear Form for Fig. 2.21 from *Nuclear Forum*, Special Supplement;
British Telecom for article from *BT Business News* and extract from A Guide to Working from Home' (p. 139);
Jean-Claude Chesnais for article on p. 105 'Africa's population explosion spurs exodus of youth to Europe' (reprinted in the *Guardian*);
Development Board for Rural Wales for Fig. 4.38 advertising 'Rural Wales';
The Economist for Figs 1.40, 6.25 and 3.30 and other material sourced to *The Economist Book of Vital World Statistics; A Complete Guide to the World in Figures*. Copyright © 1990 The Economist Books Ltd;
Financial Times for Figs 6.34, 'Aluminium gets top marks for publicity' by Kenneth Gooding, 11.9.91, Fig. 5.27 'UK "green" farming scheme extended' by David Blackwell, 21.11.91, graph on p. 209, 'Net resource flows to developing countries', Jan. 1992, and article on p. 47, 'Cold comfort on global warming' by John Hunt, 8.11.91;
Friends of the Earth for material in Fig. 2.24 from pamphlet on Nuclear Power;
Green Flag International Ltd for Fig. 6.41, from their pamphlet on 'Conservation Tourism', 1990;
Greenpeace for Figs 1.41, 2.21, and graphs on p. 46 from their report on Global Warming and 'The Greenhouse Effect';
Guardian News Service Ltd for Fig. 3.26, 'From a virtuous to vicious circle', 27.5.91; p. 34, 'Sahel awaits the rain', 22.4.88; graphs from 23.4.91, 24.5.91 issues, and various headlines (pp. 34–5);
The Controller of Her Majesty's Stationery Office for Figs 2.22 from *Employment Gazette*, diagram on p. 203 from 'Energy Efficiency Begins at Home', 1991, Fig. 10 on p. 7 *Regional Trends 25*, 1990, and table on p. 104 from Key Data, 1990, OPCS; Table 1 on p. 104 from Office of Population Censuses and Surveys/General Register Offices for Scotland and Northern Ireland, *Regional Trends 25*, 1990 and Table 2 on p. 104 from OPCS *International Migration 1988*, series MN no. 15, 1990;
Hodder & Stoughton Ltd for diagram on p. 46 'The greenhouse gases' from S. Boyle and J. Ardill, *The Greenhouse Effect*, New English Library, 1989;
The Independent for Fig. 3.31 'Planners plot the course of Europe's 'hot banana'' by Nicholas Schoon, *The Independent*, 14.6.91 and headline, 26.5.90 (p. 34);
Marriott Howard Publicity Ltd for Fig. 3.32, advertisement of the Port of Felixstowe;
Minority Rights Group for Figs 2.5 and 2.7 from their report on Guatemala, 1989;
The Observer Ltd for charts and tables from various editions of *New Internationalist* Fig. 1.32 from *NI*, No. 169, March 1987, and Fig. 5.28 'Planting Poverty' by Barbara Dinham, *NI*, No. 172, June 1987;
Oxfam America for Fig. 2.9 from S. H. Davis & J. Hodson, *Witness to Political Violence in Guatemala: The Suppression of a Rural Development Movement*, 45, 1982;
Pergamon Press for graphs on p. 138, from article by Nilles, *Transportation Research*, Vol. 22a, No. 4, 1988, Fig. 3.35, from D. Domanski, 'Public attitudes to local industrial development and the quality of life in Poland', *Geoforum*, Vol. 21, No. 2, 1990, Figs 5.18, 5.19 and 5.20 from A. J. Jansen & H. Hetsen, 'Agricultural Development and Spatial Organisation in Europe', *Journal of Rural Studies*, Vol. 6, No. 4, 1990, Figs 5.21, 5.22 and 5.23 from *Journal of Rural Studies*, Vol. 7, No. 3, 1991, and Fig. 5.25 from K. Knickel, 'The ecological effect of recent farming changes in the Federal Republic of West Germany', *Journal of Rural Studies*, Vol. 6, No. 4, 1990;
Peters Fraser & Dunlop Ltd for Fig. 4.5, cartoon, 'Village Christmas' from Posy Simmonds, *Very Posy*, Jonathan Cape, 1981;
George Philip Ltd for graphs from *Philip's World Atlas*, 1991;
The Reading Newspaper Company Ltd for Fig. 2.18 from 'Tory in 'I'll quit' threat' by A. Day and A. Wilson, *Reading Chronicle*, 26.4.91;
Reed International Books for Fig. 6.38 from Katie Wood and Syd House, *The Good Tourist*, Mandarin Paperbacks;
Routledge for Fig. 1.1 from D. Drew, *Man–Environment Process*, Unwin Hyman, 1983, and Fig. 4.3 from Peter Gould, *The Geographer at Work*, R & KP, 1985;
Sunday Mail for headline, 21.1.90 (p. 35);
Unilever PLC for Figs 5.29 and 5.30 from 'Unilever Plantations: Developing Agriculture in the Developing World';
John Wiley and Sons, Ltd for Figs 2.25, 2.27, 2.28, 2.29 and 2.30 from R. W. G. Carter and G. W. Stone, 'Mechanisms associated with the erosion of sand dune cliffs' in *Earth Surface Processes and Landforms*, eds Kirkby and Richards, Vol. 14, 1, Feb. 1989;

Every effort has been made to trace all the copyright holders, but if any have been inadvertently overlooked the publishers will be pleased to make the necessary arrangement at the first opportunity.

The authors and publishers wish to acknowledge the following photograph sources:

Allsport/David Cannon Fig. 2.31; Geoff Bernard/Panos Pictures p. 202; Martin Bond/Science Photo Library Fig. 6.20; Mark Boulton/ICCE Fig. 1.30B, p. 95 bottom; Sue Bolton p. 82 right, p. 83 bottom, Fig. 3.18; Canada Centre for Remote Sensing Fig. 1.26; Maria Luiza Carvalho/Panos Pictures Fig. 6.15; Chester College/Keith Hilton Fig. 1.27; G. & P. Corrigan/Robert Harding Picture Library Fig. 5.10; Crown Copyright Fig. 1.15(a), (b); Sue Cunningham/Panos Pictures Fig. 6.2; Professor E. Derbyshire Fig. 5.13; Earth Satellite Corporation/Science Photo Library Figs 1.21, 1.23; Mary Evans Picture Library Figs 1.30A, 5.1, 5.5; Robert Harding Picture Library Figs 2.12, 5.12; Paul Harrison/Panos Pictures p. 172; Stephen Hays Figs 2.6, 2.8, p. 81, Figs 6.36, 6.37; Mike Hoggett/ICCE Fig. 1.53; Ivaldi/Jerrican/Science Photo Library Fig. 5.2; Brian Janes Figs 5.4, 5.6; Josephine Law Fig. 6.28; Norman Law p. 80, p. 82 left, p. 83 top, p. 94, p. 95 top, Figs 4.9, 4.10, 4.15, 4.16, 4.17, 4.36, 4.37, 6.14; Alain le Garsmeur/Panos Pictures Fig. 1.51; Peter Menzel/Science Photo Library Fig. 5 (p. 4); NASA/Science Photo Library Figs 1.16, 1.18; NASA/ICCE Fig. 1.12; National Remote Sensing Centre Fig. 1.20; Nissan Fig. 3.24; Edward Parker/Hutchison Library Fig. 2.11; Andy Purcell/ICCE Fig. 6.18; Bernard Regent/Hutchison Library Fig. 1.50; Roger Ressmeyer, Starlight/Science Photo Library Fig. 6.16; Andrew Ridler p. 139; Saskatchewan Research Council Figs 1.24, 1.25; Debbie Snelson/ICCE Fig. 1.33; Spectrum Colour Library Figs 6.21, 1.50, p. 195; Stephen Seque/Hutchison Library Fig. 1 (p. 1); Sean Sprague/Panos Pictures Fig. 5.8; Dagmar Strasser Figs 3.34, 3.36, 3.37, 3.38; Anna Tully/Panos Pictures Fig. 6.19; Unilever plc Fig. 5.30; Simon Warner p. 134; Weiss/Jerrican/Science Photo Library Fig. 5.3; Jasper Young/Panos Pictures Fig. 3.2.

Contents

List of double-page spreads on selected topics

Introduction – coping with change

The world is in a constant state of change. In recent times, countries such as the USSR, Yugoslavia and East Germany have disappeared from the map, whereas others such as Lithuania, Russia and reunited Germany have reappeared. Communications have continued to 'shrink' the world. Population growth has led to an increased demand for resources and consequent environmental damage. These and other major changes are the subject matter of this book.

Until recently, it was possible to plan calmly over reasonably long periods to cope with any change that might occur. With the increase in the rate of change, however, decisions have had to be made at an increasingly fast pace. Without a well defined structure for decision making to cope with these requirements, changes have not been accompanied by planning of a sufficiently high standard. Problems have therefore arisen.

A possible structure for decision making has been described elsewhere (*Decision-Making Geography*, Law and Smith, Stanley Thornes, Second Edition, 1991). This sort of process allows a decision to be taken on the basis of information surrounding one well defined objective. If the problem to be addressed is the sum total of several such items, however, other preliminary work needs to be completed to define the constituents of the problem, before solutions can be sought. The word 'problem' is in common usage to describe the sort of thing with which this book is concerned (environmental degradation, population pressure, industrial change, etc.). Each of these problems may well have positive elements, for example, the range of opportunities and experiences inherent in a multicultural society. For the sake of simplicity, however, they are referred to as 'problems', not least because it can be shown how such items can be addressed by problem-solving techniques.

The relevance of such an approach may be demonstrated by an example from everyday life with which the reader may identify. A famous band is due to appear shortly at a venue some 30 km from the home of a teenage fan. This fan has not been to a large concert before and is blessed with protective parents. The problem for the fan is how to get their agreement to see the concert.

Fig. 1 Glastonbury Festival crowds

Without any prior planning, a direct question to parents or a statement of intent might prove disastrous. The problem needs to be dissected to identify the elements it contains. If each of these elements is then addressed, there may be some hope of overcoming the problem (Figs 2 and 3).

QUESTIONS

1 Write out a list as in Fig. 2 to illustrate a problem you have at the moment; for example, how to get enough money to buy something you want.

2 Would your parents perceive any more problems than you do in attending the concert? What would they be?

The resolution of the problem has been achieved by classifying its constituent parts and attacking each one in turn. The reaction to one step of a problem determines the way the next one will be handled. Your plan for resolving the problem is shown in Fig. 3. The plan, however, may be modified if the assumptions at each stage do not operate. At each stage there is a judgement to be made which determines the next stage. It is very easy to make the wrong judgement and proceed in the wrong direction.

Somebody (parents in this example) will monitor the actions you take as the result of the decisions that have been made. If they do not like the results, their decisions next time might be very different. This is how the review of actions taken as a result of decisions can affect future decisions.

The 'linear' perception of a problem (as in Fig. 2) is usually a great over-simplification of the actual case. The problem might be better illustrated, as in Fig. 4, by a diagram which looks like a series of linked 'atoms'. All the individual elements of the decision are interlinked and the answer to one part affects all the others in some way. The resolution is usually a compromise which does as well as it can at each individual stage, without necessarily being the best answer to each one.

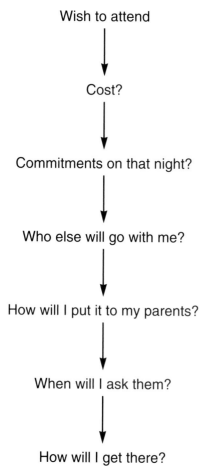

Fig. 2 The teenager's perception of the problem

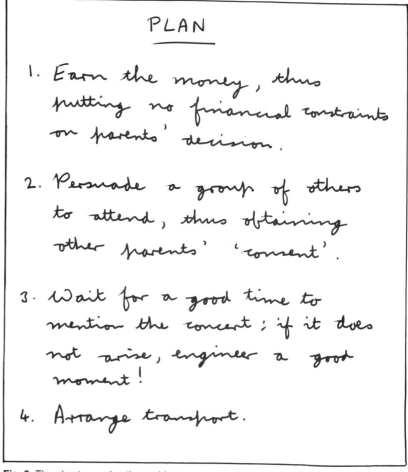

Fig. 3 The plan to resolve the problem

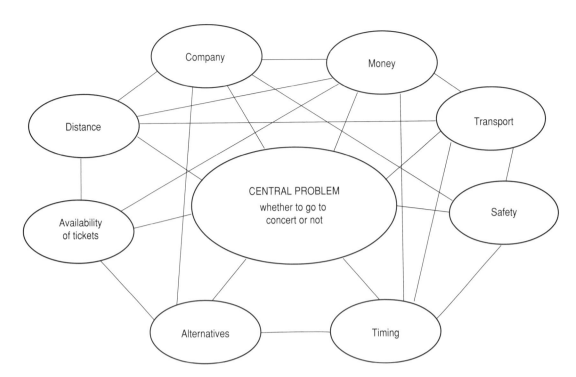

QUESTION

3 Draw a diagram as in Fig. 4 to illustrate the problem you outlined in question 1.

Through this brief investigation of an 'everyday' problem, a model for dealing with problems in general has been suggested. The steps are illustrated in Fig. 3. What we are doing is to simplify the 'atom' model into a continuous series of events in order to be able to manage it. Our model is, therefore, a simplified view of reality and the response to the problem is likely to be a compromise at best. The answer to the problem could in fact be found wanting once it has been implemented and there should always be a monitoring process built in to see whether revision is needed (the review stage).

The four main parts of this model are:

Identification
Planning (classification of elements and strategy to respond)
Action
Review

and so it is known as the IPAR model.

In this book the IPAR model will be used, but the review process will not always be relevant to the studies, other than to suggest ways in which monitoring *could* take place. The symbols  are used to indicate the application of each stage of the model to the case studies throughout the book.

The following is an example of how a geographical problem can be analysed to see how it might be tackled using this model. The problem we have chosen is one of the main concerns of many geographers in the late twentieth century and is firmly on the political agenda as well.

Does human activity affect the climate?

1 [*I*] dentification

The first step in looking at a problem is to be clear what is being talked about (identification). In this case, the terms 'human activity' and 'climate' have to be considered. The former, obviously, refers to all the industry (primary, secondary and tertiary), transport, settlements and communications undertaken by people. They have been said to affect processes which influence climate. These effects may be deliberate, as in the case of large irrigation schemes which affect soil moisture and humidity levels, or they may be 'accidental' as in the case of the deforestation of the tropics and the resulting disturbing effect on world climate. In other words, connections between human occupation and climatic variation will be sought in answer to the question.

Fig. 5 A wellhead fire in Kuwait following the invasion by Iraq in 1991. Comment on the likely microclimate changes it may have caused.

'Climate' means average atmospheric conditions at a location, in other words, average 'weather'. It is therefore composed of a number of measurable items, as revealed in the shipping forecast for 1700 hours for Wednesday, 18 September, 1991:

'Tyne, Dogger: west, backing south westerly, 5 or 6, increasing 7 later, showers, good.'

Later in the same report (weather reports from coastal stations):

'Tiree: west by north 6, recent showers, 11 miles, 1015, rising.'

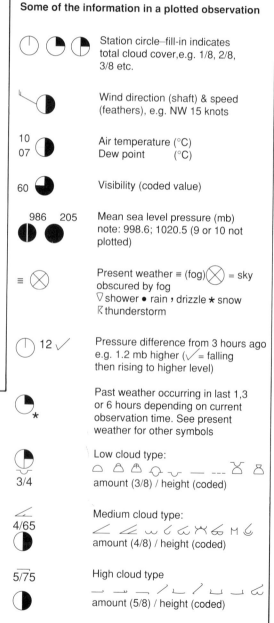

Some of the information in a plotted observation

Station circle—fill-in indicates total cloud cover, e.g. 1/8, 2/8, 3/8 etc.

Wind direction (shaft) & speed (feathers), e.g. NW 15 knots

Air temperature (°C)
Dew point   (°C)

Visibility (coded value)

Mean sea level pressure (mb) note: 998.6; 1020.5 (9 or 10 not plotted)

Present weather ≡ (fog) ⊗ = sky obscured by fog
∇ shower • rain ‚ drizzle ✱ snow
Ƙ thunderstorm

Pressure difference from 3 hours ago e.g. 1.2 mb higher (✓ = falling then rising to higher level)

Past weather occurring in last 1,3 or 6 hours depending on current observation time. See present weather for other symbols

Low cloud type:
amount (3/8) / height (coded)

Medium cloud type:
amount (4/8) / height (coded)

High cloud type
amount (5/8) / height (coded)

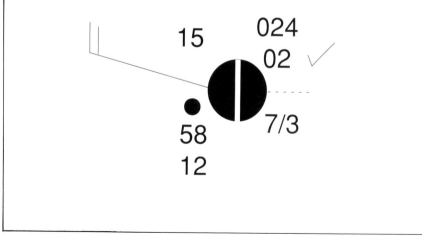

Fig. 6 A station marker from a Meteorological Office weather map may help you to identify further features

QUESTIONS

4 Read the weather information on p.4, then make a list of the meteorological items it measures (e.g. temperature, visibility, etc.).

5 Are there any further meteorological items which could be measured and which are not mentioned in the forecasts? You should produce a list of all the items that need to be measured in order to see what effect human activity has on climate. (See Fig. 6.)

2  lanning

Having identified the factors that need to be measured, an experimental example which includes areas of differing degrees of human influence might be studied. On a large scale, such an example would be a city and the surrounding countryside. On a smaller scale, it could be a school building and the surrounding playing fields. If monitoring of the elements you identified in answer to question 4 is undertaken, there should be some indication of whether the factors differ as the degree of human 'interference' (in this case, the density of buildings) also varies.

Figure 7 shows the result of monitoring the city of Leicester for temperature and Fig. 8 shows the result of mapping wind speed and direction around some school buildings. It should be obvious from just these examples that human activity does indeed affect these meteorological elements. If that is the case,

then the climate, which is an average of several such 'snapshots', would be expected to reveal a link with human activity.

Urban areas influence more aspects of their local climate than just temperature. Other ways are shown in Fig. 9. This phenomenon is known as the microclimate effect. Figure 7 shows the relationship between the built-up area of Leicester and temperature conditions on 19 August 1966. Similar relationships could be shown for rainfall: it tends to increase in severity and amount over large urban areas. In other words, there is something in the urban area that is affecting the climate. On investigation, we find that the differences between the microclimate of an urban area and that of the surrounding area can be put down to factors such as the use of fuel, building regulations and population density.

Having identified the reasons for microclimate, there is now a chance to take action to control it based on the information and to monitor any changes that occur as a result.

The reason that management of micro-climate is so important is that various conditions can be harmful to health or even to building structures. The following is a brief list of examples.

QUESTIONS

6 (a) In what ways are the built-up area of Leicester and temperature linked (Fig. 7)?

(b) How might the following explain what you have found?
   (i) heat escaping from buildings
   (ii) traffic
   (iii) differences in the type of surface (concrete and bricks v. grass and farmland)

7 How do buildings affect wind speed and direction?

Fig. 7 Temperature and built-up area in Leicester on an August day

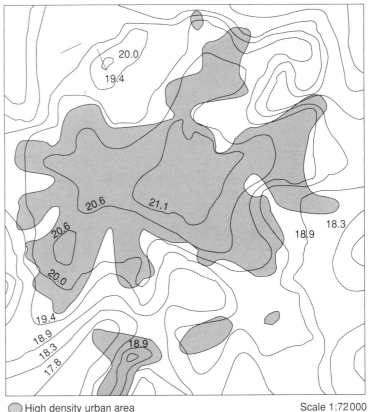

◯ High density urban area
╱ Isotherm (°C)

Scale 1:72 000

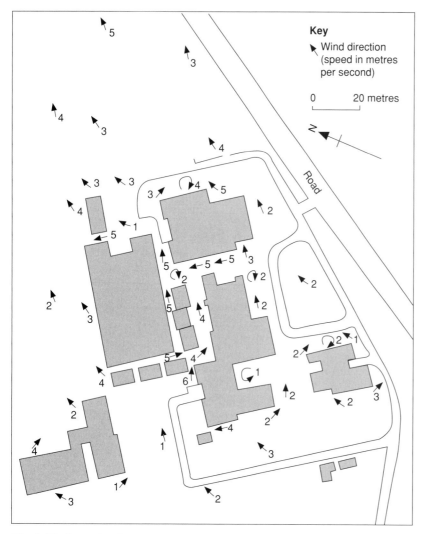

Fig. 8 Wind speed and direction round a school on an October day

ELEMENT	EFFECT AND CAUSE
Wind speed	Much higher in some places, where buildings are placed close together, for example, creating a wind tunnel effect.
Wind direction	Buildings create severe eddies and rapid changes in direction of winds.
Temperature	Can be up to 5 °C higher than surrounding area in the right night-time conditions. Heat stored by day is released from buildings and roads and is added to by heat released from central heating, cars, etc.
Humidity	The lack of vegetation and open water and efficient surface drainage can greatly reduce humidity.
Precipitation	The greater heat can cause convectional storms. Particles of dust released into the atmosphere can give rise to increased condensation and, therefore, greater precipitation.

Fig. 9 Urban microclimate

Examples of microclimate effects

i) The air in Mexico City is badly polluted because the city is in a natural basin into which air tends to sink. The burning of fossil fuels, especially by industry and cars, means that the air becomes laden with sulphuric and nitrous gases. In 1992, a plan was announced to build three huge horizontally mounted fans to disperse the pollution-laden air.

ii) In the summer of 1991, many deaths were recorded in Athens from heat exhaustion. The high Mediterranean temperatures were magnified in urban areas by polluted and therefore heat-retaining air and by the low albedo (reflectiveness) of many man-made surfaces, which leads to greater heating of the air in contact with the hot surfaces.

iii) In 1989, many structures in southern England were seriously damaged in a series of storms with high winds. These winds were channelled in urban areas and, where they passed between high buildings, were magnified (the Venturi effect).

QUESTION

8 Suggest TWO measures in each case that could be taken in a large urban area to manage (a) wind speed and (b) temperature.

 3 **Action**

Having decided how each of the items about which we are concerned could be managed, we now need to implement the decisions. In the case of a British city, the authorities in charge would be the city council, although particular decisions could still be overridden by county council or central government. No decision can be taken and implemented in isolation. What is decided in one place may well have serious repercussions for people in other areas. The best way to implement any decision, of course, is to inform people fully about it (i.e. educate them) and obtain their consent before putting it into practice.

QUESTIONS

9 Suggest how the burning of fossil fuels could be managed in a city. Think of education, persuasion, enforcement and financial inducements.

10 How are the burning of fossil fuels and microclimate linked? (Refer to Figs 7 and 9.)

QUESTION

11 (a) How thoroughly have smoke levels and sulphur dioxide levels been sampled?

(b) What is the apparent trend of the figures revealed by the survey?

(c) How would you improve this survey to increase the significance of the results?

4 Review

In this example, where the problem is that of improving the climate of an urban area, a monitoring network should be established to see whether the chosen measures are having the desired effect. We should also be on the lookout for any new developments which have not yet been identified as part of the problem. A good management system will keep an eye on developments in other areas and borrow the best and most effective management ideas.

The links between pollutants and local climate have been suggested above. Figure 10 shows the results of monitoring smoke and sulphur dioxide levels in the United Kingdom.

In the example of microclimate, it has been suggested through the application of the IPAR model that:

1. Different types of area have their own microclimates.

2. Human activities can influence climate on the local scale.

3. Management of buildings and fuel use can be effected on the local scale to the benefit of local climate.

	Smoke (micrograms per cubic metre)			Sulphur dioxide (micrograms per cubic metre)			
	1971–72	1987–88	Percentage change 1971–72 to 1987–88	1971–72	1987–88	Percentage change 1971–72 to 1987–88	Total sites[1] (numbers)
United Kingdom	62	15	−76	116	39	−66	64
North	83	13	−84	94	37	−61	4
Yorkshire & Humberside	89	23	−74	141	45	−68	4
East Midlands	50	16	−68	105	43	−59	3
East Anglia	61	12	−80	79	24	−70	1
South East:							
Greater London	43	14	−67	172	42	−76	11
Rest of South East	38	11	−71	82	39	−52	6
South West	33	8	−76	75	21	−72	3
West Midlands	70	16	−77	113	40	−65	5
North West	86	17	−80	148	45	−70	13
England	63	15	−76	128	40	−69	50
Wales	43	11	−74	69	28	−59	5
Scotland	63	17	−73	73	34	−53	8
Northern Ireland	79	37	−53	87	67	−23	1

[1]*As can be seen, the number of sites in certain regions is particularly small. Consequently great care should be taken in interpreting trends within regions.*

© Crown copyright

Fig. 10 Atmospheric pollution, 1971–72 and 1987–88

How to use this book

Each chapter in this book has a similar structure. After discussion of the background to the topic under consideration, often with a detailed example, there is consideration of a related problem. There is a great deal of scope for data manipulation by the student, guided by the IPAR model. Each chapter provides additional related data, and, with much less commentary, proposes a further problem for solution (a problem-solving exercise). Some relevant techniques are given in the Appendix, but others can be found in the companion volume *Decision-Making Geography* and in several other A-level texts.

The book provides a progression through the process of problem solving. Chapter 1 sets the scene for the current state of many of the large-scale systems of water, soil and atmosphere. It looks at the present state of stress in these systems. This includes population distribution and growth rates, and their impact on land management, and the threat to the climate from ozone depletion and the greenhouse effect. It also includes some meteorological analysis and discusses the use of remote sensing, to show where our information comes from. It deals with the ways the earth is represented in the form of map projections and the way the earth is viewed through mental maps. This will be the starting point for closer analysis in subsequent chapters.

Chapter 2 begins with the definition of 'environment' and considers how quality of environment is measured. It looks at the impact of environmental change in rural and coastal areas of Britain and considers the issues of developing aboriginal lands.

Chapter 3 considers the choices made by individuals when they decide to migrate, and the influence of environmental and political factors on their action. It links the movement of population with models of industrial development.

This theme is developed in Chapter 4, which considers the transmission of ideas and the role of the information revolution on global society. This will form a bridge into the next chapter which considers the problem of feeding the world's population.

Chapter 5 takes a global look at agriculture and the role of big business in the production of food. It analyses the impact of the Green Revolution and looks at agricultural development in China and Europe, developing many of the ideas from Chapter 1.

The final chapter will return to the global scale to consider what appropriate action can be suggested. Appropriate development strategies for sustainable development are analysed and the role of the individual considered in producing an action plan for the twenty-first century.

There is a selection of independent double-page spreads of information throughout the book. Each one looks at a particular aspect of change in geography. They also provide concentrated data which can be analysed using problem-solving techniques.

Crisis – what crisis?

- Perception of the earth is affected by map projections, personal experience and remote images.

- Population growth poses a challenge to the earth.

- Population pressure leads to environmental problems.

- The environment is in a state of dynamic equilibrium.

- Population dynamics are affected by economic and physical factors.

- Government measures can influence population change.

- Ozone depletion and global warming are two results of population pressure.

- Major environmental threats can be challenged by concerted action.

- Water resource planning poses one of the greatest future threats to regional stability.

How is the earth represented?

If we could fly over the planet earth we would notice that nearly two-thirds of its surface is covered by water. Of the remaining land area of 13 076.5 million hectares some 11% is under arable and permanent crops, the latter occupying less than 1%. A quarter of the land area is covered by permanent pasture and 31% is covered by forest and woodland. The remaining 33% is classified as 'other land'.

However, it is more important for us to consider not just the present land use, but by how much the surface of the earth is changing.

Information on change can be acquired from a variety of different sources, including personal observation. Television, newspapers, magazines and radio provide a continuous stream of information about places far and near. Many of these media use images transmitted from satellites as well as maps to give information and support stories. Still photographs and video, graphs, accounts (both written and spoken) and banks of data are available in libraries for people to scan and analyse. The computer and information revolutions have made vast quantities of data available on disc, cassette, compact disc and interactive video. Some of this information has been analysed and is used to support a particular point of view, and some is 'raw' and unbiased.

QUESTIONS

1.1 Re-draw the pie charts (Fig. 1.1), locating them on an outline world map. Use a colour key to show different land uses.

1.2 Explain the large amounts of land not given over to farming. You should refer to an atlas map and think about the factors that limit agriculture (slope, water, soil, temperature, etc.).

Crisis – what crisis?

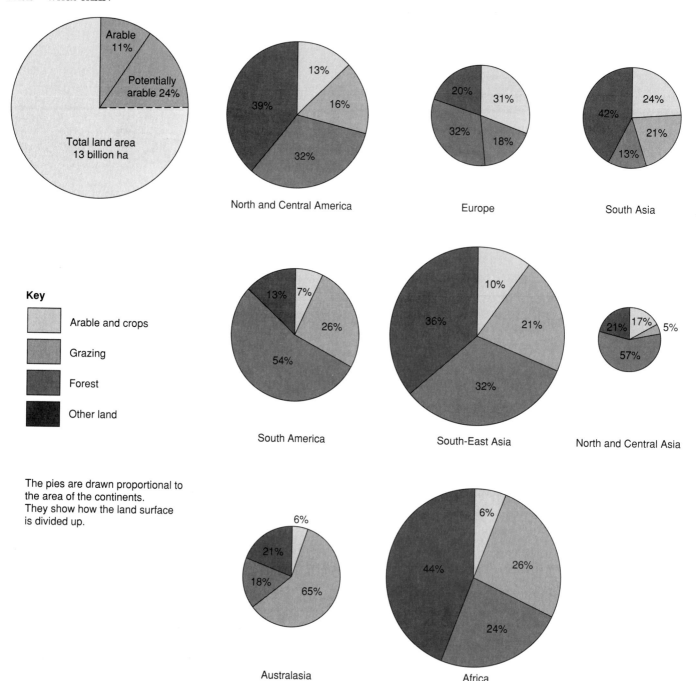

Arable 11%

Potentially arable 24%

Total land area 13 billion ha

13%
16%
39%
32%

North and Central America

20%
31%
32%
18%

Europe

24%
42%
21%
13%

South Asia

Key

Arable and crops

Grazing

Forest

Other land

13%
7%
26%
54%

South America

10%
36%
21%
32%

South-East Asia

17%
21%
5%
57%

North and Central Asia

The pies are drawn proportional to the area of the continents. They show how the land surface is divided up.

6%
21%
18%
65%

Australasia

6%
44%
26%
24%

Africa

Map projections

It is important to be aware of the bias which has been used in any set of data. Maps are no exception to this. It is obvious that the globe cannot be represented accurately on a flat sheet of paper. Some form of distortion will be necessary to represent the earth and we will carry these distortions around in our heads. They will help to form our mental map of the earth.

Mental maps can provide very powerful images. Figures 1.2 to 1.4 show a series of different mental maps of the British Isles and the USA. Figure 1.5 shows the mental map of

an 11-year-old used to describe a journey to school. The amount of detail and the selection of features by the youngster is interesting as it indicates the perception of space and the relationship between home and school.

Figure 1.6 shows two familiar views of the world. The Mercator projection has provided many generations of people with their mental picture of the world. The newer Arno Peters projection shows areas according to their actual size so that comparison is possible. It is now in such frequent use that it may become the predominant mental map of the world in future.

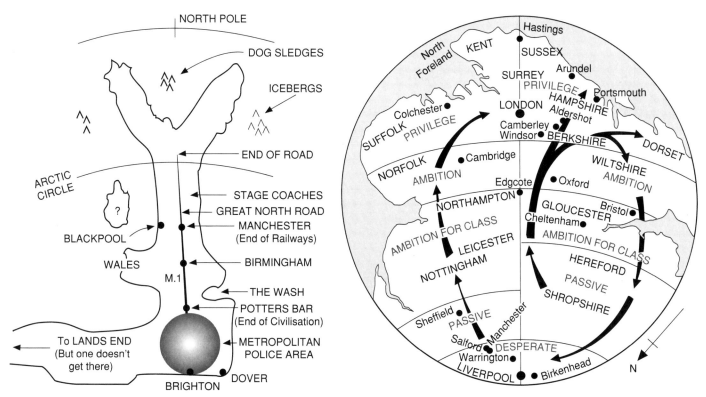

Fig. 1.2 How Londoners see the North – at least according to the Doncaster and District Development Council. Draw another map of the same area from the point of view of someone living in Doncaster

Fig. 1.3 England projected into social space – according to Professor Northcote Parkinson. This map was drawn in 1967. How and why may the situation have changed since then?

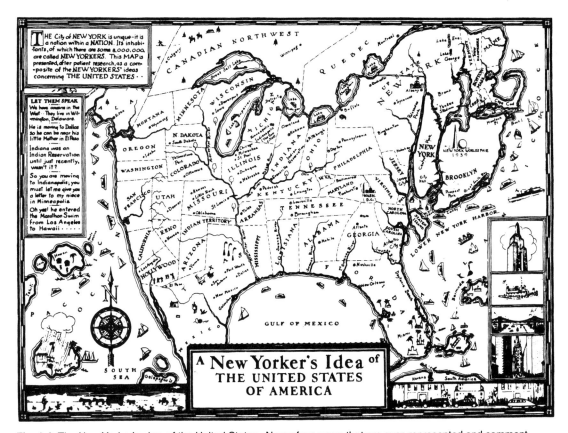

Fig. 1.4 The New Yorker's view of the United States. Name four areas that are over-represented and comment on why this may be.

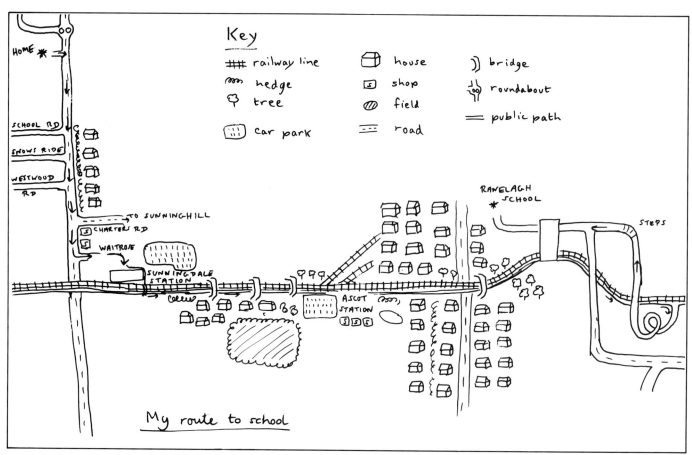

Fig. 1.5 Mental map of a journey to school. Which features appear to be most important to this person?

QUESTIONS

1.3 In five minutes, draw your own mental map of your town and compare it with those of others in your class. What features have you, decided to include? What factors give people different mental maps of their home areas?

1.4 Compare the land areas on the Mercator projection with those on the Peters projection. Which land areas show the greatest distortion on the Mercator map? Look up the actual area of the countries and compare them with the sizes on the maps. Which projection gives the fairest representation of area? Is fairness important in drawing maps of the world? Discuss this concept with other members of your class.

1.5 The way that maps are drawn affects people's perceptions of their surroundings. Comment on how the following people might react to different projections which you will find in most good atlases.

(a) A government minister from Kenya trying to raise development capital in London and being faced with a Mercator wall map behind the banker who is being asked for the loan.

(b) An American citizen trying to understand the break-up of the Soviet Union and looking at an Interrupted Mollweide's Homolographic projection.

(c) A New Zealand relative visiting the family in the UK and attempting to show them from where he comes using a Hammer Equal Area projection centred on North America.

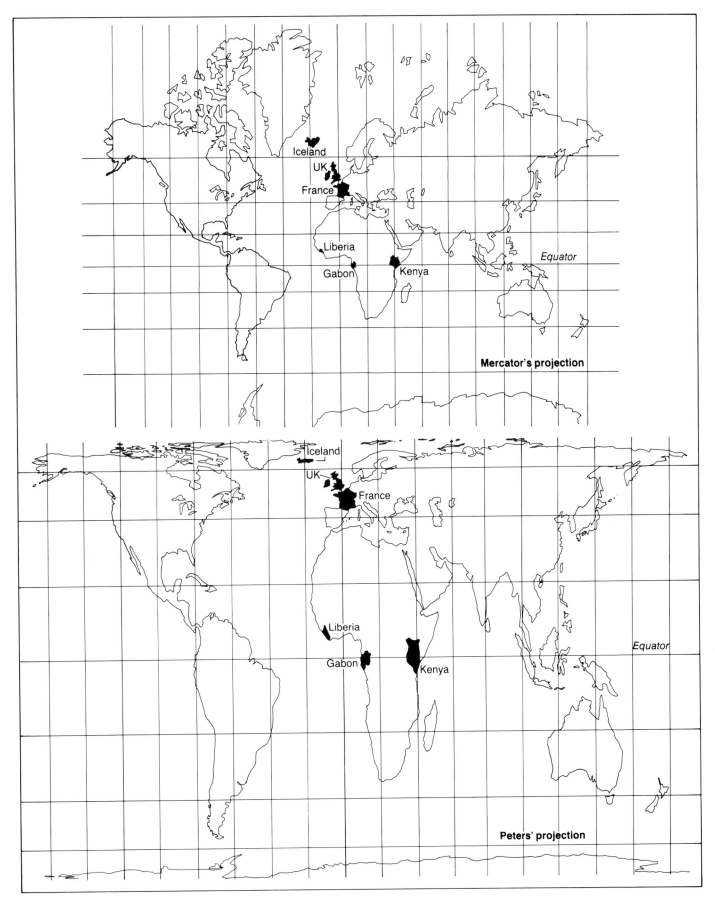

Fig. 1.6 The Mercator and Peters world maps

Map Projections

The earth is a three-dimensional object. In order to represent it on a two-dimensional piece of paper, compromises have to be made. These basically lead to one of three major distortions. The shape of the land areas, their area or the relative directions between places may be distorted. Common map projections which distort these elements are:

The Mercator Projection

(distorting area)
Size and shape are distorted more the further they are away from the equator.

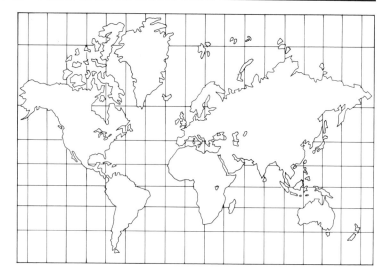

Aitoff's Projection

(distorting direction, but maintaining relative size relationships).

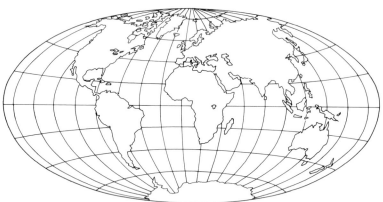

The Cylindrical Projection

(distorting shape more the further a country lies from the equator).

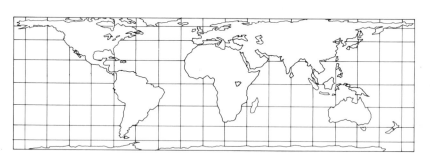

Equal area projections

One attempt at a projection which gives equal area with not too much shape distortion is the Hammer Equal Area Projection. There are many equal area projections, but the one which has found favour recently is Peters' projection (see Fig. 1.6).

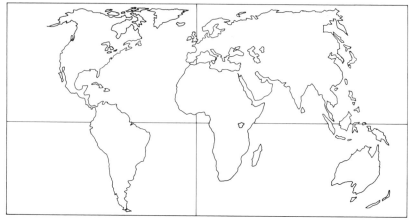

A map projection can be thought of in the following way. Imagine a glass globe at the centre of which there is a light. The borders of the countries are drawn in black on the surface of the globe. The light is switched on and the outlines of the countries are then 'projected' onto nearby surfaces. If a cylinder of paper were wrapped around the globe, touching it at the equator, a cylindrical projection would result.

Modification of the cylindrical projection (by altering the distance between latitudes) results in the familiar, but highly distorted, Mercator projection.

Cylindrical Projection

modified to a

Mercator Projection

Source of light

A further improvement on this projection can be made by 'wrapping' a cone around the globe instead of a cylinder. This gives the commonly used **conical** projection.

Another way to compromise between the elements of direction, size and shape, is to 'cut up' the globe as if it were an orange and then flatten out the pieces. This particular one is Mollweide's Interrupted Homolographic projection.

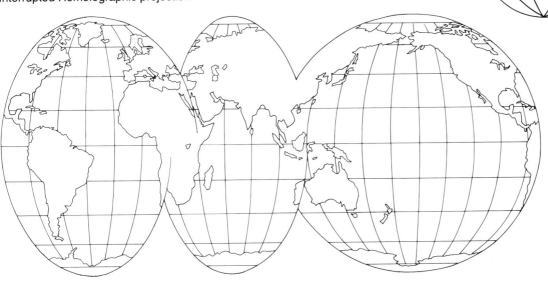

QUESTIONS
1 Look through a good atlas. The names of the map projections used are usually written in the margin of the map. Attempt to list the projections under one of three headings: True area, True shape and True direction. Which projection do you like most, and why?
2 Which projection would you use if you wished to show world population density, and why?

Remote sensing

Modern perceptions of the world may be more influenced by 'high-tech' images such as satellite photographs than they are by map projections. Anyone who has flown in an aeroplane will be able to marvel at the amount of information which can be obtained from flying over the surface of the earth. This is a form of remote sensing: gathering information about the surface of the earth without being in direct contact with it. Photographs taken from cameras mounted on aeroplanes provide a valuable source of information, but they are limited as they only give pictures from less than 10 km above the surface of the earth and they deal with the visible part of the spectrum. Figure 1.17 is a satellite photograph of Europe and North Africa taken at night using transmitted electric light. It is possible to pick out many of the coastlines and large conurbations. However, this is only a small amount of the information which can be collected by satellites.

Satellites can collect information from 700 to 35 000 km above the surface of the earth. They can provide a continuous source of data and hence can be used to monitor long-term environmental change. They can also collect information from parts of the electromagnetic spectrum which are not visible to the naked eye. They are said to have a bigger *spatial* reach in that they can give images from a greater height and therefore cover a larger area than conventional forms of imaging. They also have a greater *spectral* reach in sensing the full range of radiation waves from the earth.

Satellites collect measurements of electronic radiation on optical sensors. Radiation from

Fig. 1.7 The electromagnetic spectrum and satellite sensor bands. MSS = multi spectral scanner, TM = thematic mapper, AVHRR = advanced very high resolution radiometer, CZCS = coastal zone colour scanner

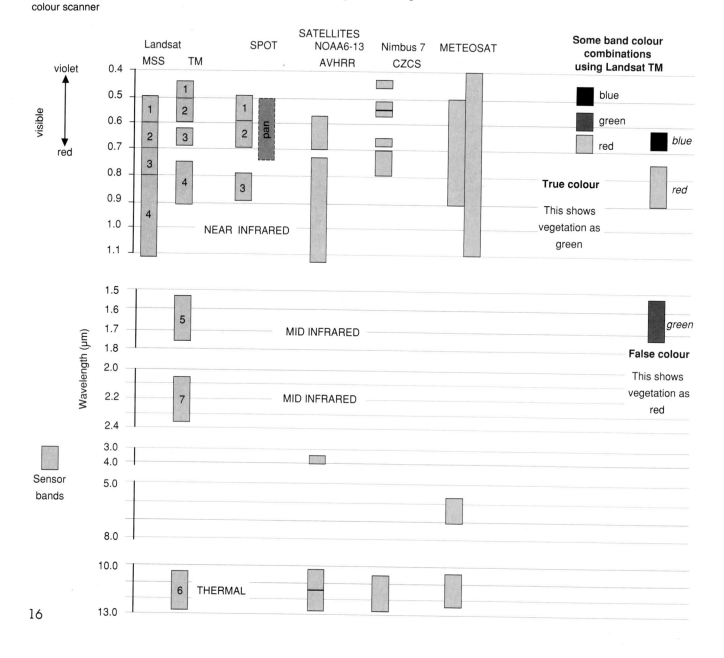

the sun is reflected, absorbed or transmitted by the earth's surface and atmosphere. This radiation is transmitted at a variety of wavelengths known as the *electromagnetic spectrum*. As some of the radiation is scattered or absorbed by the atmosphere the remote sensing equipment can only use certain 'windows' in the spectrum. Different satellites are built to use different windows, depending on the information required. Figure 1.7 shows the spectrum and the windows used by some satellites employed in remote sensing. The electromagnetic spectrum is shown on the left hand side of Fig. 1.7. The part of the spectrum which is visible occupies the top wavelengths from 0.4 m to 0.7 m. The windows used by the satellites are shown as numbered boxes.

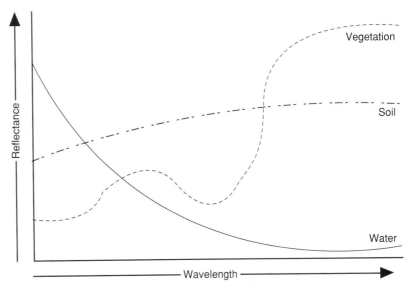

Fig. 1.8 Spectral signatures of water, soil and vegetation

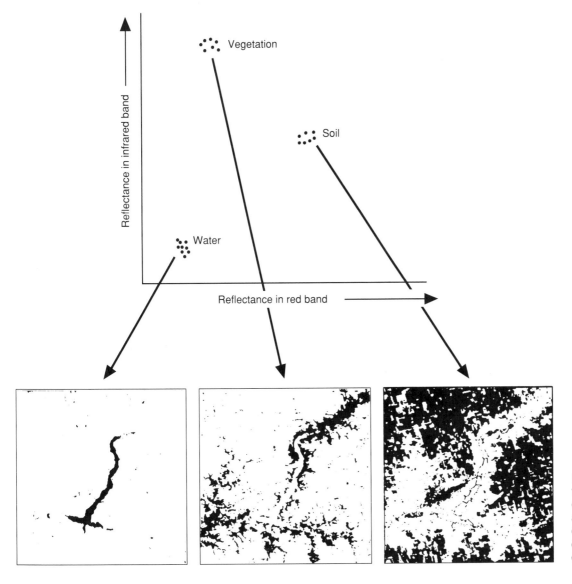

Fig. 1.9 Soil, water and vegetation pixels plotted on a graph of infrared against red band, giving distinctive clusters. These clusters correspond to the different types of land use.

In the case of the thermal mapping instruments of the Landsat 5 satellite, information is collected from the visible spectrum in windows 1, 2 and 3 and is also collected in the infrared parts of the spectrum. The information from the infrared spectrum will provide more detailed information about such factors as plant health and soil moisture which will enable a surface to be identified. The distinctive pattern of reflectance (the ratio of the radiant energy reflected by the surface to that incident upon it) for a particular surface feature is known as its *signature*.

These spectral signatures can be shown in graphical form as in Fig. 1.8. Clearly the patterns produced by water, soil and vegetation are significantly different, although at some wavelengths they could be confused as shown by where the lines cross each other. If the values are plotted for the red band (window 3) against the reflectance in the infrared band then the surface types can be more clearly distinguished. Figure 1.9 shows the distinctive clusters and how they relate to a satellite image. However, spectral signatures may change from season to season as plants grow and soil moisture varies. Careful analysis is required to understand such images.

Satellites may be launched to monitor a certain part of the earth. These are geostationary satellites which orbit the earth above the equator. The METEOSAT satellite is an example of this type of satellite. It is stationary over Europe and Africa. Landsat 5 is an example of a satellite which is in a polar orbit. Landsat orbits the earth as shown in Fig. 1.10 and is providing continuous monitoring of the earth's surface. The satellite is 705 km above the surface of the earth and it collects information from a 185 km wide strip. It will give a complete picture of the earth every 233 orbits or 16 days, although cloud cover in parts of the world will affect the quality of the images. Britain will have only 4 cloud-free scans out of 22 per year.

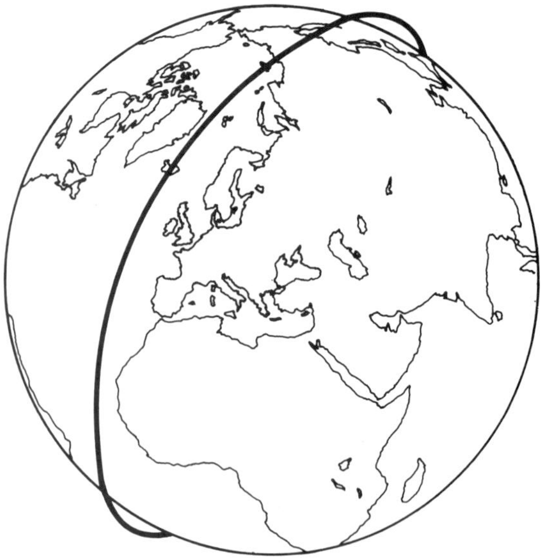

Fig. 1.10 Landsat 5 is in a polar orbit 700 km above the earth

Fig. 1.11 Remote sensing

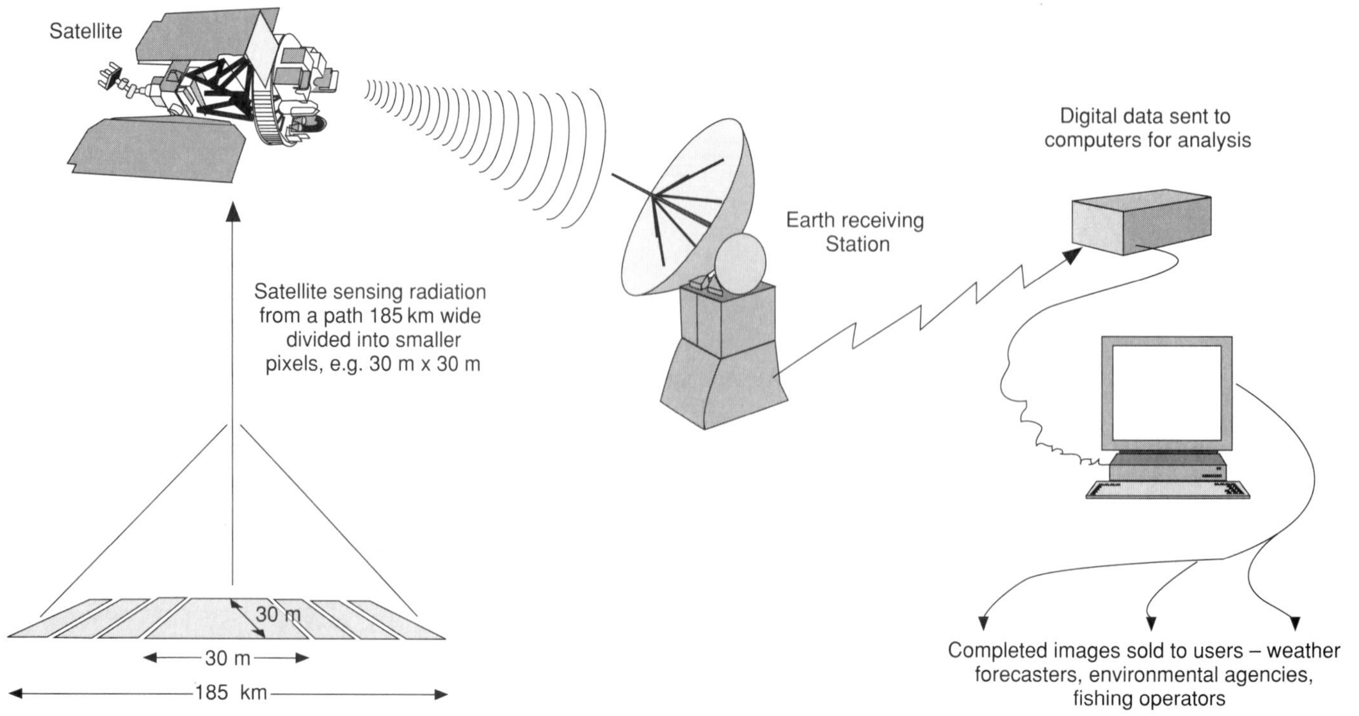
Satellite
Digital data sent to computers for analysis
Earth receiving Station
Satellite sensing radiation from a path 185 km wide divided into smaller pixels, e.g. 30 m x 30 m
30 m
30 m
185 km
Completed images sold to users – weather forecasters, environmental agencies, fishing operators

Fig. 1.12 The earth from space

QUESTION

1.6 (a) On a plain white sheet of A4 paper, draw a circle 15 cm in diameter to represent the earth as shown in Fig. 1.12. Sketch in the coastline that can be seen on the photograph.

(b) Using a good atlas, identify the area that has been photographed. Complete the coastline that cannot be seen by drawing it in with a dotted line.

(c) Sketch in the positions of the equator and tropics.

(d) Draw in the cloud cover patterns.

Figure 1.11 shows the operation of collecting data from Landsat 5. Data are collected by scanning a small unit of area and assigning an average signature to that area. The small area is known as a *pixel* and in the case of the Landsat 5 satellite it covers 30 m × 30 m. The smaller the pixel, the finer the resolution of the image and the greater the detail. This information is recorded in a digital form, as numbers ranging from 0 to 255, and it is then transmitted to a ground receiving station. Computers are used to build up an image from the data.

The operators can then decide how they wish to put the information together on a map. If information is being collected from one window only then the image can be in black and white. If information from more than one window is being used then a composite image can be produced. Colours are assigned to the information from Landsat 5 from each window so that blue is used for window 1, green for 2 and red for 3. In this case vegetation will be green and this is known as a true colour composite. However, to use the data from the infrared spectrum, 'false' colours must be used, since we cannot see infrared radiation. So vegetation appears red. The false colour composite will give more information about the stage of the growing cycle of the plant, the state of soil moisture and other factors such as the management of the land.

Remote sensing provides the geographer with both a new perspective on problems and areas and a chance to monitor the rapid changes, both physical and human, that are taking place. The following pages introduce a range of different types of remote image and show how they can be used in a problem-solving context.

Ordinary photographs taken from space vehicles, such as that shown in Fig. 1.12, are useful partly because they present a very familiar image. Colour film is 'panchromatic' and picks up light in a very similar way to the human eye. For example, vegetation appears green because it absorbs most wavelengths of light except green. This light is reflected and our eyes detect the vegetation as green. It is fairly straightforward, therefore, to interpret the resultant photographs.

In the area around the tropics, the general circulation of the atmosphere takes the form shown in Fig. 1.13.

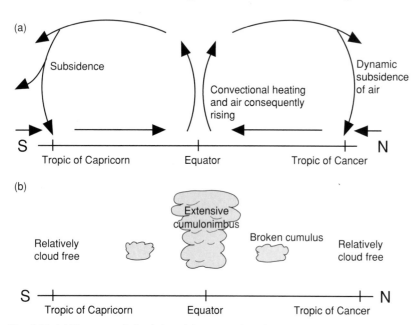

Fig. 1.13 (a) The general circulation of the atmosphere between the tropics. **(b)** The resultant cloud formation

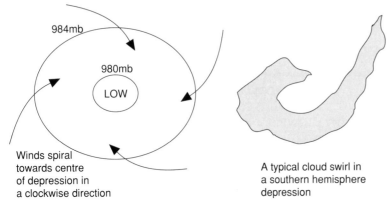

Fig. 1.14 A southern hemisphere depression

QUESTION

1.7 (a) On your sketch for question 1.6 (a), identify the equatorial cloud and label it to show how it was formed.
(b) Identify the cloud-free areas associated with the tropical subsidence belts. Label them and, with reference to the atlas, label the deserts at these locations.

In the sub-Capricorn area on the photograph, swirls of cloud can be identified. These are associated with dynamic uplift of the air where warmer, tropical air flowing towards the south meets cooler, Antarctic air flowing towards the north. The features formed at the junction (*front*) between these two air masses are called *depressions*. Since the photograph is of the southern hemisphere, the circulation in such weather systems is opposite to that in similar systems in the northern hemisphere (Fig. 1.14).

QUESTION

1.8 (a) Identify three low pressure systems on your sketch.

(b) Comment on the usefulness of colour satellite photography to weather forecasting.

Another form of remote sensing is radar imagery. If aerial photography were to be used to predict rainfall, it could only provide a best guess. That is because the incidence of rainfall would have to be inferred from the clouds that could be seen. A technique which actually detected falling rain would be better. That is why radar is used. This sweeps the area below the clouds detecting, amongst other things, falling rain. The results have to be interpreted, as all sorts of other items can be picked up, from aircraft to flocks of birds. If used with a synoptic chart, the radar picture can be very useful. Figures 1.15(a) and (b) show two consecutive radar pictures, indicating the rainfall on a Monday afternoon.

The heaviest rainfall is shown on a radar picture by orange colouring, followed by yellow and dark blue.

Fig. 1.15 (a) A radar picture of rainfall at 1400 h

QUESTION

1.9 (a) Describe the location of the rainfall on Monday at 1400 hours.

(b) By 1500 hours, which of the following had occurred?
(i) The rainfall had decreased in intensity.
(ii) The main belt of rainfall had moved east.
(iii) The rainfall belt had diminished in size.
(iv) Showers had developed in south Wales.

(c) In view of the changes you have noticed, what would be your prediction for rainfall in East Anglia over the next six hours?

Fig. 1.15 (b) A similar picture one hour later

In October 1988, the space shuttle *Discovery* passed over the Aswan Dam and Lake Nasser in Egypt. An ordinary panchromatic photograph was taken (Fig. 1.16). Another use of such photographs is to aid the interpretation of environmental change and topography.

QUESTION

1.10 (a) Draw a sketch of the outline of the lake, the tributaries, the Aswan Dam and the River Nile.

(b) Compared with a high level in 1981, the level of Lake Nasser had fallen considerably by 1988. Identify from the photograph the former lake shores (which can be seen most clearly in the lower left corner of the picture). Add this to your sketch and label it.

(c) Identify and label an extensive area of desert.

(d) Comment on the usefulness of panchromatic photography in the identification and management of environmental problems.

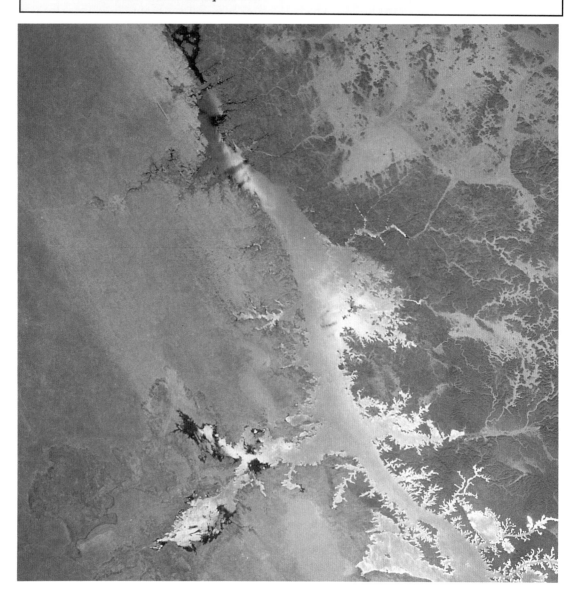

Fig. 1.16 A panchromatic photograph of part of the Nile Valley

Fig. 1.17 A photo-mosaic of Europe and North Africa

Photographs taken from space at a time when the area being photographed is experiencing night time can also be a useful interpretive tool. This picture (Fig. 1.17) was taken from a height of 825 kilometres above Europe and is a mosaic composed of the results of several passes above the continent. All cloud and land details have been filtered out to provide a photograph of city lights. As such the picture is one of population density.

QUESTION

1.11 **(a)** Identify and give examples of the following from the photograph:
  (i) a major river valley picked out in lights
  (ii) a well populated coastal area
  (iii) a sparsely populated part of the British Isles
  (iv) three capital cities.

(b) For what purposes could a photograph of night-time light emission be used?

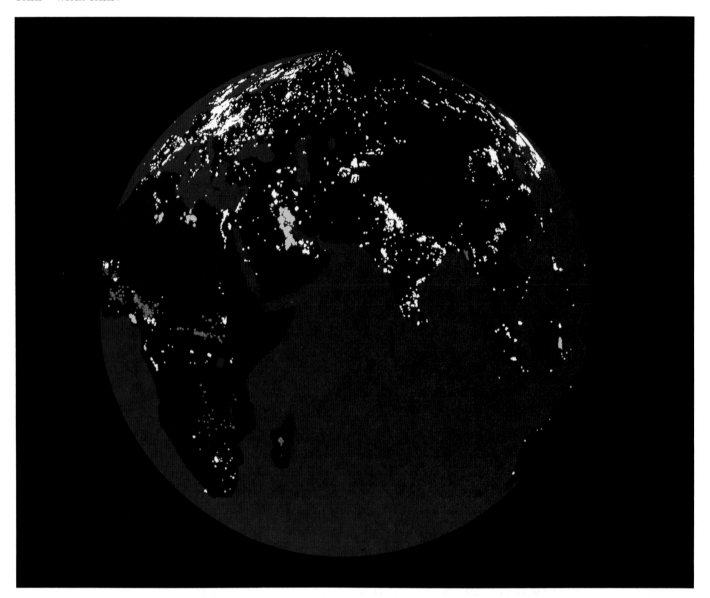

Fig. 1.18 A visible/infrared image of the world at night

This photograph (Fig. 1.18) was produced by recording at the visible/infrared part of the spectrum. It shows three main categories of 'light'.

- The white is, once again, city lights.
- The yellow shows natural gas flares associated with oil fields.
- Red areas indicate agricultural burnings.

QUESTION

1.12 (a) Identify on the photograph and name:
(i) an area of major burning associated with forest clearance
(ii) a major oil producing area
(iii) a major conurbation in South East Asia
(iv) three capital cities.
(b) In what ways is this photograph useful for indicating:
(i) urbanisation
(ii) the location of resources
(iii) environmental degradation?

Fig. 1.19 A Landsat image of the Dead Sea

Remote sensing is a very useful tool in identifying and understanding the physical processes operating on the surface of the earth. Features such as volcanoes can be monitored and their impact measured.

Figure 1.19 is a Landsat image of the Dead Sea, Jordan. The Dead Sea lies between two parallel faults. The rate of earth movement can be measured by comparing satellite images, and governments can be alerted to potential dangers. Although this area has been relatively inactive in recent years, a movement of the Dead Sea slip fault occurred in 1927 at Safed and caused some 500 deaths.

The false colour of the image shows the vegetation on the west bank of the Jordan in comparison with the arid regions to the East.

QUESTION

1.13 (a) How is vegetation represented on the photograph and how are arid regions shown?

(b) Using an atlas, identify national boundaries which cross the area.

(c) For what reasons might land on either side of the river be disputed?

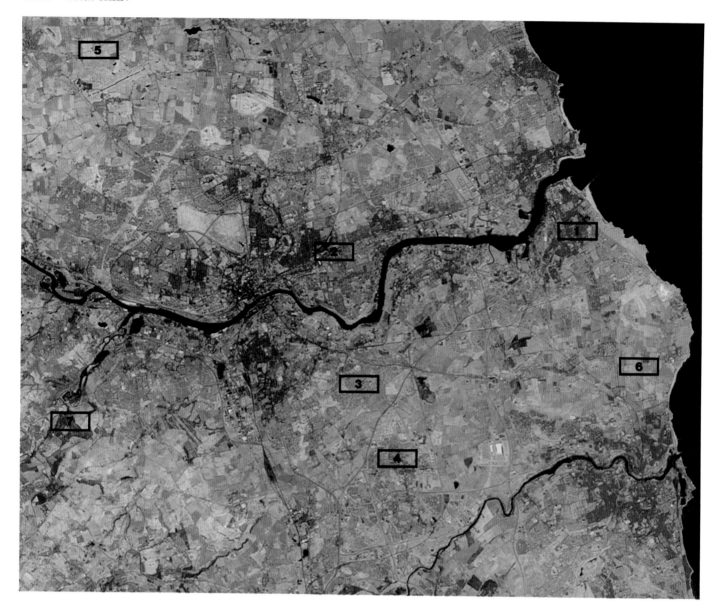

Fig. 1.20 A Landsat false colour image of Tyneside

KEY TO SELECTED LAND USES

Colour	Main land use	Example
Dark blue	Heavy industry	1
Mottled dark blue	Heavily built-up area such as a town centre	2
Mid-blue/pale green/yellow	Suburban housing with playing fields	3
Mottled pale to mid-blue	Suburban houses and gardens	4
Field patterns:		
blue	Ploughed or recently planted	5
red and orange	Standing crops and grass	6
Dark brown/black	Moorland and woodland	7

Figure 1.20 is a false colour Landsat composite of Tyneside. The key to the image is given below it. You will need the 1:50 000 Ordnance Survey map of Tyneside (sheet 88 second series) to help you analyse the photograph.

QUESTIONS

1.14 (a) Make a tracing of the photograph and use the map to identify and label the following:
- the rivers
- the major settlements
- the main roads, railways and the airport
- leisure areas such as the golf courses and the Town Moor north of Newcastle
- the Nissan car plant in the western suburbs of Sunderland.

(b) Describe the location and layout of Washington new town. Compare the layout with the layout of Sunderland.

(c) Comment on the pattern and likely growth of settlement in the area of the Landsat photograph.

1.15 (a) Construct a 10 × 10 grid on tracing paper to fit over the image.

On the tracing draw the shape of the coastline and the river Tyne.

Now try to decide on the major land use in each square and shade in the tracing to produce a generalised map of land use. Use the land use categories in the key.

When you have finished, describe the pattern of land use, with particular mention of the location of heavy industry. Why is the industry located here?

(b) Now make a second tracing to the same size. Number the grid lines from 0 to 9 in both directions starting from the bottom left corner and use it to test the hypothesis that: 'Agricultural land use changes with distance away from the major built-up area'.

Draw up a copy of the following table:

Random point number	Land use	Straight line distance to the edge of the built-up area

Use a random number table to generate 100 six-figure grid references. At each grid reference identify the land use at the point and complete the table. You may wish to work in groups to share out the work so that four people can do 25 points each.

Calculate the percentage for each land use and the average distance from built-up areas for agricultural land use.

Apply significance testing – Appendix, p. 223.

(c) Write a short comment on the application of remote sensing and in particular on its use in sampling spatial patterns and monitoring environmental change.

Fig. 1.21 A false colour Landsat image of the San Francisco Bay area, California

Figure 1.21 shows the San Francisco Bay area. This area is well known for tectonic plate movement. The Pacific plate is moving north-westwards at a rate of 6 cm a year. The earthquake of 1906 was caused by a sudden displacement of 6.4 m along the San Andreas fault. This large displacement was the product of parts of the fault locking up and the build-up of pressure. After this there was a large and sudden displacement known as an earth-quake. In October 1989 an earthquake measuring 7.1 on the Richter scale was caused by movement of the fault beneath the Santa Cruz mountains, south east of San Francisco. Although the epicentre was 90 km away from the built-up area, waves from the earthquake entered the bay area and were amplified by the soft fill and muds around it. This resulted in 28 deaths and damage to 28 000 homes and businesses.

Remote sensing can assist the mapping of large-scale features such as plate margins. It can complement ground surveys and can

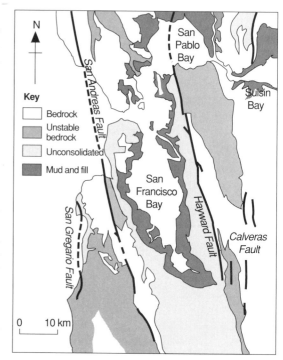

Fig. 1.22 The San Francisco Bay area

Fig. 1.23 An un-enhanced Landsat image of the same area

enable large-scale map up-dating of building areas and infrastructure which may be located in geomorphologically unstable areas.

QUESTION

1.16 (a) Make a tracing of the coastline and the bay area from the false colour Landsat image. Use the image and the map (Fig. 1.22) to indicate the built up area (blue), the San Andreas fault and the Hayward fault.

(b) Draw an annotated diagram to show the development of the 1989 earthquake.

(c) Red shows the redwood forest. In which season do you think this image was taken?

(d) Figure 1.23 is another Landsat image but has not had false colours added. It shows a green patchwork of salt beds at the southern end of the bay. The differences in colour are due to different populations of algae indicating varying salinities. Compare the two images and comment on the benefit of using false colour.

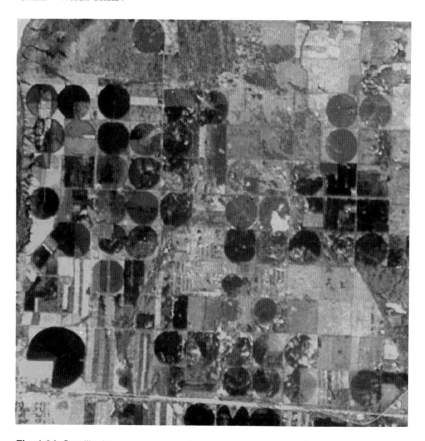

Fig. 1.24 Satellite image showing central-pivot irrigation in Saskatchewan, Canada

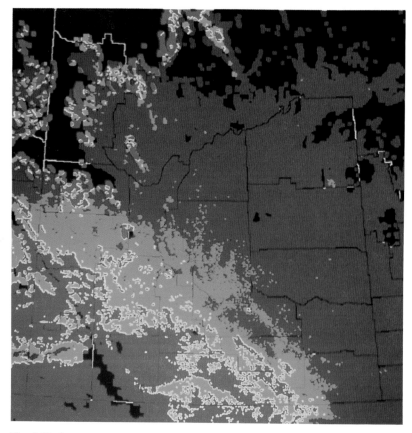

Fig. 1.25 An enhanced colour image illustrating a drought index in an area of Saskatchewan

Satellite images can be used by farmers to warn them of changing soil conditions. Figures 1.24 and 1.25 were produced by the Saskatchewan Research Council for farmers. Figure 1.24 shows the presence of salt in the soil. This is indicated by the red colour. Over 2 million hectares of Saskatchewan can be affected by saline conditions and early detection can avoid a reduced crop yield. Figure 1.25 shows areas of the province classified by a drought index. Red shows areas where the yield may be reduced by 50 to 97% and the light green shows losses of less than 50%. Normal yield is shown by the dark green colour.

This information can help farmers to plan ahead. It can help them to decide on the relative amounts of seed, fertiliser and herbicide inputs and can show them where yields have been reduced by salinity, weeds, poor drainage and excess herbicide application.

QUESTION

1.17 (a) What do the circles indicate in Fig. 1.25?

(b) How do soils become saline in irrigated areas? What action can farmers take to reduce salinity?

(c) How applicable would this remote sensing technology be to countries in the developing world?

Fig. 1.26 shows the delta of the Mackenzie river in northern Canada. Sediment is shown as red on this false colour Landsat image, while the black circular features are lakes in the tundra. The area of the image and the difficulty of the terrain make it impossible to monitor changes on the ground. However, by monitoring satellite images taken over a period of time changes in the sediment flow and the nature of the tundra and permafrost can be measured.

Fig. 1.26 The Mackenzie delta

QUESTION

1.18 (a) Make a tracing of the Landsat image and label the main channel, the delta, the main area of sediment deposition, the distributaries, an oxbow lake and the lakes in the tundra.

(b) Comment on the usefulness of satellite imagery in monitoring large-scale features in areas of low population density.

31

Geographic Information Systems

The development of the computer has made it possible to store a vast amount of information. This information can be retrieved and manipulated to change some of the parameters and can be analysed in terms of new factors. Continuous monitoring of the earth by satellites provides huge amounts of data which need to be used in conjunction with data collected in more conventional ways. Figure 1.27 shows a computer screen displaying a number of maps showing information collected from a variety of sources. In this case the information is on elevation, natural vegetation, roads, rural population, stream networks and national parks. These maps can be superimposed to provide the analyst with a composite image. Such a system is known as a *Geographic Information System* or GIS.

A GIS would be capable of storing a vast amount of information. Data from remote sensing could be input directly into the system to ensure that the system was correctly updated. This makes it a highly valuable management tool for a number of commercial and public companies. Any organisation interested in spatial patterns will have a use for GIS. This will include companies involved in marketing and advertising, as well as planners and public utility companies providing gas and water.

The new generation of satellites is just beginning to be launched, including the European ERS-1 which combines a number of functions. This satellite will measure sea temperatures and changes in the surface of the sea. It will measure aspects of the global weather including surface wind patterns as well as providing continuous data on the changes occurring on the land surface. As well

Fig. 1.27 A display showing elements of a Geographic Information System

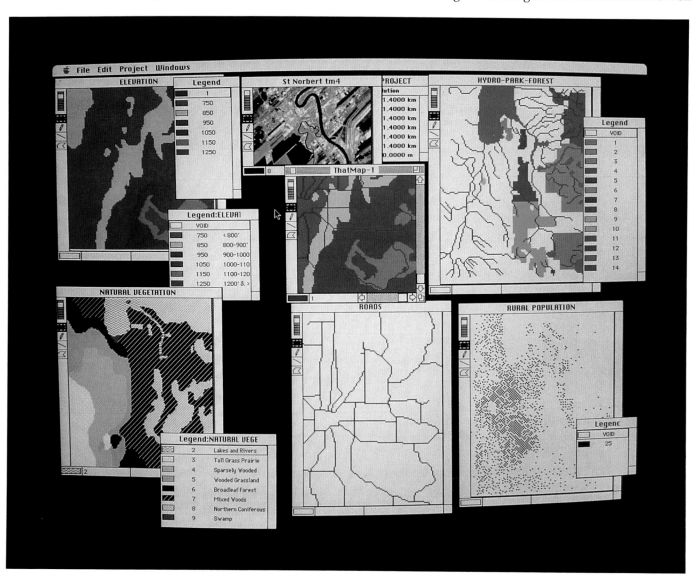

as further satellites to provide data, developments in the future will lead to the construction of additional land stations and a more complete grid of data-collecting stations. This will mean that information about the earth will be more complete in its coverage. It is important to be able to store this information and to get access to it quickly when it is needed. Hence GIS will be a valuable system to help monitor environmental change.

Population issues

Many of the environmental problems of the earth can be related to population growth and to poverty. Is it high population growth rates which bring about poverty or does the condition of being poor lead to high population growth?

Figure 1.28 shows two ways of representing these relationships. Diagram A shows how population growth may affect poverty. It shows that, although there may be the same level of resource availability, there are more people so everyone gets a smaller share. An increase in poverty leads to an increase in environmental problems as farmers are forced to cultivate land which is unsuitable. It might be too steep and removal of the vegetation cover may leave the soil vulnerable to soil erosion, as in northern Thailand. Yields from the land may diminish as a result and the family of the subsistence farmer may have less to eat. The environment is unable to support the population; this acts as a restraint upon further population growth as the death rate increases due to malnutrition and diet-related diseases. This is an example of negative feedback, where an increase in one factor causes an increase in a second factor so that the system re-establishes an equilibrium and may even return to the original level. This is shown by the graph (a) in Fig. 1.29.

Diagram B in Fig. 1.28 represents a different perspective on the situation. Here poverty is shown as the trigger mechanism. This leads to increased population growth as families have more children to compensate for high death rates. The children provide labour for the farm and an 'insurance' for looking after the old people. This can lead to the same environmental pressures and deterioration of the environment, which may lead to greater poverty. This also shows positive feedback in the system, with a worsening of the situation as the cycle proceeds.

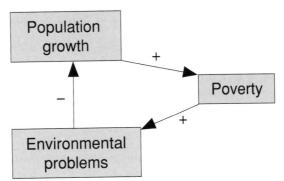

A. Negative feedback

Fig. 1.28 Two possible causes of environmental problems

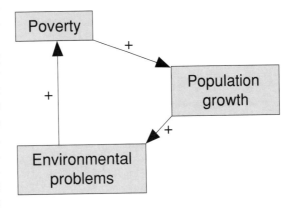

B. Positive feedback

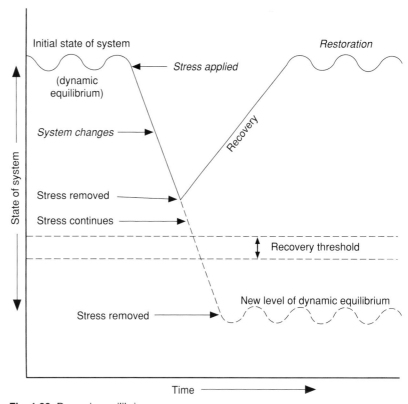

Fig. 1.29 Dynamic equilibrium

Major World Issues

Scientists identify growing danger of global warming

Independent 26-5-90

Sahel awaits the rain

Michael Hulme

THE RAINY season is due to start over most of the semi-arid zone of the Sahel in Africa next month. Farmers, especially, are waiting anxiously.

The last 20 monsoons in Sudan, in the eastern Sahel, have brought rainfall well short of the average for the 20th century. Twenty years is a long time for Sahelians – nearly half their average life expectancy. It is also long enough for climatologists to define a new climatic environment, much less favourable than the wetter decades of the colonial era.

There are at least three different levels of explanation.

At a local level, more intensive land use in the Sahel (which also covers Mauritania, Mali, Niger, Senegal, Burkina Faso and Chad) has led to a reduction of surface vegetation. This reduces the amount of energy reflected from the land and enables larger loads of dust to enter the atmosphere. These consequences are thought likely to reduce rainfall.

At a global level, rainfall reduction in the Sahel is linked with forces in the Pacific Basin ("El Nino" events in which a huge area of the eastern Pacific warms by several degrees), and the possible shift of whole belts of the atmosphere's circulation towards the equator.

Between these local and global extremes there is an intermediate level of explanation which has yielded the most promising results in terms of both understanding and forecasting.

The temperature difference between the oceans of the northern and southern hemispheres is a key. With a relatively warm south Atlantic, the moist monsoon airflow into the Sahel is weakened; with a relatively cool south Atlantic the monsoon is enhanced.

What is now clear is that for the last 20 years or so the south Atlantic has been relatively warm (see diagram). This has therefore undermined the rainfall regime of the Sahel.

What remains less clear is the reasons for the warming of the southern oceans.

• *Dr Michael Hulme is Lecturer in Climatology at Salford University*

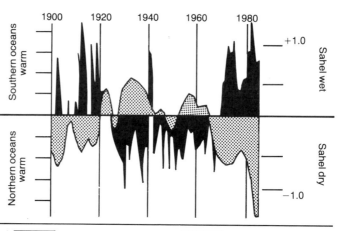

Ocean warmth — Rain in Sahel

Guardian 24-4-88

Guardian 21-9-90

City starves quietly — and prays for aid

Ozone pact in jeopardy

By Andrew Morgan Environment Correspondent

CHINA is threatening to boycott an agreement to phase out the ozone-damaging gases chloro-fluorocarbons at the intergovernmental conference in London this week.

Sunda Correspondent 24-6-9

It is the 'Mother of oil spills' but can nature fight back? **John Vidal** reports on the ecological catastrophe unfolding in the Gulf

The 462 million gallon question

Guardian 1-2-91

Volcanoes back from the dead can catch scientists off-guard

Disaster usually comes, says **Tim Radford**, from mountains the experts see as benign

WHEN the volcano in the Mount Unzen complex near Nagasaki erupted earlier this month, the Japanese were ready. Geologists — mindful that records showed the volcano killed around 15,000 people in 1792 — had predicted that another eruption was imminent.

Above all they were ready because there has been, since at least 1965, a new understanding of earth sciences called tectonics, after the huge rigid tectonic plates which make up the earth's surface and which float on a mantle of semi-molten rock.

This understanding has made both earthquakes and volcanic eruptions, in theory at least, predictable. When Mt Unzen exploded on June 3, people were already leaving the area. But with advance notice, others were arriving to see the phenomenon.

Among the 38 who died in Japan were an American geologist who came to study the eruption, and several journalists reporting on it.

Guardian 13-6-91

Toxic swill that is the country's dirtiest river

Sunday Correspondent 13-5-90

Danger pesticide found in chocolate

Sunday Mail 21-1-90

Streets of Athens emptied by smog

Helena Smith in Athens

UNPRECEDENTED air pollution sent hundreds of Athenians to hospital with breathing and heart problems yesterday and prompted a government warning that people should keep off the streets.

The centre of the capital, under a haze of pollutants, was nearly deserted. Only a group of tireless Greens were prepared to brave a third day of sizzling heat to corrode their lungs in a march to protest at the lack of long-term pollution controls by the ruling conservatives.

"Private cars have to be banned from the city, green space increased and industry dismantled if we're not going to die from this problem," said Thanassis Papaconstantinou, a leading member of the Ecologists-Alternative.

The photochemical cocktail known to Greens as the *nefos* or "cloud" usually attacks around noon when warm, windless weather traps pollutants in the lower atmosphere. Yesterday, however, the *nefos* broke all records, casting its shadow by 9am.

By midday, the environment ministry released a curt statement saying that ozone levels had reached the unheard-of ratio of 393 mg per cubic metre of air. Nitrogen dioxide was registered at 382 mg per cubic metre. Both figures were well above the 300 mg danger level. Sirens wailed as ambulances took Athenians to clinics and hospitals.

Stefanos Manos, the environment minister — who likes to call himself the *nefos* minister — announced that restrictions on cars would be expanded from a small segment of central Athens to a large area of the capital today. Those vehicles allowed on the road, he said, would have to carry at least four people.

Guardian 20-6-91

QUESTIONS

1 Study the cuttings from recent newspapers. Try to work out what the major issues are and to classify them according to whether they are issues dominated by the physical or human environments.

2 Discuss the classification you have arrived at with the rest of your class. Are there any which could go in either column?

3 Make a list of the major issues affecting the earth today. Do not restrict yourself to geographical issues. How many of them have a direct or indirect connection with geography? What conclusion do you draw from this?

4 Start to make a newspaper cuttings collection to illustrate world and local issues. Locate them around an appropriate map on your class noticeboard.

The thesis of the Reverend Thomas Malthus, writing at the end of the eighteenth century, describes the situation in Fig. 1.28A. (See also Chapter 6.) He saw the imminent breakdown of environmental systems as being the fault of population growth. Put simply, his view was that population would outstrip the ability of the earth to feed the population and a calamity would follow. Population would grow by geometric progression and would double every 25 years whilst agricultural production would only increase arithmetically (Fig. 6.9, p. 196). The solution to the problem as seen by Malthus was that population growth could be curbed by 'moral restraint' or through the positive checks on population growth provided by famine, disease and drought which would act to keep the population within the capacity of the earth to support them (the *carrying capacity*).

However, the Malthusian scenario did not come about on a world scale as predicted. For example, new agricultural areas were opened up in the Midwest of the USA which increased the global food supply. Later, the developments of the Green Revolution, including genetic engineering to produce hybrid seeds and developments such as irrigation, became available (see page 156). Many scientists and technologists agree that solutions can always be found to problems whenever major disaster looms.

Population and resources

While the main problem may not be to do with the total amount of resources, it may be something to do with the distribution of and access to them. The earth is, after all, rich in supplies of minerals, power and natural resources.

The biosphere is made up of a series of interacting ecosystems powered by the sun. Within an ecosystem food chain, producers and consumers have evolved in a state of dynamic equilibrium. An increase in a population in the food chain due to a change in the energy input into the system will lead to changes in other parts of the ecosystem. These changes may bring the system back into equilibrium through a series of negative feedback loops if the stress on the system is removed in time. A new level of equilibrium may result if the stress is maintained. These situations are shown diagrammatically in Fig. 1.29.

As humans evolved they have dominated many of the ecosystems of the earth. Inventions and technology have allowed them greater control over ecosystems and have given them more options for management. Grouping of people in settlements led to specialisation, in which groups of people were dependent on others. Hence farmers have provided food for towns and have developed strategies to maximise their output.

Establishing systems of agriculture provided the first stimulus to population growth. In 8000 BCE it is estimated that the world's population numbered 10 million. These people were nomadic or semi-nomadic. By the Common Era the population had increased to 260 million. The growth rate was still very slow by modern standards and was of the

Fig. 1.30 Mechanisation of farming has meant that people now have far greater control over their environment and can change it more swiftly

order of 0.06% per annum. However, the population doubled in the next 1700 years and increased by over five times in the following 200 years. By 1991 the world's population was estimated at 5.4 billion. The United Nations have estimated that the population for CE2000 will be in the region of 6.4 billion. This would mean that the global population would be increasing by 85 million people each year with three births every second. A graph of world population growth is shown in Fig. 1.31.

Looking further into the future is fraught with uncertainty, but the population estimates for the world range between 11.6 billion and 14 billion for the end of the twenty-first century. This is the date when it is thought the global population will at last become stable.

Understanding population change

Much of this increase is due to the reduction in mortality in developed countries and increasing life expectancy. However, life expectancy is also increasing in the developing countries. In India, for example, life expectancy in 1930 was 37 years. By 1974 it was 52 years and by 1990 the figure was 57 years. This change in death rate has to be set against a decrease in fertility. Low fertility was a feature of the developed countries but is now showing in the statistics for some developing countries. According to a survey carried out by the US Agency for International Development, fertility rates have declined from 6.1 to 4.2 births per woman. The largest falls have been noted in the countries with the largest populations. This compares with the European figures which show a decline from 2.6 to 1.6 births per woman. In the UK the rate has declined from 2.1 to 1.8. The reasons for this change are associated with an increase in the education level of women, the availability of contraception (birth control), and changes in attitudes towards family life.

Uncertainties exist whenever estimates of population are made. The effect of AIDS on the global population is very uncertain. Estimates for the number of carriers of the HIV virus in 1991 varied between 5 and 15 million people. At present the disease has not had a significant effect on population statistics but it could in the future. Its effect could be marked, as it may well affect the most fertile and economically active sections of society (Fig 1.32).

The current situation in the world has a

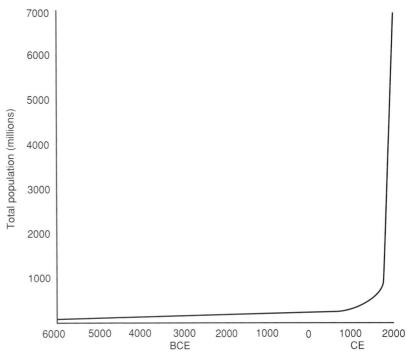

Fig. 1.31 World population growth

Malthusian ring to it as food production has fallen behind population growth in 27 of the 39 sub-Saharan countries. However, agricultural scientists have estimated that the world could produce 25 times the current food output if appropriate management techniques were employed. The problem would seem to be one of distribution rather than capability. For example, the average consumption in the USA is 3658 calories per day, while in India the mean figure is 1880. The World Health Organisation suggest that a mean requirement is 2400 calories.

The Chinese experience

China has made considerable efforts to control population growth. It has 25% of the world's population and has a relatively slow-growing economy. There had been efforts made since the 1950s to reduce fertility by discouraging early marriage and encouraging contraception. The average age of marriage in China is 18 for women and 20 for men. However, the Chinese population continued to grow quickly due to the success in reducing the death rate. In 1979 the one-child policy was introduced. This involved parents signing a pledge to have only one child. They were rewarded with incentives which included cash allowances, extra paid maternity leave, improved housing, extra land allocation, free medical and education facilities and extra grain allowances. These benefits were removed if they had a second

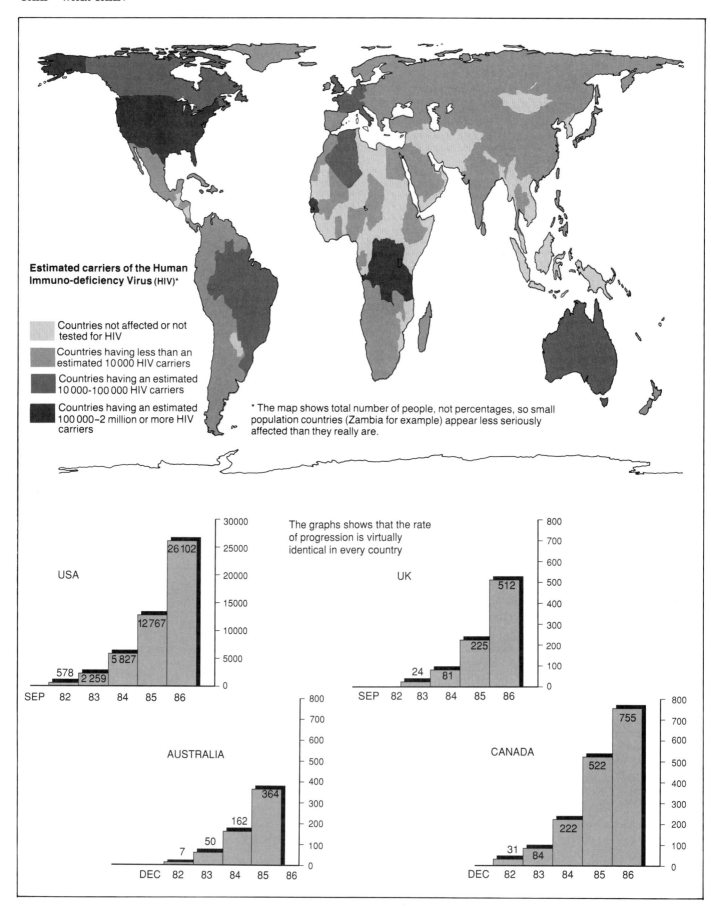

Fig. 1.32 The world AIDS epidemic

Fig. 1.33 A poster for the one-child policy

child and penalties such as salary reduction were implemented if they had a third child.

The policy was unpopular because it was against both Confucian traditions and Marxist ideology. Also the people were concerned about who would care for them in old age. The Chinese government responded by introducing pensions and state care for the elderly. These policies led to a decrease in the growth rate of the population, an increase in the standard of living, later marriage and later first pregnancy.

The fertility rate in China was 5.99 between 1965 and 1970 but 2.36 between 1985 and 1990. It is now predicted that the population will double every 72 years rather than in 21 years as it did between 1949 and 1970 and that population stability will be reached by the year 2000 (when a fertility level of just over 2 is reached).

Associated problems

To understand the global population system fully we have to consider the role of power and politics. Over time people have sought to have access to resources beyond their lands. This desire to control extraction and movement of natural resources has led to the growth of empires. Development of transport has seen the movement of products to the centre of the empire and hence the development of wealthy consuming areas living off the producing areas. This is also true today in thinking about the relations between the developed and developing world. It is no accident that Western Europe has reached a high level of development while much of the African continent is very poor. The two are in part linked by the history of European colonisation of Africa. Two recent reports have stressed the relationship between the developed and developing world. The Brandt report *North–South: a programme for survival* was published in 1980, and in 1987 the Norwegian Prime Minister reported back to the United Nations with her report entitled *Our Common Future.* More will be included on the latter report, the Brundtland Report, later in the book (Chapter 6).

The people of the planet earth are its greatest resource. They are capable of producing great works of art, of seeking after knowledge and of producing rich and lasting cultures.

However, many people are currently unable to realise their potential. They do not have their fair share of the riches of the earth. In fact they live without access to many of the basic needs of life as they are understood in the West and they do not have a voice in the way these resources are allocated.

World Population

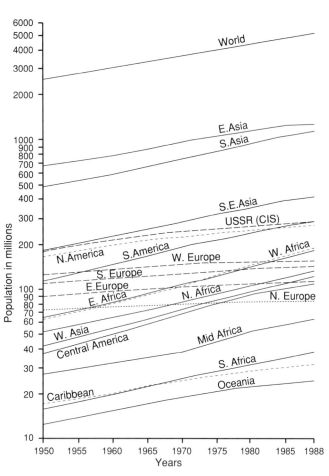

World population growth by region

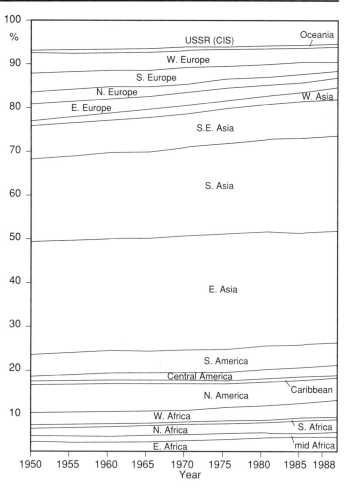

Cumulative percentage graph of population growth by region

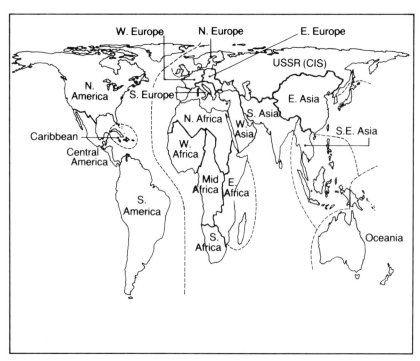

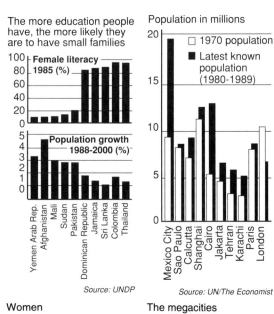

The more education people have, the more likely they are to have small families

Female literacy 1985 (%)

Population growth 1988-2000 (%)

Yemen Arab Rep., Afghanistan, Mali, Sudan, Pakistan, Dominican Republic, Jamaica, Sri Lanka, Colombia, Thailand

Source: UNDP

Women

Population in millions

☐ 1970 population
■ Latest known population (1980-1989)

Mexico City, Sao Paulo, Calcutta, Shanghai, Cairo, Jakarta, Tehran, Karachi, Paris, London

Source: UN/The Economist

The megacities

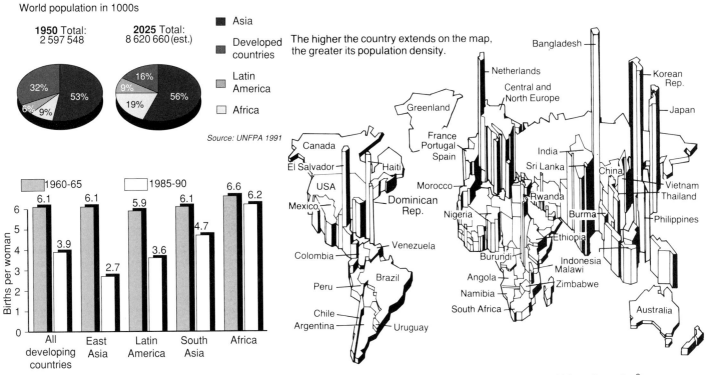

Around the world

World population in 1000s

1950 Total: 2 597 548

2025 Total: 8 620 660 (est.)

- Asia
- Developed countries
- Latin America
- Africa

Source: UNFPA 1991

The higher the country extends on the map, the greater its population density.

1960-65 | 1985-90

Fertility trends in the developing world, by region

High-rises — relative population densities around the world (people per km²)

QUESTIONS

1 (a) The graph showing world population growth by region is a semi-log graph. Look at the axes and suggest why it is called 'semi-log'.

(b) Why is a logarithmic scale useful to illustrate statistics as widely spread as the population figures for Oceania and The World?

2 The steepness of the lines shows the rate of growth.

(a) Classify the regions illustrated on the graph into
(i) faster growing regions,
(ii) slower growing regions.

(b) Do the fast growing regions have anything in common? Explain your answer.

(c) In which of the regions you looked at in (a) are most of the 'megacities' located?

3 What is the relationship between female literacy and population growth? What are the reasons for any relationship you may have found?

4 The other main graph shows the share of world population and how it has changed since 1950.

(a) How is a cumulative percentage graph constructed?

(b) Name one region which has increased its share of the world population over the period shown.

(c) Name one region whose share has declined.

5 The diagram headed 'Around the world' shows pie charts for 1950 and 2025. The last figures illustrated on the cumulative percentage graph are for 1988.

(a) Re-classify the regions shown in the cumulative percentage graph into the categories given in the pie chart (Asia, Developed countries, Latin America and Africa). Determine the percentage share of world population in each of these regions.

(b) Draw a further pie chart for 1988 using the new categories.

6 Suggestions for future work
Collect items from news reports, newspapers and magazines and produce a wall display showing the current state of affairs regarding world population. Use the information to suggest how world population growth may affect economic development, urbanisation, agriculture and any other relevant issues.

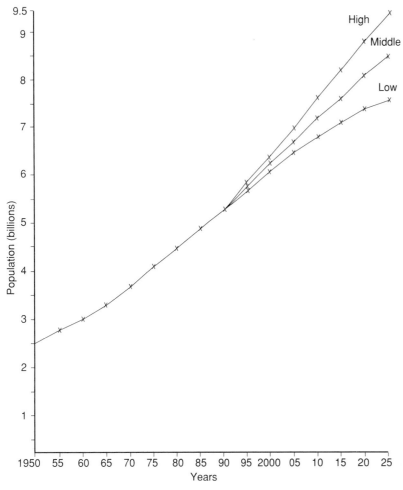

Fig. 1.34 Predictions of world population growth

A recent survey estimated the population of the earth to be 5.4 billion. This population has the following characteristics:

1. *Nourishment.* 450 million people are starving or ill-fed.
2. *Infant mortality.* 19 children per 1000 die before their first birthday in the North, 93 per 1000 in the South.
3. *Primary school enrolment.* A huge increase since 1950 has achieved 73.9% enrolment.
4. *Literacy.* Less than 50% of women are literate and 66% of men.
5. *Housing.* 75% of world housing has been classified as sub-standard, with sanitation being the biggest problem.
6. *Social protection.* National spending on social protection ranges from 0 to about 50% of the Gross National Product.
7. *Civil liberties and political freedom.* 80% of the population of the North have freedom to express their point of view whereas the figure for the South is only 20%.
8. *Employment.* Over 30% of the workforce is unemployed or underemployed.
9. *Life expectancy.* This ranges from about 40 years to over 70 years.

Predicting trends

World population was 5.4 billion and rising in 1991. By the year 2000 the figure could be as high as 6.4 billion. This would be the equivalent of the current population of China being added to the global total between these dates.

These figures are estimates based on current rates of growth. The estimates of world population are shown on Fig. 1.34 and they show the high prediction and low prediction to the year 2025.

Changes in population have been related to a model of demographic transition. This is shown in Fig. 1.35 and shows the population of a country passing through a series of stages as development takes place. The total population is shown as an 'S' shaped curve reaching stability in the last stage. The main problem with the world's population is that many countries are still at the earlier stages of population growth. It is argued that some countries will remain in a low stage as they struggle to emerge from the vicious cycle in which they find themselves.

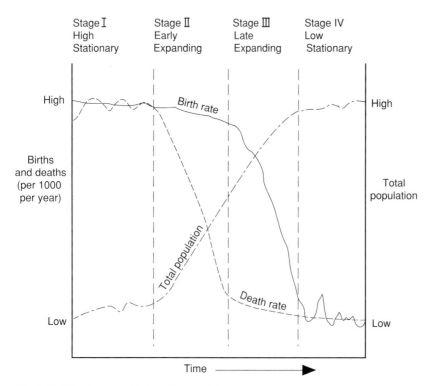

Fig. 1.35 The demographic transition model

QUESTIONS

1.19 Use the data given in the table (Fig. 1.36) to estimate the stage each country has reached in the demographic transition model. Which countries will show a major growth in population? (You can confirm your answer by looking at the population projections for the year 2010.)

1.20 Use the table to test the following hypotheses relating to population growth.

(a) The highest birth rates are in the countries with the lowest GNP.

(b) People live longer in countries with a high GNP.

(c) The highest death rates are found in countries with the lowest % living in towns.

(d) A high rate of contraceptive use is related to a low birth rate.

(e) Poorer countries have a higher fertility rate.

You could test these hypotheses and any others you think are relevant by using Spearman's rank correlation (Appendix, p. 225) and by drawing scattergraphs with best fit lines to show the information. How good are the correlations? Try to account for any residuals which do not fit the overall hypothesis.

1.21 Try to group the countries from the sample into four or five categories and write a short paragraph for each category describing the demography of the group. Discuss the criteria you have used for grouping the countries together.

1.22 Essay: Define the term 'over-population'. Using actual examples wherever possible, outline the problems that are caused by a country perceiving itself to be overpopulated.

Country	Pop. estimate mid-1991 (millions)	Birth rate per 1000 pop.	Death rate per 1000 pop.	Natural increase (ann %)	Pop. doubling time in years at current rate	Pop. proj-ection 2010 (millions)	Infant[1] Mortality	Total[2] Fertility	Life expect-ancy	% Population under 15/ over 65	Urban pop.	% married women using contra-ception	Per capita income ($)
Libya	4.4	37	7	3.1	23	7.1	64	5.2	67	44/3	70	NA	5 410
Burkina Faso	9.4	50	17	3.3	21	17.2	121	7.2	52	48/4	9	NA	310
Kenya	35.2	46	7	3.8	18	45.5	62	6.7	63	50/2	22	27	380
South Africa	40.6	35	8	2.7	26	66.0	52	4.5	64	40/4	58	48	2 460
Israel	4.9	22	6	1.6	43	6.1	10	3.0	76	32/9	90	NA	9 750
Bangladesh	116.6	37	13	2.4	28	176.6	120	4.9	53	44/3	14	33	180
Thailand	58.8	20	7	1.3	53	70.7	39	2.2	66	35/4	18	68	1 170
China	1151.3	21	7	1.4	48	1420.3	33	2.3	69	27/6	26	71	360
USA	252.8	17	9	0.8	88	299.0	9.1	2.1	75	22/12	74	74	21 100
El Salvador	5.4	35	8	2.8	25	7.6	55	4.6	62	44/4	43	47	1 040
Barbados	0.3	16	9	0.7	102	0.3	9	1.8	76	28/10	32	47	6 370
Brazil	153.3	27	8	1.9	35	207.5	63	3.3	65	35/5	75	66	2 550
Denmark	5.1	12	12	0	1732	5.1	8.4	1.6	75	17/16	85	63	20 510
France	56.7	14	9	0.4	169	58.8	7.2	1.8	77	20/14	73	75	17 830
UK	57.5	14	12	0.2	330	59.8	8.4	1.8	75	19/16	87	83	14 750
Hungary	10.4	12	14	−0.2	–	10.5	15.7	1.8	70	21/13	59	73	2 560
Italy	57.7	10	9	0.1	1155	55.9	8.8	1.3	76	17/14	72	78	15 150
New Zealand	3.5	17	8	0.9	75	4.0	10.6	2.1	74	23/11	84	70	11 800

1. Infant deaths per 1000 live births
2. Average number of children born to a woman during her lifetime

Fig. 1.36 Selected statistics

Ozone depletion and the greenhouse effect

The incidence of some natural disasters has increased steadily throughout the last 30 years. These include flooding, storm damage, drought and famine. These have occurred at a time when dramatic changes have been measured in the atmosphere.

One of the most worrying impacts of population changes on the natural system is depletion of the ozone layer in the atmosphere. This is particularly alarming because the ozone layer in the stratosphere, some 15 to 30 km up in the atmosphere, protects life from the harmful effects of ultraviolet radiation. In small doses this radiation causes sunburn, but it can produce skin cancer and eye cataracts in larger doses. Some studies have shown that plant productivity can also be affected. A 25% increase in ultraviolet radiation can reduce the yield of the soya bean by the same amount.

This depletion of ozone was first reported in 1984 by scientists from the British Antarctic Survey. They noted that a hole had appeared in the ozone layer above Antarctica. The main cause of this is said to be the release of chlorine from chlorofluorocarbons (CFCs), composite chemicals used in aerosol propellant, refrigerant gases and many other applications. The chlorine is released by reacting with ice crystals in the upper atmosphere and destroys the ozone in the spring when it reacts with sunlight. Figure 1.37 shows a series of maps of the ozone hole over Antarctica.

Exactly the same problem has now been found closer to the developed world. Satellite measurements of the northern hemisphere have found a belt of depleted ozone between 30 degrees and 50 degrees north. This could have harmful effects on young plants and agricultural yields could be affected. Part of the reason for this depletion in the northern hemisphere could be the amount of sulphuric acid droplets in the atmosphere. Much of this has been input into the atmosphere by volcanic eruptions but human activity also plays a part. The depletion of ozone in the northern hemisphere is currently measured at 8%.

Changes in the ozone layer are also connected with the *greenhouse effect*, which may lead to global warming, as CFCs are also involved in this. The threat of global warming stems from the increasing atmospheric concentration of 'greenhouse gases' which trap the heat given off by the earth as shown in Fig. 1.38. These gases include carbon dioxide,

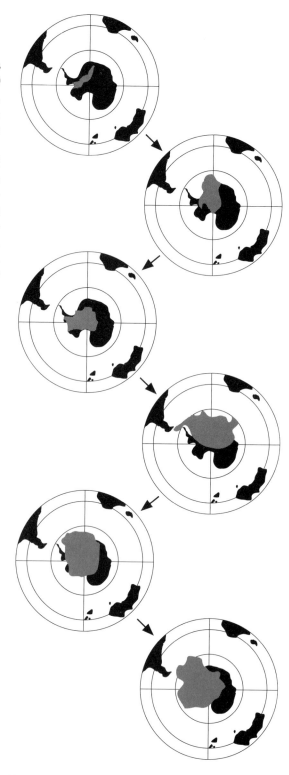

Fig. 1.37 The hole in the ozone layer over Antarctica as it develops over one season

methane, nitrous oxide, chlorofluorocarbons (CFCs) and water vapour.

Carbon dioxide concentration has increased from 315 parts per million (ppm) in 1958, when measurements of the atmosphere were started, to the current level of 353 ppm. This figure accounts for 57% of greenhouse gases and the main source of the additional carbon dioxide is from burning fossil fuels (coal, oil and natural gas). Another 13% of the total comes from deforestation. The rate of increase is 0.4% per annum and it is predicted that global temperatures could rise by 1.5 to 4.5 degrees Celsius as a result. Some scientists have predicted that changes may be highly variable and that changes of 25 to 43.5 degrees Celsius could occur in the polar regions. Figure 1.39 shows some predictions for the major regions of the earth. These figures have been derived from large-scale computer models of the processes acting within the atmosphere and are known as General Circulation Models.

Concentrations of the other gases are currently much lower, but they are potentially more damaging. Methane is emitted from wetlands, rice paddies, livestock and from warming permafrost. Its volume is increasing at an annual rate of 1% and it contributes 12% of the additional greenhouse gases. CFCs are present at a concentration of 0.000 225 ppm but are increasing at a rate of 5% per annum. These make up 25% of the greenhouse gases. Nitrous oxide makes up the remaining 6% and is given off by burning fossil fuels and from deforestation. However, it has a slow growth rate of 0.2% per annum.

Knowledge of all these problems is necessary for planning a sensible course of action.

A International action has been agreed by some governments to reduce the production and use of some of the main contributors to global warming. The situation was first recognised in 1974 and in 1985 the United Nations Environment Programme instituted the Vienna Convention of 43 nations. This convention led to the Montreal protocol (1987) on substances that deplete the ozone layer. A further amendment was signed by the same parties in 1990. This protocol agreed that the production and consumption of CFCs, halons and carbon tetrachloride should be phased out by 2000 and methylchloroform by

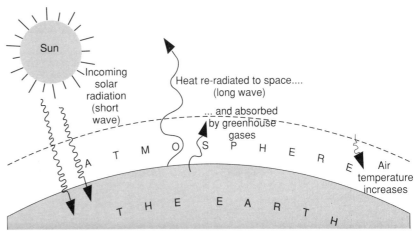

Fig. 1.38 The greenhouse effect

2005. These are all substances used to propel aerosols, to act as coolants in refrigerators and as solvents for cleaning electrical components. In addition, many companies in the developed world have stopped producing and using CFC propellants in aerosols and, under public pressure, now advertise 'environmentally friendly' and 'ozone friendly' products. Action has therefore been taken on both the voluntary and government levels.

QUESTIONS

1.23 The drive to decrease population growth rates and to do something about the ozone depletion has come from the governments of the developed world. The developing world has fewer resources to implement such action. Do you think the developed world should expect the developing world to do anything about these issues? Explain your answer.

1.24 Do you consider that problems such as global warming and ozone depletion are the responsibility of governments, or should individuals be involved in their resolution? Outline the reasons for your answer.

Area	Temperature		Precipitation	
	Winter	Summer	Winter	Summer
North America	+2 to 4°C	+2 to 3°C	+15% increase	+5 to 10% increase
South Asia	+1 to 2°C	+1 to 2°C		+5 to 10% increase
Sahel	+1 to 3°C	+1 to 3°C		Decrease
Southern Europe	+2°C	+2 to 3°C	Increase	−5 to 15% decrease
Australia	+2°C	+1 to 2°C		+10% increase

Fig. 1.39 The predicted effect of global warming on some of the world's regions by CE2000

Global Warming

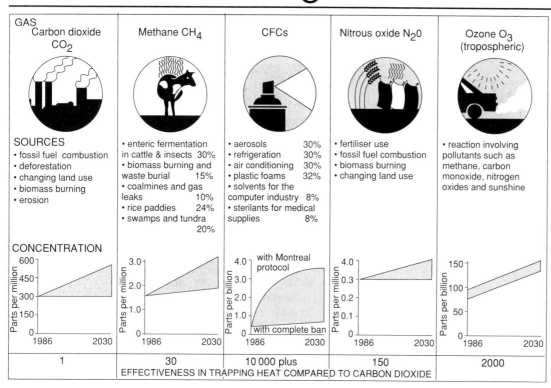

GAS Carbon dioxide CO_2	Methane CH_4	CFCs	Nitrous oxide N_2O	Ozone O_3 (tropospheric)
SOURCES • fossil fuel combustion • deforestation • changing land use • biomass burning • erosion	• enteric fermentation in cattle & insects 30% • biomass burning and waste burial 15% • coalmines and gas leaks 10% • rice paddies 24% • swamps and tundra 20%	• aerosols 30% • refrigeration 30% • air conditioning 30% • plastic foams 32% • solvents for the computer industry 8% • sterilants for medical supplies 8%	• fertiliser use • fossil fuel combustion • biomass burning • changing land use	• reaction involving pollutants such as methane, carbon monoxide, nitrogen oxides and sunshine

The greenhouse gases
(after S. Boyle and J. Ardill)

CONCENTRATION

1	30	10 000 plus	150	2000

EFFECTIVENESS IN TRAPPING HEAT COMPARED TO CARBON DIOXIDE

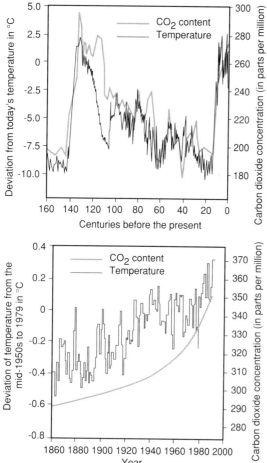

CO₂ content of the atmosphere and temperature change (Greenpeace)

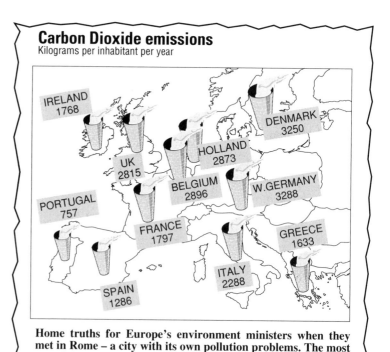

Carbon Dioxide emissions
Kilograms per inhabitant per year

IRELAND 1768
DENMARK 3250
HOLLAND 2873
UK 2815
BELGIUM 2896
W.GERMANY 3288
PORTUGAL 757
FRANCE 1797
GREECE 1633
SPAIN 1286
ITALY 2288

Home truths for Europe's environment ministers when they met in Rome – a city with its own pollution problems. The most surprising figures are for Denmark, the Netherlands and West Germany, the three countries with Europe's strongest ecology lobbies.

Carbon dioxide emissions (kilograms per inhabitant per year)

Cold comfort on global warming

John Hunt on assessments of the effect on crops in Asia and Brazil

AGRICULTURE AND the coastal fishing industry in south-east Asia could be seriously affected by global warming according to the first detailed survey into the regional impact of the "greenhouse" effect.

There could be extremes of weather resulting in droughts, floods and frosts accompanied by sea level rises of 10 to 30 cm by the year 2030, it says. This would cause extensive damage to the fish and prawn industry, which provides an important source of protein in local diet.

Over the next 30 years rice yields in Malaysia may fall by 12 to 22 per cent because of higher temperatures. There would be higher rates of evaporation and substantially increased need for irrigation.

In some areas, however, climate change could be beneficial. Frosts and floods in the south of Brazil might damage coffee and citrus growing, but rainfall increases in parts of south-east Asia might compensate for high evaporation and extend the area of rice cultivation.

The report, The Potential Socio-Economic Effects of Climate Change, was produced by the governments of Indonesia, Malaysia, Thailand and Vietnam and there was a similar study by Brazil.

The United Nations Environment Programme supported the project and the report was edited by the Environmental Change Unit at Oxford University.

For Indonesia, Malaysia and Thailand computer models were used to simulate the possible effects of climate change. Findings were based on a doubling of atmospheric carbon dioxide, the main greenhouse gas, by the year 2030. It was assumed that current trends in emissions would continue, causing an increase in mean annual temperature of C 3° to C 4° (F 5.4° to 7.2°) by 2050.

"Even if greenhouse gas emissions were halted by the year 2030 global sea level would continue to rise by 40 cm by 2100, levelling off a century or so later," it says. In Indonesia maize yields might fall by between 25 and 50 per cent. Improved growing methods could mitigate this but thousands of farm labourers and farmers could lose their livelihoods.

Indonesian rice yields could decrease as a result of higher temperatures and reduced water but the drop could be held at 4 per cent by increases in late season rice production.

Increased rainfall could mean a 30 per cent increase in the irrigation area of the Brantas and Citarum basins in western Java. But heavy rain would also mean increased soil erosion resulting in the loss of 2,000 tonnes of soya bean production in the upper Citarum River basin, 2,500 tonnes in the Brantas basin and 2,700 tonnes in the Saddan River basin. Soya bean yields could frequently fall more than 10 per cent but increased productivity might partly offset this.

In Malaysia the reduction in rice yield would "significantly affect levels of farm income". Many farmers might be forced to seek alternative income, with the poorest relinquishing their land and levels of rural poverty increasing.

The practice of growing two rice crops a year would have to be limited to a smaller area and the effect on national rice output could be substantial. Malaysia's rice production, which satisfies 60 per cent of demand, could be cut to less than 50 per cent of demand.

The east coast of Peninsular Malaysia could become too wet for rubber cultivation with rainfall interfering excessively with tapping. Rubber production, currently valued at M$3.6bn (£750m), could be reduced by 15 per cent.

Much of Malaysia is low-lying coastal plain and sea level rises could cause substantial losses of agricultural land, mangrove forests and fisheries.

In the Suratthani province of southern Thailand, rising sea levels could inundate 37 per cent of the coastal area with the loss of 4,200 hectares of agricultural land.

A study in Ayuthaya Province, Thailand, indicated that the main rice crop could increase by 8 per cent. But this was not consistent with results for Chiang Mai which suggested rice yield would decrease by 5 per cent.

Vietnam says that more research is needed into the effects of climate change but over the long term it could have a significant impact on agriculture. The Red River and Mekong River deltas are major agricultural areas and a substantial reduction in their output would have consequences for the country as a whole.

Brazilian studies concentrated on the current impact of climate variation as a guide to future climate change. Dry spells every year in the highly fertile agricultural region of Brazil's mid-west cause substantial losses in yield of rice and maize.

The report concludes that there is still great uncertainty in predicting climate change but says countries must begin to explore useful responses.

Financial Times 8-11-91

World carbon dioxide emissions 1988 (million tonnes carbon)

	Solid fuel	Liquid fuel	Gas	Total	Per capita
USA	493.6	566.4	238.6	1310.2	5.3
USSR (CIS)	425.3	334.4	302.6	1086.0	3.8
China	487.9	86.9	7.5	609.9	0.56
Japan	82.9	152.8	23.5	269.8	2.2
Germany	78.0	75.0	25.1	182.7	3.0
India	117.4	35.3	3.5	163.8	0.2
UK	66.7	55.0	27.8	152.5	2.7
Poland	106.0	11.9	5.4	125.3	3.3
Canada	28.9	54.9	32.5	119.4	4.6

USA carbon emissions (1988)

	% of total
Residential	8.6
Commercial	5.2
Industrial	15.7
Transport	36.8
Electrical utilities	33.7

QUESTIONS
1. What are the main causes of global warming?
2. To what extent does the carbon dioxide content of the atmosphere appear to be linked to temperature?
3. Using actual examples, explain why global warming matters.
4. To what extent are carbon dioxide emissions linked to population levels?
5. One solution that has been suggested to this problem is a carbon tax, whereby the main users (and therefore the culprits) pay more to continue their use of fossil fuels than they do now. Make out a case in support of governments introducing such a carbon tax.

Fig. 1.40 Some attempts to monitor the situation

A. AIR POLLUTION (tonnes per year)

	SOx	Dust particles	NOx	CO2	HC
OECD	53 892	15 448	37 992	134 945	37,459
Australia	1 479	271	915	3 704	423
Austria	325	50	201	1 126	251*
Belgium	856	267	317	839	339*
Canada	4 650	1 907	1 942	9 928	2 100
Denmark	452	47*	245	577a	197
Finland	587	97b	284	660c	163*
France	3 512	483	2 561*	6 620	1 972*
West Germany	3 187	696	2 935	11 708	2 490
Greece	546*	40*	217*	695*	130*
Ireland	217	94	71	497	62
Italy	3 211d	386d	1 585d	5 487d	1 566*
Japan	1 259	133	1 340		
Luxembourg	24		23		11*
Netherlands	462	162	553	1 450	493
New Zealand	88*	21*	89*	566*	38*
Norway	150	28d	2 036	81	59
Portugal	266	119*	116	533*	159*
Spain	2 543*	1 521c	937*	3 780	843*
Sweden	502	170b	318	1 250	410
Switzerland	126	28	196	711	311
Turkey	714*	138*	380*	3 707*	2 011*
UK	4 836	290e	2 264	4 999	2 241f
US	23 900	8 500	20 300	76 100	23 000

* Estimate   a Mobile sources only
b 1978   c 1979   d Excludes industrial emissions
e Emissions from coal combustion only
f Total hydrocarbons

B. WASTE DISPOSAL AND RECYCLING (tonnes per year)

	Municipal	Industrial	Hazardous/special	Paper and cardboard	Glass
OECD	352 890	1 299 604	286 591		
Australia	10 000	20 000*	300	31.8	17.0
Austria	1 727a	31 000*	200	36.8	44.0
Belgium	3 082	8 000	915	14.7	39.0
Canada	16 000	61 000	3 290	18.0*	12.0*
Denmark	2 161	1 317	125	31.0	32.0
Finland	2 000	15 000	124	30.0	20.0
France	15 000	50 000	2 000	33.0	26.0
West Germany	19 387	55 932	5 000	41.2	37.0
Greece	2 500	3 904			
Ireland	1 100	1 580	20	15.0	8.0
Italy	15 000	35 000*			38.0
Japan	41 530	312 000	666	49.6	54.4
Luxembourg	131	135	4		
Netherlands	6 510	3 942b	1 500	50.3c	62.0
New Zealand	2 160	300b	50*	19.0	53.0d
Norway	1 970	2 186e	120	21.1	
Portugal	2 246	11 200	1 049	38.0*	14.0
Spain	10 568	5 108	1 708	44.1	22.0
Sweden	2 650	4 000	500	40.0	20.0
Switzerland	2 500		120	38.0	47.0
UKf	16 668	50 000	3 900	27.0	13.0
US	178 000*	628 000g	265 000	20.0	8.0

* Estimate   a Household waste only
b Non-chemical waste only
c Recycled from the paper industry only
d Includes reusable bottles
e Wastes from the chemical industry only
f England and Wales only   g Includes waste waters

C. ANNUAL EMISSION OF GREENHOUSE AND OZONE DEPLETING GASES 1950–86

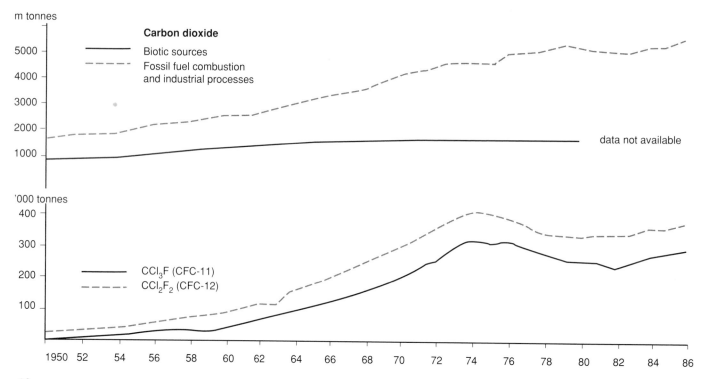

Monitoring of the side effects of population growth is still in its infancy. Techniques for measuring these effects are still being refined (and in some cases, invented) and monitoring is at best patchy. Only since the 1980s have some governments taken the threats to the environment seriously and many individuals (and governments) still ignore them even now.

Some attempts at monitoring are illustrated in Fig. 1.40.

Problem-Solving Exercises

A. Planning to reduce inputs into the atmosphere

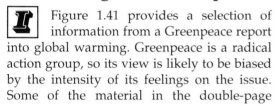 Figure 1.41 provides a selection of information from a Greenpeace report into global warming. Greenpeace is a radical action group, so its view is likely to be biased by the intensity of its feelings on the issue. Some of the material in the double-page spread on global warming is also from this source, but some is from other bodies.

Use the information provided in the double-page spread (pp. 46–7) and the information in Fig. 1.41 to identify the various elements of the problem of global warming.

THE ROLE OF TRANSPORT

Here we have some bitter choices to make. The combustion of one litre of petrol in a car produces around 2.5 kilos of carbon dioxide. Cars and light vans produce around 15 per cent of global carbon dioxide emissions, and are the fastest growing source of carbon dioxide. In Britain we now have 21 million cars on ever more congested roads and we will shortly have 25 million. Six thousand new cars take to the road every single day. There are several environmental prices paid for this social nonsense, as city and country dwellers alike are beginning to discover. And the social nonsense needs to stop.

We need to stop subsidising private motoring and begin massive funding of public transport. The clear alternative of an integrated public transport system is there for the having and must now be given priority. The environmental folly of two or three car families, of subsidised company cars, of ever-increasing road building plans – all this must be confronted and the alternative sanity made into political reality. We need to stop subsidising private motoring and begin the massive subsidising of public transport. It is an argument you will have heard in other areas; it is a key component of any solution to the Greenhouse Effect.

What you can do
* Use your car less. Set a maximum annual mileage of at least 20% less than you drove last year.
* When you replace your car, make fuel consumption the top priority in your choice of new car.
* Burn only unleaded petrol.
* When you buy a new car, consider only models already fitted with catalytic convertors.

What industry can do
* Develop and introduce energy saving vehicles and fuels as a first priority.

What the UK government can do
* Remove all subsidies on company cars.
* Require all new cars manufactured in or imported to the UK to average a minimum of 100 mpg by 1999.
* Require local councils to draw up plans and implement the banning of private cars from city and town centres by 1999.
* Invest heavily in the planning and development of an excellent integrated public transport system.

Fig. 1.41 Extracts from Greenpeace report

Fig. 1.41 (*cont*)

AGRICULTURE

Current agricultural practices are making a significant contribution to the Greenhouse Effect. Methane, partly produced from agricultural sources, is providing 18% of the Greenhouse gases. Nitrous oxides, produced in part from fertilisers, represent a further 6%. Global warming may lead to massive shifts in agricultural production being forced upon us. Right now we need to eat far less meat and graze far fewer ruminants. But nothing is easy; we could all become vegetarians tomorrow, and the rice fields of the East, which feed such a high proportion of the world's population, would still be contributing terrifying amounts of methane to the atmosphere. The answers can only be global – and radical.

What you can do
* Eat less meat and dairy produce.
* Do not eat hamburgers from companies associated with forest destruction in the Third World.
* Ask for and purchase organically grown produce as much as possible. Your purchasing decisions will influence the planning decisions of food retailers and consequently of the farming communities.

What the UK government can do
* Create incentives for farmers to switch out of beef and dairy production and into organically grown crop production.
* Implement restrictions on the use of nitrogen fertilisers.

ENERGY EFFICIENCY

The quickest and most cost effective way to reduce CO_2 emissions to the atmosphere is to implement a crash programme of energy saving and efficient energy use.

For instance, every kilowatt hour of electricity burned means 1 kilo of CO_2 released into the atmosphere from the power station. And every litre of petrol burnt in you car means 2.5 kilos of CO_2 released from your car exhaust.

By cutting back on energy use we can instantly affect the amount of CO_2 emission – by some 127 million tonnes if we saved energy and used energy with maximum efficiency.

The rich countries of the world must take the lead in saving energy. They burn most of it and are responsible for the lion's share of the global warming. It will not be possible for the rich countries to persuade poorer nations to forego high energy industrialisation plans unless the rich nations have developed and tested the low energy technologies on which human survival will depend.

What you can do
* Use your car less.
* When you come to buy or replace anything that burns energy buy the most energy efficient model. Demand to know the energy use of the products you buy.
* Decide to cut your fuel bills by at least 20% across the board. Then work out for yourself how best to achieve that – by better home insulation, for instance, or by buying energy saving equipment.

What industry can do
* Every company must commit itself to a provable reduction in energy use and should aim for absolute reductions in its energy costs.
* Companies should monitor and publish inventories of solids, gases and liquids (aerosols) released to the atmosphere from their factories. This is now required by law in the USA.
* Manufacturers should label their products to show energy use.

What the UK government can do
* Make a commitment to reduce UK CO_2 emissions by 20% by the year 2000, and by 50% as soon as possible after that.
* Make an immediate commitment to zero energy growth (absolute reductions).
* Enforce energy labelling.
* Require utilities to adopt pricing policies which will discourage rather than encourage excessive use.
* Use tax measures to raise the basic prices of all sources of energy on an annual basis from 1992 to help meet the targets to reduce energy use. Use the resulting revenue to invest in energy efficiency technologies, to make grants for their adoption by

Fig. 1.41 (cont)

industry, to fund energy efficiency schemes for low income households, and to assist Third World countries in the development of energy conservation.

* Require power utilities to prove that each new power station planned is necessary. They would need to show that all other options for producing and conserving energy have been investigated and have proved insufficient to meet the need.
* Invest in energy efficient technologies for fossil fuel power stations (which are currently only 35% efficient).
* Invest in the development and installation of renewable energy technologies.
* Take a lead amongst the international community in pressing for energy efficient societies.
* Work towards international agreement on CO_2 and energy use reductions.

WHY TREES MATTER

Destroy a tree and you destroy a natural means of 'soaking up' carbon dioxide. Burn a tree and the very burning aggravates the Greenhouse problem. Burn a whole forest and you engage in a peculiar act of social suicide.

In October 1988 a small American electricity company, Applied Energy Systems in Virginia, announced a plan to plant 15 million trees in Guatemala – an area of a thousand square kilometres. They estimated that this was the amount of forest needed to absorb the 387, 000 tonnes of carbon dioxide per year from their 180MW coal burning power station.

Few vested interests would be this imaginative. Reafforestation cannot solve the Greenhouse Effect. But it can buy time – maybe thirty or forty years – in which to reduce the Greenhouse gases.

Meanwhile, of course, we continue to burn trees everywhere and in parts of the Third World to slaughter the rain forests. It is no use criticising countries like Brazil – they're using the land for cattle ranching, crops and mining to finance the debts they owe to countries like us. We need a far more imaginative attitude to these debts which are crippling so many of these countries – perhaps a 'debt-swap' arrangement that writes off debt for protecting areas of rainforest.

THE ROLE OF THE THIRD WORLD

The rich nations of the world have few moral lessons to offer. They are the countries that have produced the Greenhouse Effect. Twenty years ago it would have been conventional wisdom that we wanted the Third World to be able to develop in the way that we have.

Not any more. The huge and expanding populations of Third World countries must be persuaded from going down the same road. We must not export the technology of the inefficient power station, the private car and the CFC aerosol. We must export energy efficient technologies – which are, in any case, more relevant to Third World societies. We must give them the lessons we have learned about agricultural chemicals and toxins. We must restrain the aggressive practices of certain multinational timber companies. We should cancel debts. We should acknowledge in every way the help we must give the Third World in our fight to save the planet. If we do not, they are likely to pursue every short cut to feed, house and sustain their own growing populations. The rich countries have just acknowledged a bitter lesson: our first duty is to pass it on to the Third World countries and help them implement the alternatives. Without them we are lost.

What the UK government can do

* Write off Third World debts in exchange for agreements from debtor countries to invest in energy efficient technologies and reafforestation schemes.
* Penalise multinational corporations operating in the UK which have member companies involved in forest destruction programmes in the Third World.
* Finance the exchange of energy efficient technologies, technologies which reduce CO_2 emissions and renewable energy technologies between the UK and the Third World.
* Ban the export of CFCs and other ozone depleters, and help to provide Third World countries with CFC-substitute technology.
* Instigate a World Fund for coping with Greenhouse related disasters.

What alternatives are open to governments and individuals to stop the input of harmful substances into the atmosphere? Complete the sections of the grid (Fig. 1.42). For each entry try to think of the implications of such action on society in general, and on the living standards of individuals.

Element of global warming	Cause	What can ...		
		Western governments do?	Governments of developing countries do?	Individuals do?
Transport				
Agriculture				
Energy efficiency				

Fig. 1.42 The Impact Grid

QUESTIONS

1.26 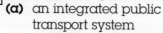 What effect could the following have on solving the problem of global warming:
  (a) an integrated public transport system
  (b) a large investment in commercial systems for producing alternative energy
  (c) public boycott of products made from tropical hardwoods?

1.27 What inducements can you think of for reducing the emissions from motor cars? Can the number of cars be reduced or could they use their fuel more efficiently? Try to brainstorm as many different ways of solving the problem as you can. Group your solutions under suitable headings and discuss them with the rest of the class.

1.28 What can governments and individuals do to play their part in reducing the output of greenhouse gases? Study the information given in this chapter and try to work out at least two things that each of the following could do to improve the situation:
  (a) an individual living in a developed country such as the UK
  (b) the government of an industrialised country
  (c) the government of a developing country where population is rising quickly and the expectation of rapid development is high
  (d) the director of the World Bank approving applications for development capital for the Third World.

1.29 Evaluate the following options for the long-term reduction and elimination of global warming. How realistic are they? What are the obstacles to implementing such strategies?
1. *Abandon growth.* Industrial society treats the natural world as an endless store of resources to be plundered and exploited. Consumerism and economic growth are the twin gods of modern life. Defeating global

warming may mean that we have to rethink our relationship with our natural surroundings, learning to love the earth as well as ourselves.

2. *Reduce the use of fossil fuels.* Carbon dioxide is one of the main greenhouse gases. Much of this is released from burning oil, coal and gas. Cutting our use of these resources and changing our dependency on these fuels would stop the build-up of carbon dioxide. This would fundamentally change the world's energy system.

3. *Boost alternatives.* Research into non-polluting sources of renewable energy could help us move away from our dependence on fossil fuels. At the same time work could be done to improve energy conservation by reducing the amount of energy we use and improving energy efficiency so that we do not waste energy.

4. *Ban CFCs totally.*

5. *Save the trees.* Stop countries pursuing policies of deforestation so that the trees can remove the carbon dioxide. The clearing of trees for farming and grazing accounts for 13% of global warming.

6. *Fight for fairness.* The economies of the Western world have become wealthy due in part to cheap fossil fuels. In an attempt to develop, countries of the Third World have incurred vast debts. These are now crippling many Third World countries. Poverty is now a huge threat to the environment. Restructuring of the world economy in favour of the poor is critical to fighting global warming.

7. *International action.* These effects are not confined to national boundaries. A global action plan is required in which all the countries of the world unite to work together.

B. Global warming and the supply of water – a case study from the Middle East

Background

Despite the fact that much of global warming will be the result of the indulgences of countries in the developed world, some of the major impacts will be found in developing countries. These impacts could be multiplied as countries experiencing rapid population growth aim to increase food production and control raw materials. This in turn could lead to political unrest and even international confrontation. Many past disputes have developed over competition for territory and resources and these may increase as the demand for these commodities increases and the supply becomes more scarce. All nations require a continuous supply of food, water, fuel and raw materials and the need for access to these resources is a powerful driving force for conflict. There is a growing recognition that a country's security is dependent upon political stability and environmental security. Both these requirements must be satisfied to achieve full

security. This may mean, for example, that whole drainage basins need to be controlled so that the people of a country can gain the full benefits of a secure water supply.

The Middle East is one region where the relationship between these factors can be seen to operate. Water is essential to the development of agriculture in an arid area. Seasonal temperature variations are very wide, precipitation is irregular, and much of the region does not receive adequate rainfall. High rates of population increase and urbanisation lead to increases in demand for water for domestic and industrial uses. Water is in constant demand for irrigation schemes. Control of the supplies of water is therefore vital to the economic and social well-being of the countries of the region. While conflicts over oil reserves and territory appear to be the major disagreements in the area, disputes over water have occurred.

Figure 1.43 shows the planned use of the basin of the Tigris–Euphrates. The basin of the Euphrates covers 444 000 square kilometres and this is divided between Turkey (28%), Syria (17%), Iraq (40%) and Saudi Arabia (15%). However, 62% of its inputs come from within Turkey. The area of the Tigris basin is of similar size but over half of its area is in Iraq. Development of these basins is vital to economic progress in the region, but the supply of water is scarce and is less than the planned demand. The Turkish Grand Anatolia Project (GAP) plans to transform nearly 10% of the area of Turkey into a vast grain-producing region. This area would require 10 000 million cubic metres of water each year to irrigate the 700 000 hectares. Syria has plans to use a further 7000 million cubic metres. The amount of water available to Iraq would be reduced from 30 000 million cubic metres to 11 000. This is at least 2000 million cubic metres short of what the Iraqis need to implement *their* development schemes.

This has already created tension in the area when the flow of the river was interrupted in January 1990. If the GAP scheme is fully implemented it could cut Syria's share of the water by 40% and Iraq's by 80%. When Syria completed the Al-Thawra dam in 1975 Iraqi troops were rushed to the border as a show of strength.

The basin of the river Jordan is also the scene of conflict. Figure 1.44 shows the area concerned. Israel gained territory after the 1967 war with her Arab neighbours. The previous boundary had been the 1949 armistice line. However, following the 1967 war Israel claimed areas of the Golan Heights in Syria and the West Bank from Jordan. The River Jordan is now the frontier between Israel and Jordan.

This had the effect of allowing the Israelis to control the water resources of the Jordan basin. Water from the Golan Heights feeds into the headwaters of the Jordan via the Sea of Galilee. Also, the water resources of the aquifers (see Fig 1.49) under the West Bank passed into Israeli hands. Plans to capture the headwaters of the Litani River in Lebanon have not been discounted by Israeli hydrologists.

The Israelis pump water from the Sea of Galilee into a series of pipes and canals which make up the National Water Carrier. This takes water to Tel Aviv and on to feed the orange groves of the Negev Desert. Water is being redirected into the Sea of Galilee from the River Yarmuk to provide extra supplies. This is leaving the discharge in the river Jordan very low. As the discharge drops so the water becomes more saline. At present 90% of the water in the West Bank is used by Israelis with the remainder being used in the Palestinian villages.

Jordan's plans to dam the River Yarmuk were stopped in 1967 when the dam on the river was destroyed. Plans to build the Unity dam with World Bank finance depend on a peaceful settlement to the political problems of the area.

The Egyptians have also been very concerned about the flow of water in the river Nile. They are concerned that Israeli water engineers have been working in Ethiopia and Uganda, planning irrigation schemes that could reduce the amount of water reaching Egypt.

Exercise

You are to present a report to the United Nations Environment Programme (UNEP) on the Nile and Jordan Basins. You should indicate the problems of water use in the

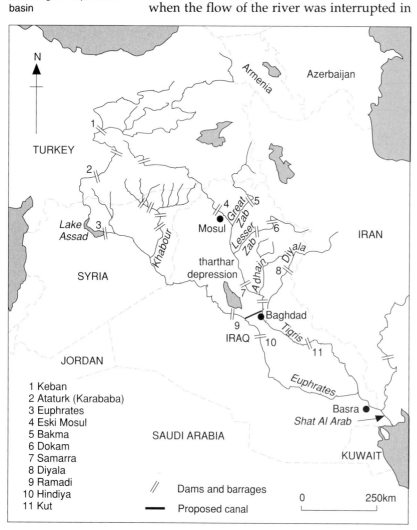

Fig. 1.43 Water projects in the Tigris–Euphrates basin

1 Keban
2 Ataturk (Karababa)
3 Euphrates
4 Eski Mosul
5 Bakma
6 Dokam
7 Samarra
8 Diyala
9 Ramadi
10 Hindiya
11 Kut

Dams and barrages
Proposed canal

0   250km

basins against the background of global warming and then try to present management solutions. Use all the relevant information in this section. You should use the following questions to help you structure the report.

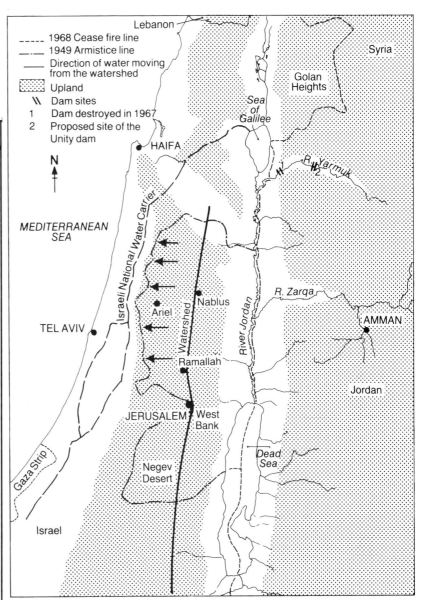

Fig. 1.44 The Jordan basin

QUESTIONS

1.30 Draw a climate graph for Jerusalem on circular graph paper, similar to those shown in Fig. 1.55. Describe the climate of the area using this and the three climate graphs in Fig. 1.55 and information from your atlas.

1.31 Now use the information from the GISS general circulation model (Fig. 1.45) to draw sketch graphs for the four locations to show what the predictions will actually mean to this area.

What effect will this change have on the hydrology of the area? Using the example of the Nile's hydrograph (Fig. 1.48) and the information relating to evaporation rates, draw a sketch hydrograph to show the predicted changes in discharge.

1.32 Draw a suitable graph to show the likely changes in the populations of the Middle East countries and the changes to the urban populations.

1.33 Many of the schemes in the area involve building dams. These can bring problems as well as advantages. Identify the likely changes to agriculture downstream of some of the major dam projects. The example of Egypt may assist you.

1.34 Write a summary of the likely problems of water supply in the area in the future.

1.35 Describe the changes which have taken place in the Jordan basin and produce a model for one of the basins to show an equitable use of water in an area where several countries are competing for the supply. Remember the Unity dam could still be built.

1.36 Describe six steps you would consider to be necessary in implementing your plan. Remember, you have to try to sell the plan to the countries concerned. How much would you allow the countries concerned to be involved? Would you require the services of an international agency to oversee the running of the project?

1.37 How would the situation be monitored? Suggest a series of indicators to measure the effectiveness of the plan.

Fig. 1.45 Drainage basins
of the Middle East

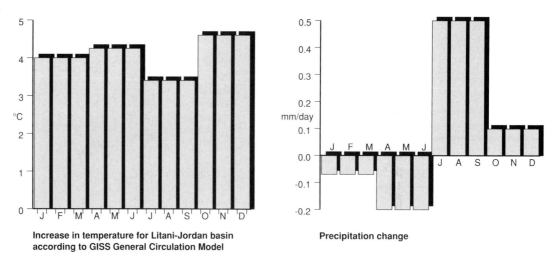

Increase in temperature for Litani-Jordan basin
according to GISS General Circulation Model

Precipitation change

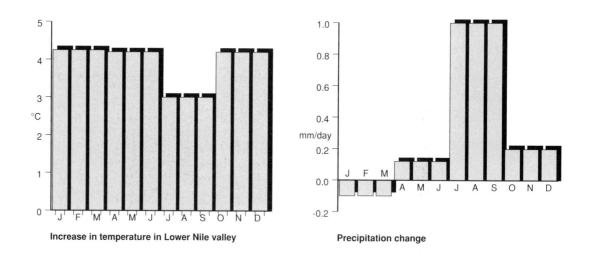

Increase in temperature in Lower Nile valley

Precipitation change

	J	F	M	A	M	J	J	A	S	O	N	D
Jerusalem °C	9.90	10.5	12.0	17.5	20.5	22.5	23.8	24.2	23.2	21.2	16.3	11.1
mm	132	132	64	28	3	<1	0	0	<1	13	71	86

Fig. 1.46 Population data
for selected Middle
Eastern countries

A. Population data 1960–89

	Population size (millions of people)						
	1960	1965	1970	1975	1980	1985	1989
Egypt	25.5	29.4	33.1	37.0	42.3	46.8	51.4
Ethiopia	20.0	22.6	25.5	28.8	31.1	36.5	48.7
Sudan	11.2	12.5	13.8	16.5	18.7	21.6	24.2
Israel	2.1	2.6	3.0	3.5	3.9	4.3	4.5
Jordan	1.7	2.0	2.3	2.7	3.2	3.5	4.1
Lebanon	1.9	2.2	2.5	2.8	2.7	2.7	2.9
Syria	4.6	5.3	6.3	7.4	9.0	10.6	12.2

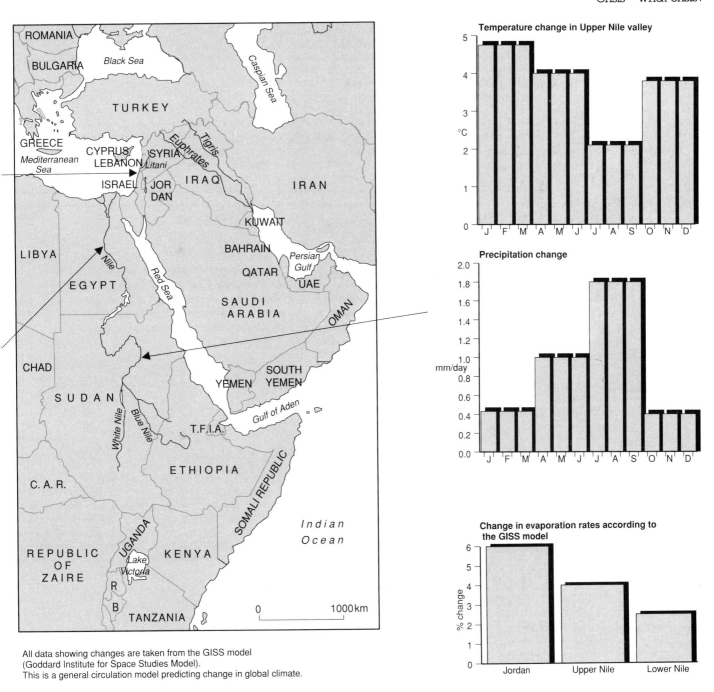

All data showing changes are taken from the GISS model
(Goddard Institute for Space Studies Model).
This is a general circulation model predicting change in global climate.

B. Population growth rates 1965–90

	Population growth rate (average annual percentage change)				
	1965–70	1970–75	1975–80	1980–85	1985–90
Egypt	2.2	2.1	2.5	1.9	2.3
Ethiopia	2.3	2.3	1.5	3.0	2.8
Sudan	2.0	3.3	2.3	2.7	2.9
Israel	2.8	2.8	2.1	2.0	1.7
Jordan	2.9	3.0	3.3	1.5	4.0
Lebanon	2.6	2.2	−0.8	0.1	2.1
Syria	3.0	3.2	3.4	3.0	3.7

Fig. 1.47 The regional context for water planning in the Middle East

Country	Area (000 km²)	Arable (000 km²)	Forest (000 km²)	Food intake (cals/day)	GNP per capita ($)	Debt ($m)	Debt as % of GNP
Egypt	995	25	0	3183	700	15 229	49
Sudan	2376	124	483	2314	400	5 729	78
Ethiopia	1101	140	265	2149	140	1 223	26
Iraq	434	55	15	2789	NA	NA	NA
Israel	20	4.2	1.2	3062	5630	15 149	70
Jordan	97	4.1	0.4	2498	1710	1 940	48
Lebanon	10	2.9	0.7	2995	NA	182	NA
Syria	184	58	4.9	3010	1680	2 305	14
Turkey	771	273	202	3002	1230	15 396	30

Fig. 1.48 The Jordan valley

Figure 1.44 shows that the Jordan basin is the 'river basin in which competition for water is stronger than anywhere else in the world' (Malin Falkenmark). Climatic warming may increase evaporation rates, leading to lower soil moisture. The bordering states – Israel, Jordan, Lebanon and Syria – have all tried to develop the area in isolation and Israel has resisted these changes by the others with force. The occupation of the West Bank by the Israelis has ensured that the rainfall in the West Bank would sufficiently recharge the aquifer (see Fig 1.49) supplying half Israel's water needs. Unless there is co-ordinated effort to redistribute the water the Arab states could face acute shortages in the middle of the 1990s.

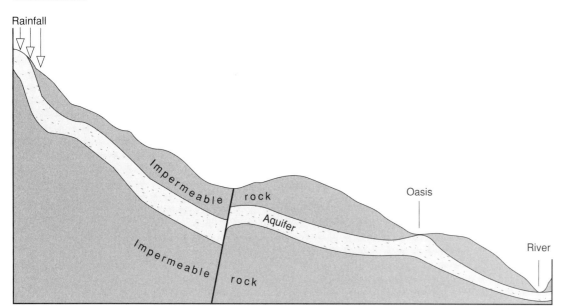

Catchment area

Rainfall

Impermeable rock

Aquifer

Impermeable rock

Oasis

River

Israel's gross domestic product has increased six times since 1960. This rate of economic progress has put considerable strain on its water resources. It is estimated that Israel's renewable water resources are 1500 million cubic metres per years, with an additional 300 million cubic metres added through re-user programmes. The demand for fresh water is about 1700 million cubic metres per year. However, the country suffers from the problem of deteriorating water quality. Increased levels of sewage discharge are causing nitrate build-up, and the Jordan river is being polluted by oil spills. Eutrophication is occurring in the river due to the discharge of agricultural fertilisers.

The increased use of irrigation is leading to the development of saline soils, which is affecting the water quality. These are the six main options open to the country:

1. Developing shared agreements with their Arab neighbours.
2. Restructuring the economy to place less emphasis on agriculture.
3. Acquiring more water resources by conquest.
4. Importing water by tanker from a friendly country such as Turkey.
5. Desalination of sea and lake water.
6. Improvement in water recycling.

Fig. 1.50 Israel

Fig. 1.51 The occupied
territories

The water resources of the West Bank are now critical to Israel. Israel takes 40% of its water from this source. There are three major aquifers in the West Bank. Israel exploited two of them before the 1967 war. The third has now been accessed and gives an additional 66 million cubic metres annually. 4.5% of the water resources of this area are used by the Palestinians. Demand for water from the new Israeli settlement of the area is increasing very quickly and is now 33% higher than the area can supply. In addition the water quality is suffering. The aquifers are being contaminated by sea water, and the water is being polluted by pesticides. The water table is falling and supply could be heavily curtailed in the future.

Fig. 1.52 The Nile

The Nile flows through a number of countries but it is Egypt which makes most use of the river. However, the water needs of Sudan and Ethiopia are increasing and additional pressure is being put on the resource. Both of these countries are expanding their agriculture and are using pesticides and fertilisers as well as extracting water for irrigation. At present water quality is good but could deteriorate with the increased chemical run-off.

Historically, relations between Egypt and Sudan have been good. The population of Sudan was small and water was available from alternative sources. In the Aswan High Dam agreement of 1959 Egypt gained rights to 48 billion cubic metres per annum while Sudan was granted 18.5 billion cubic metres. However, with increased desertification in Sudan the country has turned to irrigation on a large scale and demand could rise by 10 billion cubic metres annually.

In addition, Ethiopia is beginning to make more use of the Blue Nile by developing a number of irrigation schemes. The Blue Nile provides 82% of the Nile's water and Ethiopia is planning to reduce the discharge of the Blue Nile by 4 billion cubic metres per annum.

Figure 1.54(a) shows some of the hydrological characteristics of the Nile. Figure 1.55(a) shows the hydrograph for the Nile at Aswan and the climate graphs for Cairo. Figures 1.55(b) and (c) are the climate graphs for Khartoum in Sudan and Addis Ababa in Ethiopia. Figure 1.54(b) shows the hydrograph for Aswan in a more conventional way and also shows the effect of the dam on the silt concentration allowed through the dam. The effect of the dam has been to arrest the transport of sediment which formed a vital addition to the soils of lower Egypt and the Nile delta. Salt incursion in the delta and a reduction in natural fertility of the floodplain soils have been the result. Changes in the farming practices in Sudan and Ethiopia, along with global warming, could bring the situation to crisis point.

Fig. 1.53 The Aswan High Dam

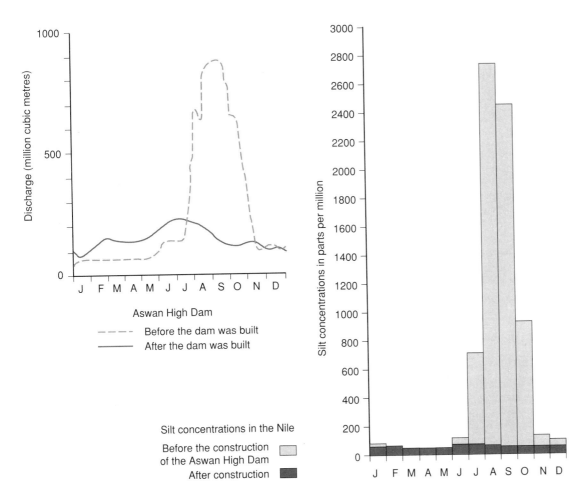

Aswan High Dam

- - - Before the dam was built
—— After the dam was built

Silt concentrations in the Nile

Before the construction
of the Aswan High Dam

After construction

Fig. 1.54 The Nile flow at Aswan

61

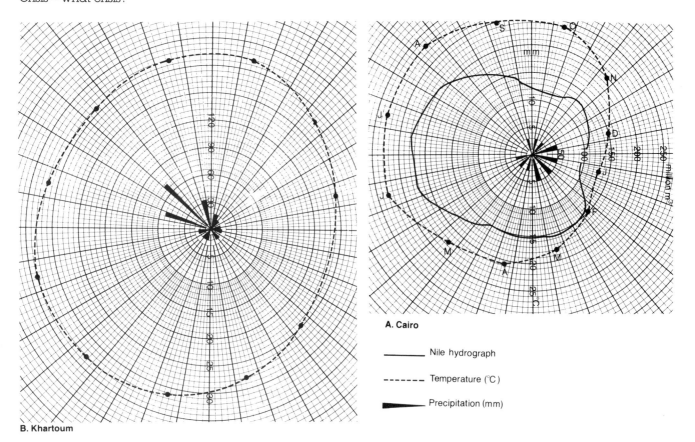

A. Cairo

——————— Nile hydrograph

------- Temperature (°C)

◣ Precipitation (mm)

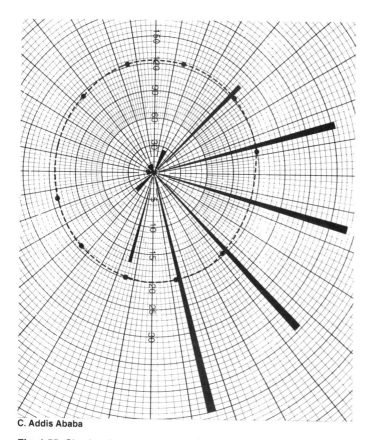

B. Khartoum

C. Addis Ababa

Fig. 1.55 Circular climate graphs for selected stations on the river Nile

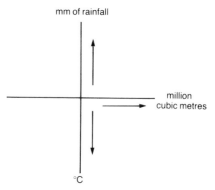

mm of rainfall

million cubic metres

°C

...It appears that the warmer temperatures and lower rainfall will affect the supply of surface water and the replenishment of groundwater supplies. Evaporation could increase by 5–20% and soil moisture could decline by a similar amount. These impacts on water supply are expected to occur gradually over the next 50 years. Population is growing at 2.5% annually and industrial and agricultural output are increasing as well. Climate warming will directly impact existing water supplies and the economic and demographic changes should be viewed in the context of broader environmental changes that will stress the region even more than at present...

Fig. 1.56 Extract from a UN report

The environment – someone else's problem?

- 'The environment' can be defined in several ways and the definition determines the perception of it.

- Measurement of the environment is a complex matter.

- Different views of 'the environment' can lead to conflict between aboriginal peoples and 'development'.

- There are different options for using environments and the selection of the right one is a sensitive problem.

- There is a difference between the political view of development and the personal view (NIMBY).

- The automobile poses a serious threat to the environment.

- Some environments are particularly sensitive to change.

- Changes in the environment can be monitored by Environmental Impact Assessment exercises.

Definitions

The term 'environment' is one which is used in all sorts of contexts and with growing frequency. It is applied at the scale of a single room in a house or in a global connection. The reason for the growing frequency with which the word appears is that there is great concern that what is called 'the environment' is declining in quality.

The word itself means 'surroundings' and is therefore usually used as a human-centred term. Its geographical use is often in an ecological sense, seeing the surroundings as a collection of interrelated phenomena. It is the fragility of these relationships which has become ever more obvious as threats to the global environment, such as deforestation, pollution and global warming, have been observed and measured.

In the past, the environment was seen as a resource to be exploited (see Chapter 6). This view led to the clear-felling of large areas of forest (e.g. in Italy), exhaustive mining and careless disposal of waste (e.g. south Wales coal mining) and the hunting to extinction of valuable species (e.g. the great auk). As more and more problems started to emerge from such policies (soil erosion, pollution of streams and loss of habitats, for example) the prevailing view of what the environment was changed, as did views on how it could be managed. Conservation began to be promoted as a means to save the environment for future generations. The key to the success of the new view is to see humans as part of the environment and not as external agents who can use it at will.

In this respect, the general view of the environment is reverting to that long held by native peoples. The view of the North American Indians, for example, was expressed by Chief Seattle:

'There is no quiet place in the white man's cities. No place to hear the unfurling of leaves in the spring, or the rustle of insect's wings … And what is there to life if a man cannot hear the lonely cry of the whippoorwill or the argument of the frogs around the pool at night? … Whatever befalls the earth befalls the sons of the earth. If men spit on the ground, they spit on themselves. This we know – the earth does not belong to man, man belongs to the earth. All things are connected like the blood which unites one family. Whatever befalls the earth befalls the sons of the earth. Man did not weave the web of life; he is merely a strand in it. Whatever he does to the web, he does to himself.'

Chief Seattle was talking about something which is beginning to find its way back into the Western way of thinking. This is the 'quality of life'. In order to derive greatest benefit from the environment, people are beginning to realise that they must not see it purely in economic terms. Indeed, many of the world's major development schemes are now subject to Environmental Impact Assessments (EIAs see p. 94) before they are given the go-ahead. The United Nations and the World Bank, amongst others, insist on a structure similar to that shown in Fig. 2.1 in order to ensure that the environment does not suffer significantly and may even benefit from the development.

An example of this fresh look at the environment is provided by Unesco (The United Nations Educational, Scientific and Cultural Organisation). This instigated a 'Man and the Biosphere' programme in the 1970s which set up representative conservation schemes in the world's major ecosystems to show how sensitive conservation can protect and enhance these areas. It promoted long-term studies so that the schemes were underpinned with scientific knowledge rather than guesswork.

QUESTIONS

2.1 (a) Write your own definition of the word 'environment'.

(b) Ask a range of other people to define the word and write down their answers. If you found any differences in their replies, try to explain why this was the case. Does their viewpoint reflect the age of the person, their sex or their job, for example?

2.2 (a) What is meant by the term 'quality of life'? Again, write down your answer.

(b) How does 'quality of life' relate to the environment?

Measuring the environment

Monitoring what is happening to the environment necessitates measuring its principal constituents. In order to be measured, they first have to be identified. Generalised classifications of components may be a starting point, even though the 'built environment' of cities is obviously very different from the 'natural environment' of forests, for example. Such a classification is shown in Fig. 2.2.

When BP Oil started to develop the Wytch Farm oilfield in Dorset, extensive studies were made of the environment as it stood and of the likely future impact of oil exploitation. For example, in 1985 the Institute of Terrestrial Ecology published a survey entitled *Poole Harbour: Ecological Sensitivity Analysis of the*

Fig. 2.1 The place of the environment in development schemes

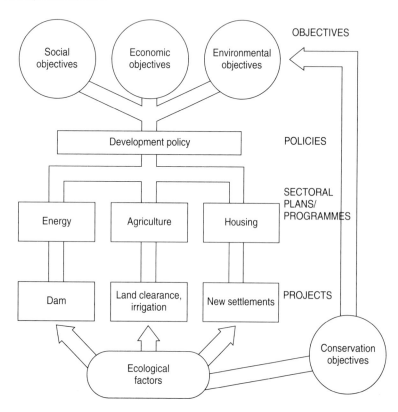

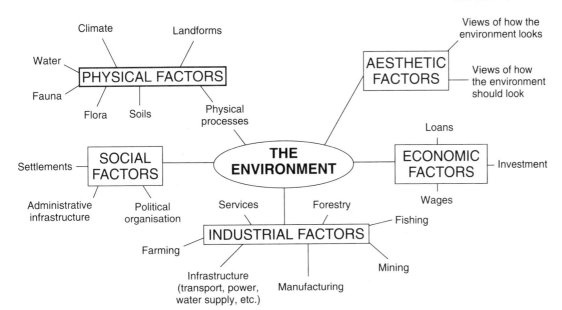

Fig. 2.2 Some of the principal constituents of 'the environment'

Shoreline. This was in response to the supposed sensitivity of certain parts of the shallow bay to pollution by water-borne oil. The survey was based on the classification of shoreline sensitivity established by Hayes *et al* (1980). Hayes recognised ten categories of shoreline in order of increasing vulnerability, as shown in Fig. 2.3. Unfortunately, this system classifies nearly the whole of Poole harbour as either 9 or 10, so some modifications were made to take into account effects such as local variations in drainage characteristics, depth of disturbance and water table behaviour. The result of this survey is shown in Fig. 2.4.

QUESTION

2.3 Suppose there were a danger of pollution of the water courses in your area by oil spillage. Suggest an ecological sensitivity classification of these bodies (streams, small rivers, large rivers and ponds). Think about how easily the oil could affect the entire range of wildlife in each habitat and how quickly it would be flushed through the system.

---

1. *Exposed rocky headlands* where wave action keeps most oil offshore and biomass is often low.

2. *Eroding wave-cut platforms* from which oil is usually removed quickly by waves.

3. *Fine-grained sand beaches* into which most oil does not penetrate far, from which it can be removed mechanically and where recovery (of, say, amphipods) may occur relatively quickly.

4. *Medium- and coarse-grained beaches* where oil may penetrate, making cleaning difficult, but may be removed naturally within months.

5. *Mixed sand and gravel beaches* which oil may penetrate rapidly and where it may persist for long periods.

6. *Gravel beaches* into which oil penetrates most deeply and may persist, but where the biomass is often low.

7. *Exposed compacted tidal flats* which oil does not readily penetrate but where, as established by the Amoco Cadiz oil spill, biological damage may be extensive.

8. *Sheltered rocky coasts* where oil may persist for many years in what is often a biologically-rich shoreline type.

9. *Sheltered estuarine tidal flats* which are vulnerable areas of high biomass and diversity and where long-term persistent oil may prevent re-colonisation by some species.

10. *Sheltered salt marshes*, the biologically most productive type, where oil may have very damaging and persistent effects.

Fig. 2.3 Sensitivity ranking of shoreline types

Fig. 2.4 A shoreline environment sensitivity map for Poole Harbour

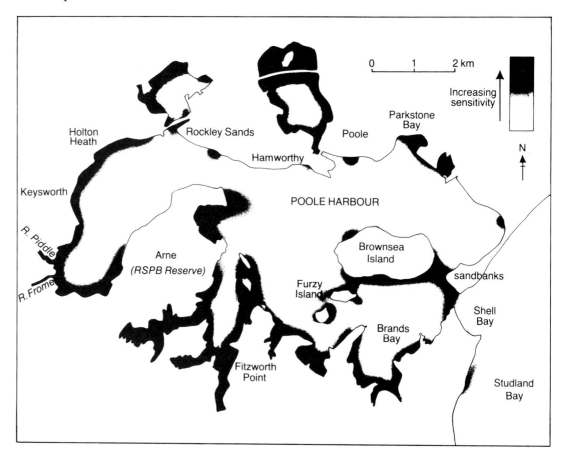

Conflict as a result of environmental perception

Conflict has raised awareness of the fact that different people view their surroundings in a variety of different ways. The Kurds have tried on a number of occasions in recent history to get the world to acknowledge their right to nationhood. The bitter confrontation between the Palestinians and the state of Israel is another example. Civil war in Yugoslavia is yet another armed struggle between people sharing the same area but having different views about the way it should be organised.

Many tribal groups find it difficult to make their voices heard. Yet they and their environments may be under considerable threat. These environments may be very important to the future management of the earth and the tribal people may be able to teach valuable lessons in their management. Groups which have been very active and are exceptions to this include the Penan of Malaysia who have been steadfast in their blockading of logging vehicles and the Inuit of Canada and the Australian Aborigines who have both staged successful occupations of military bases built on their lands.

The countries of Central America have significant ethnic Indian populations, as shown in Fig. 2.5. The Maya of Guatemala have a rich history, being the direct descendents of the Maya architects who constructed cities in the tropical rain forests of Central America. These people support many of the virtues we would support in Western society. They are hard working, honest and derive respect and status by a commitment to service for the community.

They have survived the centuries of European colonisation, but since Guatemala gained independence in 1821 they have been marginalised by a government set on a process of 'ladinoisation' or westernisation. The response by the Maya was to organise agricultural co-operatives and better health care. These initiatives have been brutally repressed by the government of Guatemala. A report from the Minorities Rights Group (Fig. 2.7) summarises the present position of inequalities and land rights.

Government policy in Guatemala is to restructure the economy on the basis of large units of land geared to growing crops for export. These plantations are heavily supported by agro-industrial mechanisation.

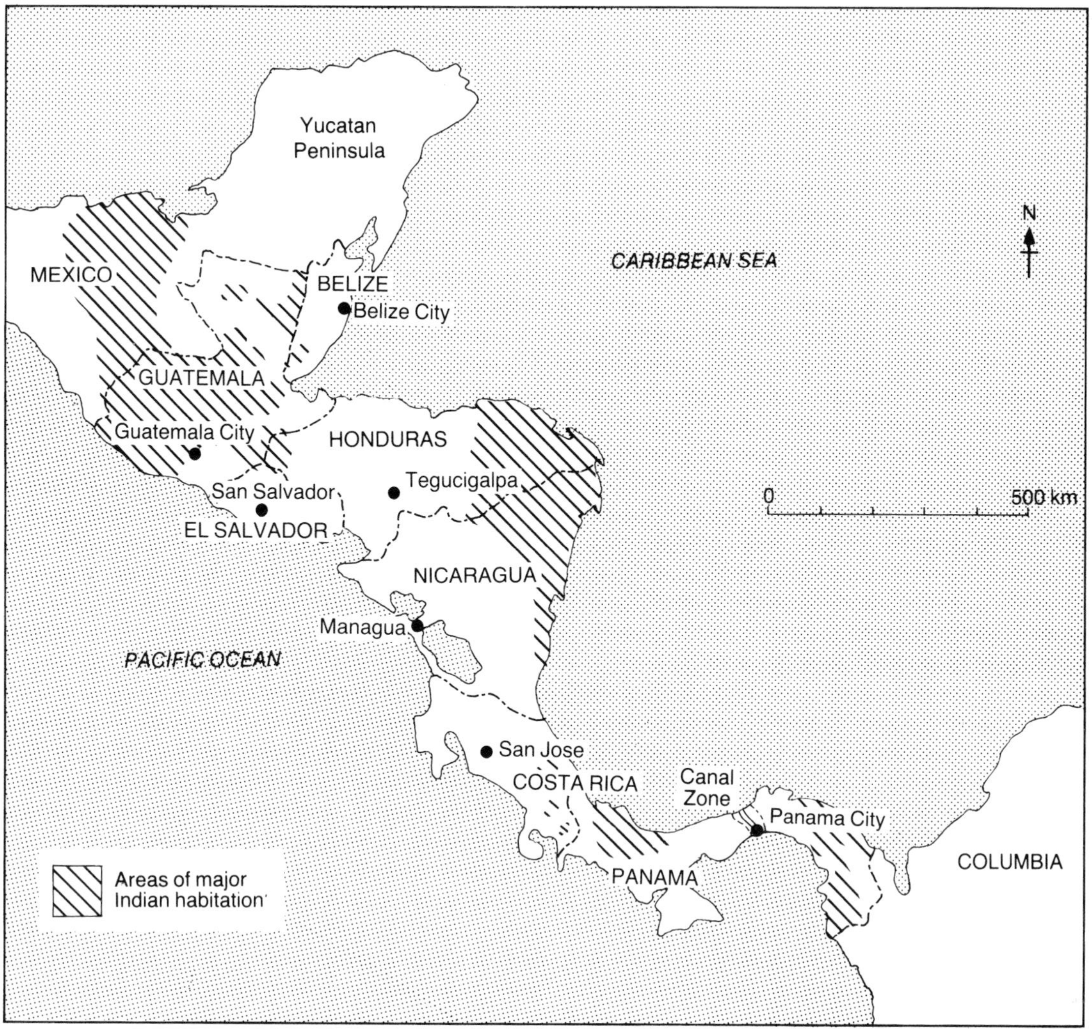

Fig. 2.5 Indigenous peoples in Central America

Central America – a quick reference

	Area (km²)	Total population	Population density (km²)	Estimate of ethnic Indian population*	% of total population
Guatemala	108 889	7 100 000	65	2 700 000 (official)	38%
				3 600 000 plus (unofficial)	50% plus
Belize	22 963	150 000	6.5	15 000	10%
Honduras	112 088	3 595 000	32	250 000	7%
El Salvador	21 393	4 813 000	225	960 000	20%
Nicaragua	148 000 (surface area: 130 000)	2 733 000	18 (21)	135 000	5%
Costa Rica	50 900	2 285 000	45	20 000	0.1%
Panama	75 650	1 830 000	24	100 000	5%

includes those of mixed Afro–Caribbean–Carib descent (e.g. in Belize: Maya; Ketchi; Garifuna)

(population figures from 1984)

They are being consolidated at the expense of the Indian farms. The Indians are being pushed onto marginal land for subsistence agriculture or becoming landless labourers. In 1950 there were 74 269 plots of under 0.7 hectares and by 1979 this figure had exceeded 250 000; that is 41.1% of the country's farms occupying 1.5% of the area. Figure 2.9 shows the land distribution in 1979.

Many of the Indians have been forced to work on the plantations. Currently, 650 000 Indians make the annual migration to work on the coastal plantations which produce coffee, cotton and sugar cane. The conditions in which they are forced to live were described by the International Labour Organisation as 'totally unacceptable with regard to hygiene, health, education and morality'.

Fig. 2.6 A local market in Central America – Chiapa, Mexico

INEQUALITIES

Guatemala's 'natural people', as the Maya term themselves, face racial discrimination, poverty and abuse. In the rigid order of society the Indians are at the very bottom, their infant mortality rates may be as high as 134 per 1000 live births compared to a national average of 80 per 1000. Life expectancy for indigenous people is 16 years lower than that for ladinos*, largely the result of the concentration of 80% of the country's health resources in Guatemala City.

Only 19% of indigenous people over seven years of age are literate, compared to nearly 50% of ladinos. An under-resourced bi-lingual educational programme means most teaching is in Spanish, even when a school is available nearby. Poverty is also a factor – most indigenous families need children to perform basic tasks from an early age and there is little or no spare cash for the pencils and notebooks that must be bought.

The economic crisis has hit the Mayan people hardest. According to the government's own figures, the average family of five needed the equivalent of $3.70 in 1988 just to satisfy subsistence needs. Yet at least 43% of the population were living on less than this and the buying power of the minimum wage had fallen substantially.

LAND RIGHTS

A close spiritual association with the land is the basis of indigenous culture and it has been the denial of land rights that is most responsible for the destruction of their lifestyle. Expropriation of land began in the colonial period and continues today. The land crisis, the result of expropriation, population growth and the pressures of agro-industrial mechanisation, means that 95% of Indian families are now landless or farming small holdings of less than 7 hectares – the minimum necessary to support a family.

This forces thousands of highland Indians to work in the coastal plantation areas, harvesting coffee, cotton and sugar cane. Here they are housed in open sleeping barns, condemned by the ILO as 'totally unacceptable with regard to hygiene, health, education and morality'. Minimum wage rates are not enforced and sickness is rampant, especially from malaria and air-sprayed pesticides.

*A ladino is a person of mixed white and Indian blood.

Fig. 2.7 Minority Rights Group report on Guatemala

Fig. 2.8 Poor farmers have to resort to clearing steep, unsuitable land in Guatemala

Fig. 2.9 Land distribution in Guatemala in 1979

Size of farm units (hectares)	Number of farms	Percentage	Surface area (hectares)	Percentage
Less than 0.69	250 918	41.1	60 871.1	1.5
0.69 to 6.99	296 654	48.7	608 083.2	14.7
7.00 to 45.00	49 137	8.0	774 974.3	18.4
45.01 to 902.00	13 158	2.1	1 793 618.6	42.7
More than 902.00	477	0.1	955 921.6	22.7
Total	610 344	100.0	4 193 468.8	100.0

QUESTIONS

2.4 Using the figures on land distribution in Fig. 2.9 construct a Lorenz curve (see Appendix, p.227). What does this show? If current trends continue, what will the shape of the curve be in several years time?

2.5 Using the information supplied in this chapter, summarise the current state of the Maya Indians.

2.6 The situation in Guatemala has come about because the government wants to restructure the economy to give it an export bias, whilst using the Indians as a cheap labour force. Comment on this in terms of the most effective use of resources for a developing country. Should the people be considered a 'resource'?

2.7 Organise a class discussion on the question 'Should development be the same as westernisation?'

2.8 Collect information about other minority groups. Information can be obtained from:

The Minority Rights Group
379/381 Brixton Road
London
SW9 7DE

The response by the rural Indians has been to turn to the co-operatives sponsored by the Catholic Action groups. These groups have received aid from the Peace Corps and USAID programmes. The number of co-operatives has grown rapidly, with nearly 60% of them in the upland areas. They have been successful as a way of effecting transfer of technological skills, introducing new farming techniques and fostering business skills such as marketing. Moreover, increased access to education has led some Indians to develop a greater political consciousness which has led in turn to a movement calling for Indian rights.

The reaction of the government was to massacre many Indians. It is estimated that the death toll is in excess of 20 000. Some of the survivors have been resettled in 'model villages' and some have joined the increasing number of international refugees. A large Maya community is found to the north in Mexico, for example.

Development options in the tropical rain forest

 The tropical rain forest is a global resource. It has a complex ecosystem and it contains many resources in the plants and trees and in the rocks beneath. Rivers running through the forest can be dammed to generate electricity and the vegetation can be cleared so that the land can be used for farmland. It is also the home for a number of native peoples. Any programme to develop the forest should consider them.

If deforestation continues at the present rate, the world is going to lose a valuable resource as well as adding to the warming of the earth, as explained in Chapter 1. Can the forest be managed in such a way that it provides goods and products and still be sustained as a resource for all of the earth's peoples? Do we have to destroy the forest to develop the area and exploit it resources?

There is a range of options available for the management of the forest. The extreme alternatives are to continue the destruction of the rain forest or to halt development completely and make the rain forest areas into national parks. However, other management strategies may exist between these extreme positions.

The ideal situation may be to go for a sustainable development strategy which would maintain a balance between the rate of removal and the rate at which the forest can grow back. This is the aim of the World Conservation Strategy. For example, sustainable development in the rain forest in Brazil would consider the use made of the forest by the Indians, the rubber tappers, collectors of Brazil nuts and the ranchers as well as the need that a developing country such as Brazil has for developing its hydroelectric potential and for mining the mineral wealth found under the rain forest. It would also consider the broader implications of climatic change brought about by global warming and the 'greenhouse effect'.

Fig. 2.10 The location of Acre

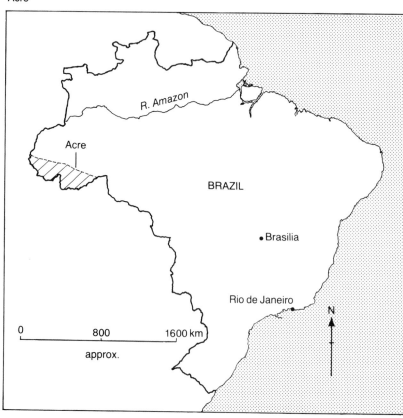

OPTION 1 Untouched forest

The forest will be able to sustain itself indefinitely and remain in balance with its environment. It will be difficult to affect the lifestyle and the level of development of the Indians, as very few jobs would be provided. However, the wood can be seen as a resource for future exploitation. Keeping the forest intact would maintain the wide diversity of plants and animals, some of which may be very useful to people in the future, not least as drugs and medicines. This option will also reduce the impact on global warming and the 'greenhouse' effect.

OPTION 2   Forest products extraction

Extraction of Brazil nuts and rubber, for example, will not harm the ecosystem, but it may provide a useful income to the local people. However, this income may be subject to wide fluctuations as demand changes in the markets of the developed world. Many of the local collectors are forced to sell cheaply to dealers and this will reduce their income and the potential for improving their standard of living. This option does not cause damage to global climate.

OPTION 3   Agroforestry

This is where small plots of the forest are cleared and the areas planted with trees which provide an annual harvest, such as coconut or jackfruit, or trees which give a longer-term return, such as teak. These trees may be native to the particular rainforest or they may be introduced from another area or country. It may be necessary to replace nutrients in the cycle: fertiliser may be required. After the first harvest, the farmer will have food and cash. This could be used to improve the standard of living. However, the income would be subject to world price fluctuations. The system would fit easily into the family system of labour and would contribute to the family eating a healthier diet. It would probably be best suited to relatively small areas or could be used to help regenerate areas which have been deforested. It would not significantly damage the global climate as long as tree cover was maintained.

OPTION 4   Growing annual crops

This could be done as part of shifting cultivation or as continuous cultivation in the same place. If cultivation were continuous the forest would have to be removed almost completely. Fertilisers would be required to replace the lost nutrients in the cycle. Farmers would need seeds and a high level of agricultural knowledge and/or experience. They might need machinery to turn the baked soil, but should beware of the problems of heavy machinery on the soil and the compaction that can follow. Farmers would benefit from income from cash crops and an improved diet, assuming that world food prices gave a good

Fig. 2.11 A rubber tapper in Acre, Brazil

return. Good services and supplies of materials would be vital. Standards of living could be made to rise. Large-scale damage to the global climate could result.

In the shifting cultivation system the differences from the continuous cultivation system would be that fertilisers would only be required when the density of population became high, making it difficult to move to a new location in the forest. Plots would be smaller and therefore the soil would be protected by vegetation. Farmers would be able to use simple machines. The forest would be damaged because the vegetation would not be allowed to regenerate before being removed again for the next agricultural cycle.

OPTION 5   'Highgrading' with replanting

This system involves taking out the most valuable timber and leaving the remainder of the forest intact. Where trees have been removed the area is replanted with seedling trees. Damage will be done to many surrounding trees and it may be very costly, as the high value trees may be scattered over a wide area. However, with fewer trees being cut the price of tropical hardwood will increase, as the developed countries still have a high demand for furniture made from the wood. The scheme would require a skilled, knowledgeable labour force, although it is doubtful that increases in wealth will be experienced by many local people. The impact on global climate would be minimal.

71

Fig. 2.12 Pastures new? Clearing the rain forest to make way for beefburger production

OPTION 6 Livestock ranching

This would involve the forest being cut down and the areas ploughed and seeded, probably from the air. To maintain the pastures vast amounts of fertiliser would be needed. This again would need to be sprayed from the air and brought in at great expense. The farms would not grow vegetables so food would need to be brought into the area. Ranching would not produce many jobs and the local inhabitants would lose their land. Ranchers would have to beware of livestock trampling and compacting the soil and affecting water run-off. They would also need to counter the inevitable invasion of weeds. The impact on the global climate could be very large due to the huge areas required to make it attractive economically.

QUESTION

2.9 A large area of 'untouched' rainforest in Acre (Fig. 2.10) has been identified by the government of Brazil as a possible development area. The area is inhabited by Indian groups and by rubber tapper communities.

The development scheme is likely to include a large 5000 hectare cattle ranch and townships providing local services. The government wants to construct a 'feeder' road from the main BR-364 highway which is to be continued into the area. It proposes to settle 9000 landless families from the dry area of north-eastern Brazil into the area over the next three years, with each family receiving 50 hectares of land.

The Brazilian government intends that this land will provide farmland for people moving from the dry, poor north east of the country. Brazil is a country with a very large international debt. It is trying to make full use of all its resources to develop itself.

Your task is to use some of the principles behind the World Conservation Strategy and make

suggestions as to the 'best' use for the land. To do this you should:

(a) Copy and complete the impact table (Fig. 2.13), giving each option a score out of 10, with 1 showing little or no change and 10 indicating a large, unwelcome change. Read through the information on each option carefully and discuss the potential impacts with your group. When you have scored each option, sum the scores. The option with the lowest score will be the one which causes least damage to the environment. You may wish to weight some of the factors if you feel that they are more important than the others.

(b) Write a letter to the Brazilian government explaining the results of your analysis and offer your recommendations about the development of this area. Remember that Brazil is a country hoping to develop itself and many of the rural Brazilians are very poor.

OPTIONS \ IMPACTS	Impact on the natural environment – the vegetation, the nutrients and compaction of the soil surface run off, food chains	Impact on the culture and economy of local people including the primitive tribes and rubber tappers	Development opportunities. Will the option lead to greater wealth, education, and health facilities? Will income be more evenly distributed?	Development infrastructure. Will the option lead to further development of infrastructure such as roads, power? Is this a good or bad thing?	Retention of development options. Does the development option allow for changes in the type of development later?	Impact on the large scale global issues, e.g. greenhouse effect	Sum of IMPACT scores
1 Untouched forest							
2 Forest products extraction							
3 Agroforestry							
4 Growing annual crops							
5 'Highgrading' with replanting							
6 Livestock ranching							

The lowest sum of scores will give you the option which provides least impact

Fig. 2.13 Impact table

	Brazil	UK
Birth rate, death rate and fertility rate (1985–90)	28.6, 7.9, 3.46	13.4, 11.9, 1.80
Age structure (1990): % under 15, % 15–64, % over 65	35.2, 60.1, 4.7	18.9, 65.6, 15.5
GDP per capita (with PPP*) 1988 ($)	2451 (24.5)	14 477 (66.1)
Population 1988 (millions) (density per km²)	144.43 (17.0)	57.08 (233.8)
Urban population as % of total (1980)	67.5	90.8
Area covered with forest (% of total land under protection)	66 (1.4)	10 (6.4)
% annual de (−) or re (+) forestation 1982–87	+1.7	−0.4

Fig. 2.14 Some socio-economic comparisons between Brazil and the UK

* Purchasing Power Parity – see p.187

Development of greenfield sites

In the developed world, greenfield sites are being sought for residential development. These new sites are either located on land adjoining an existing large settlement, or are on remote sites in the country using an existing village as a nucleus or sites with a totally different land use such as forest. Examples of these developments can be found in Berkshire and the south-east of England.

Land adjacent to Bracknell in Berkshire has been chosen for residential development. In this case the government demanded in 1980 that Berkshire build more houses than they had planned. An additional 8000 houses had to be built and it was up to the county council to decide where best to locate them. The area to the north of the new town of Bracknell was chosen to take over 2500 houses. The local people had plenty of opportunity to find out about the scheme. The local planners held a series of public meetings to discuss the merits and drawbacks of the various proposals which are shown in Fig. 2.15.

Decentralised development has seen the growth of many villages close to large urban areas. This growth may result from the building of small new estates of houses by local builders on small parcels of available land. People from the nearby town may move into one of these new houses or may buy up existing property in the village. Most of the population may work outside the village,

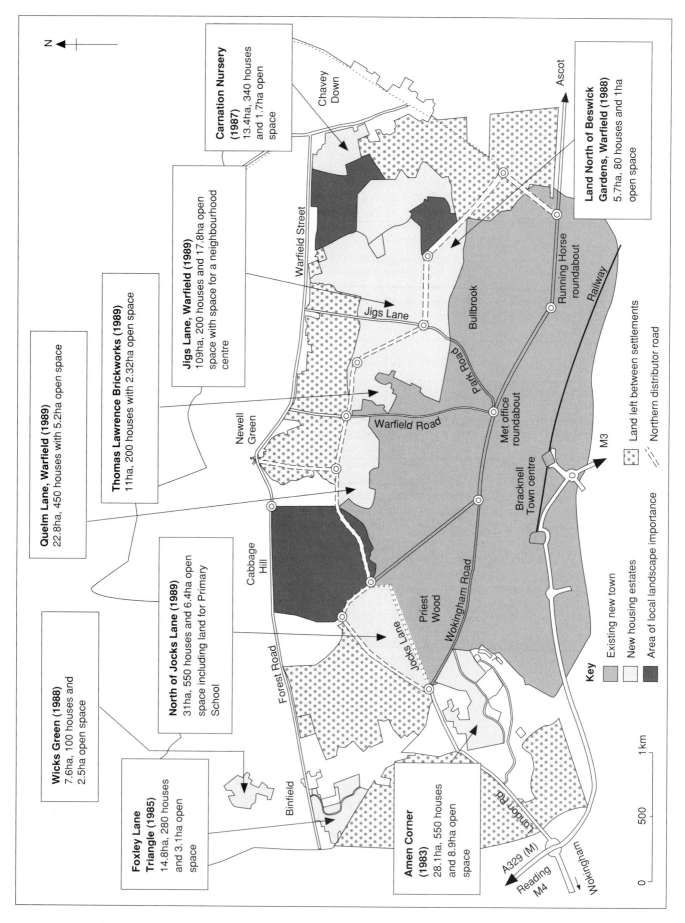

Carnation Nursery (1987)
13.4ha, 340 houses and 1.7ha open space

Land North of Beswick Gardens, Warfield (1988)
5.7ha, 80 houses and 1ha open space

Jigs Lane, Warfield (1989)
109ha, 200 houses and 17.8ha open space with space for a neighbourhood centre

Thomas Lawrence Brickworks (1989)
11ha, 200 houses with 2.32ha open space

Quelm Lane, Warfield (1989)
22.8ha, 450 houses with 5.2ha open space

North of Jocks Lane (1989)
31ha, 550 houses and 6.4ha open space including land for Primary School

Wicks Green (1988)
7.6ha, 100 houses and 2.5ha open space

Foxley Lane Triangle (1985)
14.8ha, 280 houses and 3.1ha open space

Amen Corner (1983)
28.1ha, 550 houses and 8.9ha open space

Chavey Down

Warfield Street

Jigs Lane

Bullbrook

Running Horse roundabout

Railway

Newell Green

Warfield Road

Park Road

Met office roundabout

Bracknell Town centre

M3

Cabbage Hill

Priest Wood

Wokingham Road

Jocks Lane

Forest Road

Binfield

London Rd

A329 (M)

Reading M4

Wokingham

Ascot

Key

Existing new town

New housing estates

Area of local landscape importance

Land left between settlements

Northern distributor road

0   500   1 km

N

Fig. 2.15 The north Bracknell development plan

causing these settlements to become *dormitory* settlements. In more remote villages, these houses may be occupied only at the weekend, which may give the village a dead feeling during the week (see Fig. 4.5). Examples of this smaller-scale development can be found in villages close to many towns and cities.

A further type of decentralised development has recently emerged in the form of 'private new towns'. These are small settlements on greenfield sites which have been proposed by consortia of builders. The developers call them 'new country towns'. Examples of these are Foxley Wood in north Hampshire, and Tillingham Hall, between Basildon and Upminster in Essex. The planning applications from the builders have so far produced successful protests from local action groups. They point out that areas of the countryside will be built on and the advantages of living in the countryside will be lost. The developers argue that it is better to concentrate new development on one centre rather than continue to make a series of small additions to existing villages. They contest that the best solution is one large settlement with all the amenities, rather than small additions to a number of villages with piecemeal provision of new facilities. The situation is summed up in Fig. 2.16.

At Tillingham Hall the developers, Consortium Developments Ltd, consisted of nine well known national building companies. They argued that there were six advantages to the principle of building on new sites. These included reduction of pressure on the existing settlements to expand, more economic provision of amenities and infrastructure, and reduction of pressure on agriculture due to urban growth. The builders also considered that they could pay more attention to providing an integrated community in which a variety of housing layouts and styles could be used. This would have the effect, they claimed, of increasing the supply of houses and reducing the house price spiral. The plans for the new country town are shown in Fig. 2.17 with some of the artist's impressions.

The planning applications for Tillingham Hall and Foxley Wood were unsuccessful. Local opposition was particularly strong in both cases. Opposition to local developments, be they roads, houses, or a development such as the Channel Tunnel, have led to the identification of the 'NIMBY' syndrome. This acronym stands for Not In My Back Yard and is used as a criticism of people who sympa-

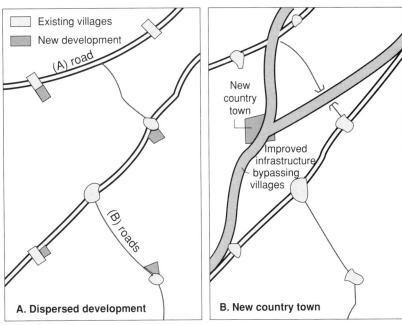

A. Dispersed development

B. New country town

Existing villages

New development

(A) road

(B) roads

New country town

Improved infrastructure bypassing villages

Fig. 2.16 Dispersal or new country town?

thise with the need for local development but do not want it to affect *them*. However, if suburban growth is going to continue it has to go somewhere. Protesters point to the amount of derelict land within the existing built-up areas and suggest that these should be developed, leaving the countryside for farming and recreation.

Figure 2.18 indicates the local strength of feeling in the Reading area to proposals to build a mini-town on the Berkshire–Hampshire border.

QUESTIONS

2.10 Collect information on planning issues from your local area. Is there a NIMBY syndrome operating in these issues?

2.11 Conduct a survey amongst a representative group of people about an issue affecting your local area. Try to draw out the factors such as age, sex and length of time lived in the area, which may affect the opinions voiced in the survey.

2.12 Should local issues be allowed to interfere with national priorities? Prepare your point of view, supporting it with research into such decisions as the Channel Tunnel rail link (see p. 96), and organise a class discussion.

High Street

Swale Park and cricket green

Commercial

Parkland

Water

Parking

Housing

Employment

Education and community

Woodland shelter belt

N

0   500 m

Fig. 2.17 Tillingham Hall

View of the centre of the country town looking west

Storm erupts over mini-town plans

TORY IN 'I'LL QUIT' THREAT

SENIOR country councillor Mrs Rosemary Sanders-Rose, has threatened to quit in a fight to halt a huge new housing scheme.

Berkshire officials are considering allowing 5,000 new homes to be built in the Mortimer/Beech Hill area — but the idea has caused a storm of protest

And this week Tory councillor Mrs Sanders-Rose said she would resign if the scheme goes ahead.

"If the plan goes to the Secretary of State for review then I will resign" she said. "I have never ever said I will resign about any issue before but I feel very strongly about this."

She is urging the council to create a green belt around Reading to protect the rural communities from further development.

The proposal for the extra houses comes just two years after the battle to protect the same Great Lea, Grazeley, site from development.

Local residents and councillors opposed the plans and eventually won.

Mrs Sanders-Rose said this week: "Once this development starts it will very quickly spread from Reading out to Burghfield and the other villages.

"It seems to me that if the jobs are north of the M4 then that's where the housing should go and there's land there to do it.

"We're not saying people can't come and live here — we're saying that we can't have this county swamped in the wrong place with houses."

Although the plans are still in the consultation period Mrs Sanders-Rose says she will step down as a councillor if it is sent to the Secretary of State as a proposal — and her majority vote on the council could cost them the go-ahead.

AROUND 500 villagers packed a public meeting this week as fury exploded over the plans.

In a defiant call to arms, local representatives at Mortimer Village Hall on Monday urged parishioners to fight the plans that threaten to submerge their own and neighbouring villages.

Addressing the audience at the annual meeting of Mortimer Parish Council, local Liberal Democrat Newbury District Councillor Alan Thorpe raised the spectre of Mortimer becoming a second Lower Earley.*

The issue, he said, was not a party political one. Everyone was agreed that the plan must go.

"I have not found a single person in the village in favour of this. We will take our share of what is genuinely needed, but we will not see our village submerged in a second Lower Earley."

There was no forward planning, said Mr Thorpe, in choosing

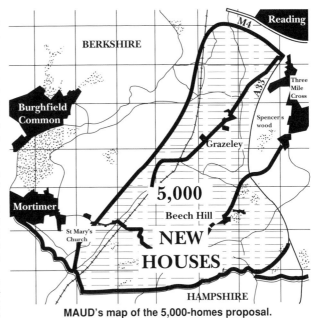

MAUD's map of the 5,000-homes proposal.

Mortimer as a prospective site for development — not only was it contrary to the local district plan, but it was unduly harsh on Newbury District.

There was no natural barrier he said, to prevent development spreading, nor had the implications on local roads or water services been properly examined.

Mrs Sanders-Rose, told the meeting that she had already received over 250 letters

opposing the housing scheme.

In a short address to the audience, Mr Ian Nalder, secretary of the recently formed pressure group MAuD — Mortimer Against urban Development — said that the homes plan was seriously misconceived. If an earlier plan to build homes in Great Lea was refused, he said then the Mortimer plan was "overwhelmingly more wrong."

Fig. 2.18 *Reading Chronicle, 26.4.91*

Figure 2.19 is a model showing the changes in the tolerance that society and small pressure groups have for new developments. It shows a marked decline in the tolerance level over the last 50 years. Is the NIMBY syndrome due to personal greed or a real concern with the environment?

Indirect measures of 'the environment'

Other measures of the environment can be made indirectly by measuring the effect on people. Such a measure is the Physical Quality of Life Index (PQLI). This is computed by giving equal weight to the three indices for child mortality, literacy and life expectancy. In other words, it reflects the human response to the environment by measuring national well-being. It therefore includes not only an attempt to measure the resources provided by the natural environment, but also how these resources are shared through economic, political and social systems. Some PQLI scores are given in Fig. 2.20.

*Lower Earley, on the southern fringes of Reading, is one of Europe's largest private housing developments

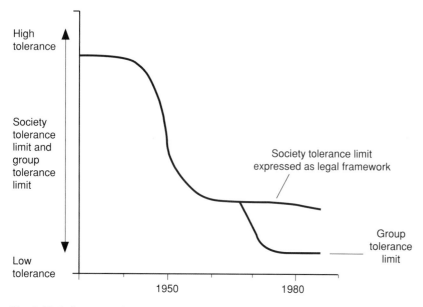

Fig. 2.19 A diagrammatic model of how society's tolerance to major developments has changed

Ethiopia	20	(High infant mortality, low literacy rate, low age expectancy)
India	44	
Colombia	74	
Sri Lanka	80	
Singapore	86	
(West) Germany	94	(Low infant mortality, high literacy rate, high age expectancy)

Fig. 2.20 Physical Quality of Life Indices

QUESTIONS

2.13 One of the most contentious types of installation is a nuclear power station. In order to ensure its environmental safety, certain aspects are monitored in the area around a nuclear site. What measurements would you suggest should be made and how should the sampling be organised to ensure that as little bias as possible comes into the figures?

2.14 Are direct measures (air, water and soil quality, for example) or indirect measures such as the PQLI more useful in understanding the environment?

There has been a recent trend in industry and commerce to claim that companies are working in an environmentally friendly manner. Product labelling often proclaims that the contents 'do not damage the environment', 'are produced without cruelty to animals' or are 'ozone friendly'. On the corporate level, headed notepaper is increasingly produced on recycled paper and companies claim that the environment is at the top of their agenda. In a speech in September 1991, however, Michael Heseltine, a Minister for the Environment, claimed that 'there is a large gap between perception and action'. Companies claimed that they were working to improve their environmental performance, but the picture created by their action 'was not impressive'. In fact, a British Institute of Management survey at about the same time stated that over half the companies surveyed could give no particular statement on the environment and 65% had nobody in a position of environmental responsibility. Very few carried out audits to make sure that their policy was not damaging to the environment. Mr Heseltine said 'I do not think this comfortable obscurity will last much longer'. Environmental audits would become essential to prove to customers and shareholders that a company was practising what it preached.

The Department of Trade and Industry (DTI) launched an Environmental Programme in May 1989. It did so 'because the protection and improvement of the environment is a major issue at home and abroad – and not least an issue for business'. It has four main objectives:

- To encourage firms to respond to environmental challenges and market opportunities at home and abroad.
- To encourage research, development and marketing of environmental technologies and products.
- To encourage best practice in waste management, and in recycling.
- To ensure that UK environmental policy takes full account of market and competitive factors and the legitimate interests of business.

The DTI has an Environmental Enquiry Point at its Warren Spring Laboratories and this provides business with easy access to information on a full range of environmental issues. It also runs two other schemes: DEMOS (the DTI's Environmental Management Options Scheme) which promotes technical advances, and ETIS (the Environmental Technology Innovation Scheme) which gives support for research in environmental technology, especially cleaner technology, recycling, waste or effluent treatment and disposal and environmental monitoring. Although a start has been made in the United Kingdom to encourage business to function in harmony with the environment, Mr Heseltine obviously believes that more needs to be done before the DTI's objectives are met.

The mechanics of measuring the environment involve the monitoring procedures themselves and the analysis of the data in such a way as to reveal trends and changes taking place. If data are collected, for example, for temperatures on every day in January over a number of years, these can be averaged out and a mean January temperature stated. The same can be done for precipitation, pressure, wind direction, soil quality, vegetation cover, water purity or any of the factors shown in Fig. 2.2.

If twenty years of measurements are taken, then the mean for that period can be obtained. If a mean for the next twenty years is similarly derived, the two can be compared to see

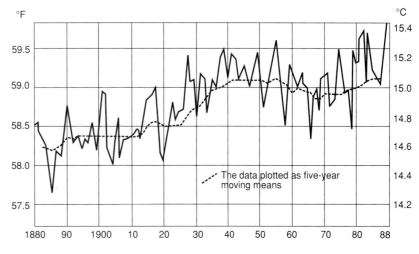

Fig. 2.21 Annual average global temperatures

whether there are any differences. This could, of course, be unsatisfactory, as a change may have occurred in the last five years of the first period and the first five of the second. This period could be hidden in the analysis.

A better way of analysing the problem would therefore be to compute *moving means* in order to assess the change over time, whilst at the same time getting rid of wild fluctuations which can obscure the pattern. The result of such an analysis of temperature figures is shown in Fig. 2.21. In this way, elements of the environment can be monitored and significant changes noted. Having identified potential problems in this way, something can be done to address them.

The problem described above is that different people view the environment differently and hence justify their own use of it. Their differences in definition pose some problems when it comes to measuring the environment. Very different pictures of the same environment can be presented by choosing to measure different aspects of it. The following items, for example, look at nuclear power from the point of view of the nuclear industry itself (Fig. 2.23, pp. 84–6) and one of its severest critics, Friends of the Earth (Fig. 2.24, pp. 87–8).

QUESTION

2.15 (a) One measure of the success and vitality of an economy is the level of unemployment it tolerates. The figures in Fig. 2.22 are the unemployment totals for the UK from 1977 to 1989. Plot them on a suitable graph using a five-year moving means technique (see Appendix, p. 224). What trends are revealed by the graph?

(b) Comment on the technique of using moving means to illustrate underlying trends. To which of the following circumstances would the technique be best suited, and why?
(i) Indicating a sudden upturn in the economy so as to impress voters.
(ii) Playing down unusual events, such as sudden rises in food prices due to bad weather.
(iii) Hiding the possibility of sudden changes in environmental conditions.

Fig. 2.22 National unemployment in the UK

Year	1977	1978	1979	1980	1981	1982	1983	1984	1985	1986	1987	1988	1989
Annual averages (000)	1163	1146	1076	1366	2174	2547	2791	2921	3036	3107	2822	2294	1797
% of employees	4.4	4.3	4.0	5.1	8.1	9.5	10.5	10.7	10.9	11.2	10.1	8.1	6.3

Changes in the environment
Physical Changes

The influences on a coastal area

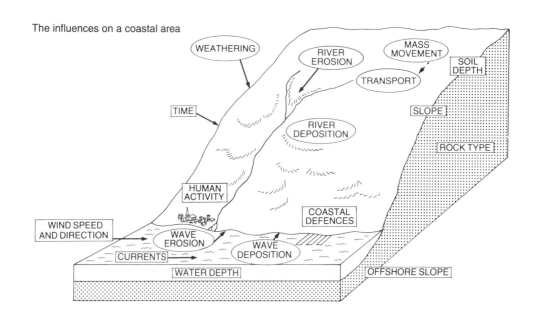

How a physical system develops

FACTORS →affect→ PROCESSES →which give→ FORM

such as vegetation type and cover, slope angle, permeability of rock, time, rainfall amount and intensity, etc.

such as downslope transfer of weathered material by mass movement processes, e.g. soil creep, slumping, avalanches, etc.

The landform is a constantly evolving result of the factor-induced processes which have acted in an area.

The coast at Hunstanton

The cliff is composed of chalk underlain by red chalk (a relatively easily eroded clayey rock). The beach is largely composed of flint pebbles which are much harder than either of the two types of chalk.

Using this and evidence from the photograph, draw a diagram similar to the one above to identify the factors and processes at work in creating the landform.

Draw a large field sketch of the scene above and label it to show the following:

FACTORS

Steeply dipping sedimentary rock
Alluvial deposit on flood plain
Sparse vegetation cover
River channel
Desert climate – infrequent precipitation, large diurnal temperature range
Denser vegetation cover in areas of lower sediment movement

PROCESSES

Rock fall on steep slopes
Mechanical weathering of rock
River erosion at edge of floodplain
River deposition
River transport of debris
Wind transport of unconsolidated material
Gulleying on steep slopes

FORM

Flood plain
Bluff
River terrace
Old river channel
Scarp slope

The valley, north of Salta in northern Argentina, is near the Bolivian border and in the rain shadow of the Andes. As such, it has a cool temperate semi-desert climate.

EXERCISE

Undertake a similar analysis of a physical landscape known to you. This could be a field example (a slope, a river valley, a cliff, etc.) or it could be completed from another photograph. Compare the factors and processes at work in the three examples (Hunstanton, Salta and your example). Under what circumstances do the most rapid changes occur to the physical environment?

Changes in the environment

The Automobile and the Environment

The cause ...

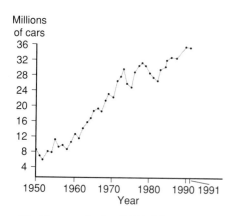

World car production (1950–91)
Source: New Internationalist

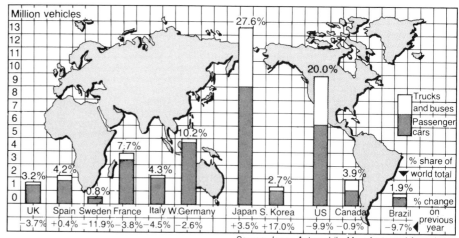

World motor vehicle production 1990

Source: Japan Automobile Manufacturers' Association

People per car (1986)

US	1.8
Canada	2.2
Australia	2.3
New Zealand	2.3
UK	2.9
USSR (CIS)	24
Sudan	229
Peru	52
China	1374

World car sales forecast (000's)*

	1990	1991	1992	1994	1996
WORLD TOTAL	35 469	34 440	35 487	38 348	40 323
Germany**	3 040	4 132	3 344	3 604	3 893
Italy	2 348	2 313	2 327	2 366	2 440
France	2 309	2 069	2 180	2 366	2 408
UK	2 008	1 602	1 787	2 184	2 288
Spain	982	897	996	1 186	1 304
EC total	12 210	12 532	12 174	13 321	14 019
Western Europe total	13 249	13 470	13 150	14 450	15 205
US	9 295	8 468	9 268	9 803	10 122
Japan	5 102	4 888	5 025	5 270	5 447
South Korea	604	695	755	872	968

World car production forecast (000's)*

	1990	1991	1992	1994	1996
WORLD TOTAL	35 867	34 382	35 599	38 517	40 528
Germany**	4 671	4 808	4 656	4 922	5 129
France	3 294	3 106	3 041	3 363	3 471
Italy	1 874	1 652	1 648	1 791	1 999
Spain	1 679	1 701	1 634	1 767	1 761
UK	1 295	1 250	1 428	1 777	1 875
EC total	13 245	12 898	12 782	14 117	14 919
Western Europe total	13 587	13 206	13 125	14 524	15 358
US	6 298	5 818	6 508	6 715	6 984
Japan	9 947	9 606	9 899	10 236	10 357
South Korea	943	1 083	1 230	1 477	1 658

*1990 actual, 1991/96 forecast. **From 1991 Germany total
includes former East Germany
Source: DRI World Automotive Forecast Report.

The effect ...

Up to one third of all land use in towns is
devoted to the car.

Every available space is used for parking.

Despite building more and more roads, it now takes twice as long to get to work by car in London as it did in 1950. The average speed of 'rush hour' traffic in London is now 13 kilometres per hour.

- The world's 390 million cars use huge amounts of petroleum (44% of all oil used in W. Europe in 1985, for example).
- Motor vehicles produce an estimated 67% of all the carbon monoxide in the atmosphere.
- All cars were banned from central Athens in September, 1991, because the photochemical smog, caused by exhaust fumes, was killing people from asthma attacks, bronchitis, etc.
- Motor vehicles produce 17% of all carbon monoxide released from combustion of fossil fuel. Carbon dioxide is one of the main 'greenhouse' gases.
- The manufacture of cars is traditionally environmentally hostile. Until recently, cars were seldom made of recyclable materials. Moulded foam, rich in CFCs (chlorofluorocarbons), non-biodegradable plastics and rare metals such as chromium are used in car manufacture.

The solution?

Traditional methods of dealing with the car problem include:

- Build more and wider roads.
- Build new intercity roads.
- Bypass bottlenecks.
- Use speed regulations to aid flow.
- Tax petrol and road usage.
- Legislate for cleaner engines, fewer emissions, greater safety, etc.

At the same time, the automobile industry is such a powerful lobby that more sales are encouraged, both to help the country's exports and to maintain employment. Meanwhile, the environment suffers.

Many town centres now have pedestrianised shopping areas

New ideas?

California will only allow companies to sell cars in the state after the year 2000 if they produce a non-polluting model in their range. This means an electric vehicle. Apart from such draconian schemes, most measures are aimed at keeping an increasingly large private vehicle fleet moving. They include the following ideas, known collectively as 'traffic calming' measures.

- 20 mph speed limits in sensitive areas.
- Banning 'rat runs', policed by the use of video cameras.
- Building speed humps.
- Narrowing roads and widening pavements.
- Encouraging the use of public transport by subsidising fares, building bus lanes, instituting park and ride schemes, increasing bus services, and building new systems (e.g. Docklands Light Railway, Sheffield Tramway).
- Pedestrianising certain areas.
- Banning travel to work by less than three people per car.

EXERCISE

Conduct a 'Traffic and the Environment' survey in an area known to you. You should collect relevant data (traffic counts, people per car, pollution figures, accident statistics) and views of people living nearby. Describe the situation as it exists at the moment. Look also for local road development schemes. Will the situation get worse? Conduct an Environmental Impact Assessment (p. 94) for the area if nothing is done to improve the situation. In view of your data, what changes would you make to the traffic management in the area you have studied? This could be shown on a map.

NUCLEAR FORUM

THE NEWS MAGAZINE OF THE BRITISH NUCLEAR FORUM

SPECIAL

SUPPLEMENT

The case for nuclear power in the UK

Nuclear energy is of great importance to us here in the United Kingdom. It is desirable to continue building nuclear power stations, both to replace obsolete plant and to supply the increasing demand for electricity.

**Dr John Gittus
Director General
British Nuclear Forum**

The constant chorus from the anti-nuclear lobby in the nuclear energy debate goes something like this: "Nuclear energy is too expensive and decommissioning costs the earth. Nuclear installations and the waste they produce pollute the environment."

These are real concerns and are not taken lightly by the nuclear industry. This article examines them.

THE COSTS

In June 1990 fifteen OECD and related countries published cost-comparisons for various energy sources.

They showed that, for most of these countries, nuclear energy was competitive in price with coal.

In the case of the Sizewell B pressurised water reactor now being built in Suffolk, Mr John Collier, Chairman of Nuclear Electric, gave these estimates (June 26 1990):

At 5 per cent discount rate:	3.4 to 4.1 pence per unit (kilowatt-hour)
At 8 per cent discount rate:	4.8 to 5.7 pence per unit
New coal-fired station:	3.5 to 4.5 pence per unit

COST: £1·8BN

COST: £0·9BN

COST: £0·9BN

COST: £0·9BN AND 52 MORE PWRs

If we follow the French and Japanese example (who in the beginning followed ours in nuclear technology) and build additional PWRs, the costs will go down.

The French, who have built over 50, now build them for half the price (£1.8 billion) of Sizewell B, largely because French industry has been able to afford to gear up for mass-production.

A comparison of fuel costs for different reactors is also instructive:

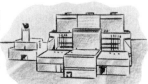

AGR FUEL: 1·1p PER UNIT OF ELECTRICITY

For MAGNOX, yesterday's reactor:	1.5 pence per unit (kilowatt-hour)
For AGR, today's reactor:	1.1 pence per unit
For PWR, tomorrow's reactor:	0.5 pence per unit

Fuel for the PWR will literally be "half-price".

MAGNOX FUEL: 1·5p PER UNIT OF ELECTRICITY

PWR FUEL: 0·5p PER UNIT OF ELECTRICITY

As for the costs of decommissioning: for the Sizewell B PWR, for every £1 we pay for its electricity we shall pay just 1 penny towards the cost of decommissioning.

Even the largest components of a PWR, the steam generators, are regularly removed and replaced with new ones. Removing the components at the end of its useful life will be just as straightforward and cheap.

HARMFUL?

One fear people have is that one of our reactors could behave like the Chernobyl reactor in the Soviet Union did in 1986.

Accidents as severe as this can *hypothetically* occur with Western reactors. But a thorough analysis done for the public inquiry on the Sizewell B pressurised water reactor found that the risk of someone being killed by such an accident is *negligible:* 10,000 times less than the risk of being killed in a car crash.

The problem with Chernobyl

The Chernobyl accident was analysed in a similar way to Sizewell B after the accident had taken place. Why should it have behaved in this manner when such accidents are so very unlikely in Sizewell B?

Chernobyl turned out to be a faulty design. The reactor was used to boil water to produce steam. If it was left to simmer, then there was a risk that it would boil dry and spread radioactive fumes far and wide.

This was what actually happened.

Britain knew better...

When British scientists were selecting a reactor design for use in Britain, they foresaw that the Chernobyl design could behave in this way and therefore rejected it.

Unfortunately the Russians had different safety standards then and selected it because it was so cheap and easy to build.

Putting Chernobyl right

The Russians have made four changes to put Chernobyl right. These changes have been applied to all the similar Soviet reactors so that in future they can 'simmer' safely.

NUCLEAR WASTE

We, like the French, are making our most radioactive waste into glass blocks.

This is such a compact method of storage that the waste from one person's lifetime consumption of nuclear electricity would be the size of a glass ash-tray.

Fifty years hence the heat from these blocks will have 'decayed' (diminished) enough for them to be disposed of in an underground repository.

Contrast that with the waste from motor vehicles: the US Government has announced that exhaust fumes now cause 100,000 deaths, from emphysema and lung cancer, every year in the USA alone.

The "high-level" waste from a lifetime's consumption of nuclear electricity would be as large as a glass ashtray.

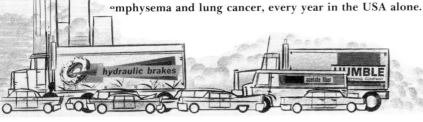

Car exhaust fumes cause 100,000 deaths in the US every year.

This *must* mean that nuclear power is a very much safer source of energy than gasoline. Indeed, if one tenth of these motor vehicle journeys were replaced by expanding the rail network, using nuclear electricity to power the locomotives, as in France, then 10,000 deaths a year would be averted.

Replacing one-tenth of America's car journeys by rail journeys, using nuclear power to drive the locomotives, would avoid thousands of deaths a year.

Fig. 2.23
(*cont.*)

THE GREENHOUSE EFFECT

The greenhouse effect is high on the public agenda. Global warming poses a real threat to our planet. People all around the world are united in their desire to do the right thing.

In the short-term, energy conservation is the least expensive of all ways of reducing greenhouse gas emissions.

But we have to *generate* energy before we have any to conserve.

Nuclear energy is a good way to generate because it only contributes *one-hundredth* of the greenhouse gases, compared to coal, per unit of electricity produced by a power station.

An alternative way of reducing CO_2 emissions is by using renewable energy sources.

Natural gas is a half-way house – per kilowatt-hour it generates about half the CO_2 that coal does.

Nuclear power in the UK already eliminates one-fifteenth of CO_2 production (40 million tonnes per year). Because France has changed to nuclear power it has almost halved its CO_2 emissions relative to ours. If the world followed France's example we would solve the global warming problem, saving around a trillion (one million million) dollars on sea-defences alone.

FRANCE'S NUCLEAR STATIONS HAVE HALVED ITS CARBON DIOXIDE EMISSIONS RELATIVE TO BRITAIN'S.

In the short-term, energy conservation is the least expensive of all ways of reducing greenhouse gas emissions.

But we have to *generate* energy before we have any to conserve. So the medium-to-long term solution has to be conservation plus "non-fossil" energy generation.

We shall *have* to rely on non-fossil fuels in a century or so, because by then we'll have burnt all the fossil fuels.

Although wind power, tidal energy, hydro-electricity, geothermal power, wave energy and solar power will all play an increased part, the real problem is to find a substitute for *coal* world-wide.

If the world followed the example of France in building nuclear power stations, around a trillion dollars (one million million) alone would be saved in building defences against rising sea levels.

Coal supplies much of the world's energy. China and India burn *1.5 billion tons* of a coal a year and will double that rate by 2000 AD.

China has more than one trillion tons of coal and so it can continue burning coal at the present rate for a thousand years.

Coal is a major contributor to the greenhouse effect.

Only nuclear-power can be produced in large enough quantities to substitute completely for coal.

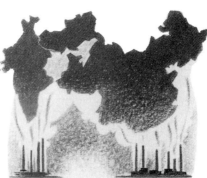

Every year China and India burn 1.5 billion tons of coal – a major contributor to the greenhouse effect – and will double that rate by the year 2000.

CONCLUSION

In respect of *costs*, nuclear energy can be competitive and decommissioning a modern PWR need not be expensive.

In respect of *pollution*, substituting nuclear for fossil fuel saves lives and can help stave off greenhouse warming.

Britain has a large export trade in nuclear fuel and other services. It needs to continue building nuclear power stations and reap for itself the advantages which these exports confer on its competitors ●

Fig. 2.24 Extract from Friends of the Earth leaflet on nuclear power

Ever since the 1950s, the nuclear industry has maintained that nuclear power is a safe, clean, cheap and essential source of energy.

But none of these claims have proved to be true.

ACCIDENTS

In addition to 'minor' incidents like leaks and discharges, which often go unpublicised, major accidents like the 1957 fire at Windscale (now called Sellafield), the partial melting of the reactor core at Three Mile Island in the USA in 1979 and the 1986 Chernobyl disaster in the Ukraine have cast a long shadow of doubt over the safety of nuclear technology.

Despite the industry's claims that the risk of accidents is low, the consequences can be serious and far-reaching.

For example, highly radioactive fall-out from the Chernobyl accident spread far and wide, over the western territories of the Soviet Republics and throughout Europe. The appalling long term consequences are only beginning to be revealed. While the nuclear authorities claimed in 1991 that there have been no health problems caused by the radiation, many Soviet health experts have condemned this, saying that the human cost of Chernobyl is far higher than the authorities will admit, and that the full effects will not show up for several more years. Even the nuclear industry has estimated that future deaths from Chernobyl will reach at least 10,000 in the Soviet Republics, and 40,000 worldwide.

WHAT ARE THE CHANCES OF FUTURE ACCIDENTS?

Eastern Europe and the Soviet Republics are bristling with old and rickety reactors. Technologically obsolete and inadequately maintained, many have the same design faults as Chernobyl. Scientists have warned that they are disasters waiting to happen.

Even in France, which has higher design and operating safety standards, the Inspector General for Nuclear Safety has indicated that there is as much as a one in twenty chance of a serious reactor accident before 2010.

In the UK, the first reactors built in the 1950s and 60s have operated well past the end of their intended lives. Inspectors fear that prolonged exposure to radiation has weakened welding inside the centres of the reactors.

IS NUCLEAR POWER CLEAN?

Nuclear power does not directly produce pollutants like carbon dioxide (the main contributor to the threat of climate change) or sulphur dioxide (which causes acid rain) in the way that coal, oil and gas burning does. For this reason the nuclear industry maintains that nuclear power is a 'clean' source of energy.

This ignores the fact that nuclear power produces radioactive pollution. Nuclear waste – as gases, liquids and solids – can remain hazardous for hundreds of thousands of years and needs careful management to ensure that it does not escape into the environment.

However, the industry has no waste management techniques to ensure such long term protection. The UK's Nuclear Industry Radioactive Waste Executive (NIREX) is planning to bury most nuclear wastes underground, despite a number of scientific concerns over the safety of this proposal.

Furthermore, the UK nuclear industry still has no plans beyond the next fifty years for the long term containment of the most radioactive wastes – 'high level' wastes.

Other gaseous and liquid wastes are routinely discharged into the air and sea, leading to contamination of the environment. This contamination is not fully monitored, and radiation 'hotspots' resulting from the discharges have been discovered.

REPROCESSING

The burden of nuclear waste is enormously increased by the reprocessing of used up, or 'spent', nuclear fuel at Sellafield. This separates uranium and plutonium from the spent fuel but produces a more than ten-fold increase in the amount of radioactive waste.

The process costs much more than the separated fuel is worth and the resulting stockpile of plutonium (a principal component of nuclear bombs) increases the risk of the spread of nuclear weapons. Moreover, plans to use plutonium as a fuel for the 'fast breeder reactor' have not proved to be commercially viable in spite of more than 30 years of costly research.

The industry itself has now admitted that reprocessing is not necessary. Despite this, the practice continues.

DECOMMISSIONING

The upward spiral of waste production continues when old nuclear power stations are taken out of service. Due to high levels of radioactivity, dismantling an old nuclear reactor could take more than 135 years and produce as much as eight times more radioactive waste than it produced in its entire working life. Recent proposals to reduce the costs of this 'decommissioning' by encasing old reactors in concrete and landscaping them into giant artificial hills fail to ensure the long term safety of this nuclear legacy.

Fig. 2.24 (*cont.*)

IS NUCLEAR POWER CHEAP?

In the 1950s, promises were made that nuclear power would be "*too cheap to meter*" – which has clearly not happened. Until the recent attempt to privatise it failed, the UK nuclear industry was able to conceal its mounting financial problems. It now admits that nuclear electricity has always been more expensive than electricity generated from coal, and that massive subsidies have kept the industry afloat.

Building nuclear reactors has taken more time and money than the industry predicted, and reactors have failed to produce the amount of power expected. On top of this, the 'back-end' costs of decommissioning nuclear reactors and managing the radioactive waste are forecast to be astronomical.

Even the most optimistic proponents of nuclear power in the UK do not foresee it becoming economic in the next fifteen years compared with other major electricity sources.

This gloomy financial outlook is not unique to the UK. In the United States, where more nuclear reactors were built than any where else in the world, high costs have led to the cancellation of all orders for nuclear reactors since the mid-1970s. France, which has the world's most ambitious nuclear programme, also has a staggering nuclear debt – by 1990, it stood at more than £23 billion.

DO WE NEED NUCLEAR POWER?

It has been argued that we need nuclear power to reduce the threat of climate change and to provide "*security of supply*" against oil price rises. However, there are other ways of achieving these aims which are cheaper and which carry less risk.

Nuclear power provides less than 20 per cent of the UK's electricity. By improving the efficiency of the ways we use and generate electricity, we could cut our electricity demand by up to 70 per cent – with no loss in standard of living, and at a fraction of the cost of nuclear power stations.

And there are other cost-effective 'alternatives'. The UK is particularly well-endowed with natural, renewable energy sources like wind and wave power. Wind energy alone could supply more than 20 per cent of the UK's electricity. By 2025, it is possible that these renewables could provide a quarter of all our energy – four times more than nuclear power does now – with far lower environmental impact.

QUESTIONS

2.16 Read the two articles on the UK nuclear industry, then summarise:
   (a) why the British Nuclear Forum think nuclear power generation is a good idea (cost, safety, alternatives);
   (b) how Friends of the Earth counter each of these arguments.

2.17 Which of the two arguments most convinces you that the authors have 'the environment' in mind when they propose their energy policy? Explain your answer (or debate the issue in class).

Monitoring environmental change

Changes in the environment provide some of the main news topics of the 1990s. Global concerns include changes in the world's climate, deforestation, desertification and soil erosion. On the local level, certain environments are very susceptible to change and are therefore cause for concern. One highly sensitive environment is the coastline. This is a rapidly changing physical environment but is now under added pressure because of its growing use as a playground and commercial resource. The factors at work on a typical coastal area are shown in the double-page spread, pp. 80–1. These factors influence the processes that are at work sculpting the landforms. If any factor changes dramatically, for example added trampling by visitors, then the processes are affected and landform development altered accordingly.

Problem-Solving Exercises

A. The coastal sand dune environment – Magilligan

An illustration of the factors and processes involved in environmental changes is provided by the coastal sand dune area at Magilligan, Northern Ireland (Fig. 2.25). The triangular area of dunes (cuspate foreland) is situated on the southern shore of

Lough Foyle at its junction with the Atlantic Ocean. Its western side is therefore presented towards relatively shallow water whose waves can only be generated over a maximum fetch of 20 km. The fetch is the distance over open water over which wave-generating winds can blow in any direction. The maximum fetch for Lough Foyle is approximately 20 km from the south west. This contrasts with the eastern side of the foreland whose shore faces the relatively deep Atlantic Ocean and whose maximum fetch is about 100 km to the north east. In addition, the wind directions, wave heights and wave periods are different (Fig. 2.26).

Magilligan is a medium to fine sandy beach ridge which is covered in loose wind-blown sands which are up to twenty metres deep in the north. The tidal range in the area is from 1.8 metres at neap tides to 3.1 metres at spring tides. With such a geology and active wave regimes, shoreline change is continuous. This can be established by the use of aerial photographs. Figure 2.27 shows the positions of the coastline over this period.

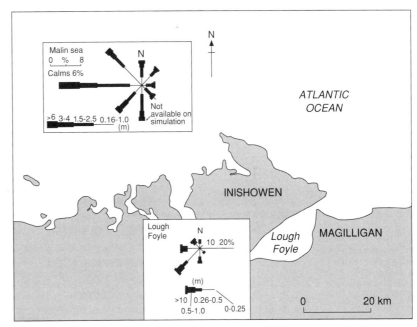

Fig. 2.25 (*above*) The location of Magilligan and the wind regimes of the Atlantic Ocean (Malin Sea) and Lough Foyle

Fig. 2.26 (*left*) Wave regimes at Magilligan

(a) Atlantic
Max. heights rarely exceed one metre
Extreme storm waves = 8 m high
Wave period range = 3.5 to 15 seconds
(mean = 8.5 s)

(b) Lough Foyle shore
Max. heights = 0.2 metres
Mean wave period = 2.5 s

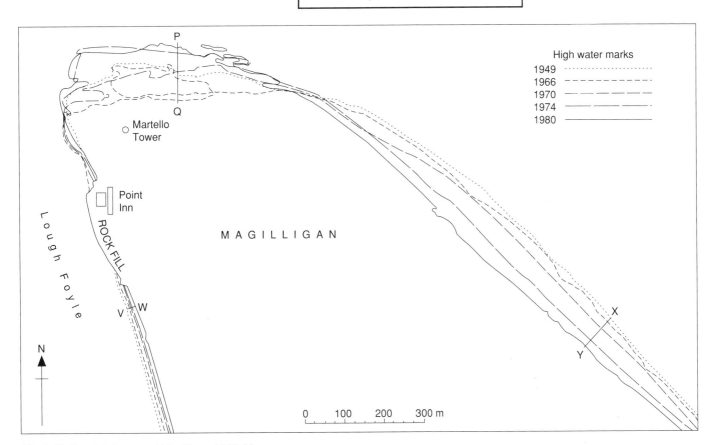

Fig. 2.27 Coastal changes at Magilligan, 1949–80

QUESTIONS

2.18 **(a)** Using measurements along line X–Y in Fig. 2.27, determine the average rate of retreat of the shoreline between 1949 and 1980 on the east coast.

(b) Using measurements along line V–W, determine the average rate of retreat between 1949 and 1980 on the west coast.

(c) Which coast of the Magilligan cuspate foreland appears to have eroded more since 1949?

2.19 With reference to the data on wave heights and fetch, explain the difference you have noted.

2.20 One area of Magilligan appears not to have changed at all over the period. Referring to Fig. 2.27 explain why this is the case.

2.21 Deposition has occurred in one area. Material eroded from the southern portions of the foreland is moved along the coast by longshore drift and is deposited at the northern end of the peninsula. (Look up 'longshore drift' in a good physical geography textbook.)
Measuring along line P–Q, establish the average annual rate of accretion (growth) of the coast between 1966 and 1980.

As you may have noticed, the coast has not changed at an even rate. You have been able to establish annual average rates of growth or retreat, but the figures are more useful as comparative figures than they are as accurate indicators of what has happened.

QUESTION

2.22 **(a)** Referring to Fig. 2.27, attempt to identify periods of more rapid retreat.

(b) At the northern end of the peninsula, growth has occurred by the deposition of shoals (deposits covered at high water) which gradually grew into islands and then merged. Using this and information in Fig. 2.27, state whether the growth of the point of Magilligan has been as predictable as the retreat of the rest of the coastline. Explain your answer with reference to currents, winds and the height of the deposited land above sea level.

Erosion of a loose sandy environment is rapid when some exceptional event occurs. In the case of the coast, this may be when particularly strong winds are experienced. Figure 2.28 shows the number of storms per year (a 'storm' equating to wind speeds of 20 knots or more for a duration of 5 hours). It also shows the storms which caused dune erosion on the Magilligan foreland.

QUESTIONS

2.23 **(a)** When were the two peaks in storm activity at Magilligan?

(b) During which periods did storm activity almost halve from its maximum occurrence?

2.24 Figure 2.29 shows the main parameters for the 22 storms since 1969 which caused dune erosion.

(a) How many of the erosional storms occurred between December and March? Why might this be significant?

(b) How many occurred during the highest spring tides in January and early February? Again, explain why this might be significant.

Apart from the parameters of the storms themselves, the resistance offered by the dune sands is important in controlling the rate of coastal retreat. The main variation here is provided by the vegetation cover of the dune. If there is little vegetation, retreat of the dune face tends to be by linear slide or avalanche. The avalanche leads to a build-up of debris at the toe of the slope which protects that slope for a while, but protection tends to be short lived (Fig. 2.30A). A more densely vegetated slope has more cohesion and slope failure tends to be by tabular slide. This also protects the toe of the slope but does so for much longer periods before the next slide occurs. On the other hand, more material is moved in one event (Fig. 2.30B). A well vegetated sand slope has much more resistance to erosion, which tends to occur spasmodically as rotational slipping, with even greater protection afforded to the toe of the slope during erosion (Fig. 2.30C).

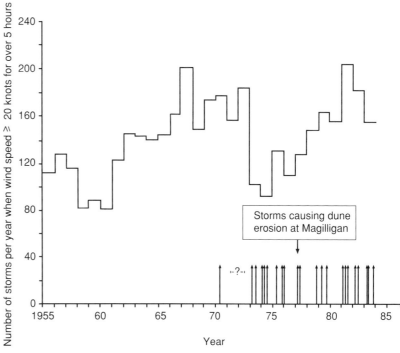

Fig. 2.28 Number of storms per year at Magilligan

Date	Mean wind velocity (m s⁻¹)	Maximum wind gust (m s⁻¹)	Mean wind direction (degrees North)	Estimated deep water wave height (m)	Storm duration (>20 knots) (hours)	Gap between storms causing erosion (days)
9 Feb 1970	15.2	31.5	010	6.1	26	—
NO RECORDS FROM AUG 1971 UNTIL OCT 1972						
9 Aug 1973	13.5	29.0	246	4.5	7	—
11 Jan 1974	13.8	26.0	248	4.9	6	152
26 Jan 1974	13.7	30.0	211	4.9	17	15
15 Jan 1975	14.1	29.5	267	4.5	11	353
7 Feb 1975	12.2	30.0	302	3.6	13	22
11 Mar 1976	12.3	21.5	309	3.6	11	396
2 Dec 1976	12.7	21.0	282	4.5	30	265
27 Jan 1977	12.4	24.5	318	4.3	27	55
5 Mar 1978	11.8	23.5	321	4.0	27	402
31 Oct 1978	14.6	25.5	346	5.5	31	241
1 Dec 1979	12.6	19.5	354	5.2	31	395
2 Mar 1980	14.0	28.5	272	5.5	27	100
26 Oct 1980	12.3	23.5	080	3.6	14	240
24 Jan 1981	15.0	35.0	261	3.6	8	90
16 Feb 1981	11.8	25.5	300	2.7	9	23
8 Apr 1981	11.9	25.0	138	4.3	28	52
17 Jan 1982	12.2	23.5	016	3.6	16	275
28 Dec 1982	13.7	32.0	247	3.6	18	345
7 Mar 1983	12.6	29.5	201	3.0	8	69
11 Mar 1983	13.2	24.0	252	4.5	24	4
4 Sept 1983	12.3	25.0	337	4.5	34	177

Fig. 2.29 Frequency of storms causing severe dune erosion at Magilligan 1969–83

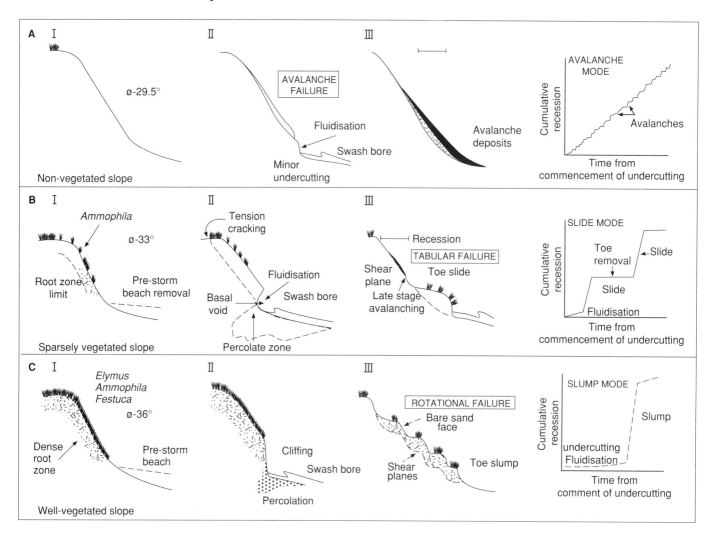

Fig. 2.30 Models of dune failure at Magilligan

A natural conclusion to draw from a study of the ways in which a dune sand slope is eroded might be that if it were vegetated, it would offer greater resistance to erosion. Unfortunately, this is only partly true. There is little difference in overall erosion rates at Magilligan between largely unvegetated dunes and well vegetated ones. The latter, although offering more resistance, tend to fail on a grander scale and therefore, over time, lose as much material as the unvegetated dunes. How, then, could the management of sand dune areas be improved?

Human interference is not a major factor at Magilligan, but a similar coastal environment in Carolina, at Kiawah Island, illustrates how dramatic the impact can be when people use a dune environment in great numbers. In 1989, a decision was made to build a new golf course on the coastal marshes at Kiawah Island. To this end, dunes were created and vegetated to give them stability. They were not subject to marine erosion as they are at Magilligan, but

extremely susceptible to the frequent strong winds of the area. This was dramatically shown by the total removal of some of them during the 1990 hurricane which ripped across the course. The dunes were, however, re-established and planted with varieties of

QUESTION

2.25 To what extent should human access be allowed to such a sensitive coastal environment as Magilligan? Discuss each of the following options.

(a) Allow free access to the entire area.

(b) Allow access to all areas, but charge for such access.

(c) Only allow access along particular paths and to certain areas.

(d) Ban all access.

Fig. 2.31 Crowds on the sand dunes at the Ryder Cup, Kiawah Island, 1991

marram grass and salt-tolerant succulents to give them stability. In this way, the course was ready for the Ryder Cup golf match between the USA and Europe in September, 1991. During that period, over 250 000 people visited the island and walked over the dunes. Consequently, enormous damage was done to them and the total rebuilding and revegetation of the dunes took six months from the conclusion of the competition.

In a similar way, tourist traffic over coastal dunes can cause major environmental damage and rapid erosion. Monitoring the changes and protecting such sensitive environments has become very important, both to ecologists who wish to preserve the environments for their unique assemblage of plants and animals and to the local authorities who often see them more as a resource, attracting visitors to the area.

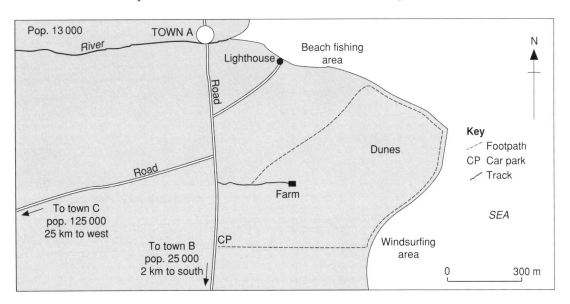

Fig. 2.32 A sensitive sand dune environment

QUESTION

2.26 The map (Fig. 2.32) shows a coastal sand dune area, similar to Magilligan. Data are given for local population and visitor activity. Draw an annotated version of the map to show how you would set up an exercise to monitor human activity in the sand dune environment. You should mark any sampling points you set up. Explain your design, particularly mentioning frequency of measurement and how the results would be used.

Environmental Impact Assessment

Before major development schemes are put into practice, a full assessment of the existing environment, the changes that would take place and the final (predicted) environment are often made. The process is built into the planning process in the United Kingdom and bodies such as The World Bank and the European Commission insist on similar schemes before committing themselves to funding 'development'. The EIA (Environmental Impact Assessment) is one means of gauging changes to the environment. The following exercise is a simplified form of the process of EIA.

1. The existing environment

The diversity and value of the existing environment are measured by putting numerical values on species, qualitative values on landscape and rarity values on sites of particular interest. One method of coming up with a figure which describes the entire environment is shown below. It only uses the visual information contained in the photograph in this instance, but could also include geological information, data on fauna and microflora and land use.

Woodland vegetation – New Forest

ENVIRONMENTAL SCORE TABLE

Increasing value

	0	1	2	3	4	5	6
Visual amenity						✓	
Range of species				✓			
Habitat value					✓		
Amount of natural vegetation						✓	
Density of vegetation					✓		
Amount of regrowth				✓			
Litter on woodland floor					✓		

2. Environmental changes

An area of woodland near Beaulieu was recently felled to produce the landscape shown on the right. Complete an environmental score table as before to show the situation immediately after felling had taken place.

Block cutting, Beaulieu, New Forest

3. Potential future changes

Many such deciduous woodland areas in the United Kingdom have been cut and replanted with coniferous woodland, a faster growing, standard 'crop' which can be harvested in about 60 years from planting. The range of species is therefore restricted. Dense vegetation gives rise to poorer habitat value, deep shelter on the floor which is covered with acidic litter. On the other hand, access for walking and picnicking may be freely available. Complete an environmental score table for the picture opposite.

Recently planted conifers, near Inverness

4. Estimating environmental impact

By using such scoring systems, the potential impact of environmental change can be estimated. In reality, monetary value could be ascribed to a number of the changes and a profit and loss account created. In the changes shown above, the value of the environment as measured by the criteria outlined in the tables would have been cut to about one third of its original value. Choose an area near your school which is likely to undergo 'development' in the future. Create as detailed an Environmental Score Table for this area as you can and measure each of the elements. Taking the example of possible housing development, suggest the impact there is likely to be on the environment.

B. Using the Environmental Impact Assessment

There is great pressure in some areas to build new motorways or bypasses to relieve traffic congestion, or to complete links in the transport network. Sometimes, the land under consideration for development is environmentally sensitive and a balance has to be struck between the benefits of building the scheme and the disadvantages of it to the local environment.

An example of this conflict is afforded by the route of the high-speed rail link between the Channel Tunnel and Central London. Figure 2.33 shows the two routes that were under consideration in late 1991. The 'direct' route, terminating at Waterloo, was the preferred route of the operators, British Rail and Eurotunnel. The other route, through the Thames marshes, the north Kent coast and in a loop across northern Kent, takes in much more 'undeveloped' land and does not affect as many existing commuters as does the direct route. The lobby from householders in southern areas of London and Kent was powerful enough to persuade the government to accept the more northerly and less direct route.

Immediately the decision was announced, in October 1991, there was opposition from both nature protection groups and the European Commission. The former argued that some of the few remaining areas of unspoilt Thames marshes would be damaged beyond repair and that wildlife, such as wintering wildfowl, would be seriously disturbed. The European Commission called for a halt to any work on the Channel Tunnel rail link because it said that the British government had not commissioned an Environmental Impact Assessment and did not know what damage would be done by choosing the route it had. In 1985, the British government had agreed to a Community Directive which set out to provide full environmental assessment before any development took place. The Community said that the British government had not completed such an assessment in the case of the Channel rail link.

An Environmental Impact Assessment (EIA) measures the value of the environment as it stands, before development occurs. It measures the range of species, scenic value, amount of vegetation, sensitivity of the environment, soil quality and the many other items which, as discussed earlier, together form 'the environment'. It then predicts the changes that would come about through development and is able to quantify those changes. Governments or developers can then see whether the proposed development can be supported, or whether it will have disastrous effects on the environment. The double-page spread (pp. 94–5) explains the idea of EIA in more detail.

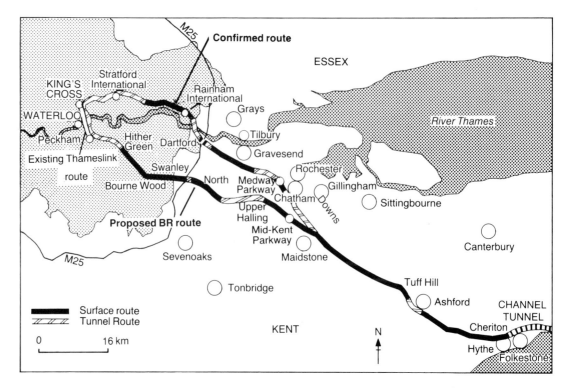

Fig. 2.33 Proposed routes for the Channel Tunnel rail link to London

Small cogs and large wheels

- *The measurement and understanding of population is important to successful planning.*
- *Population pyramids are vital tools for predicting and planning.*
- *International migrations are challenging perceptions and stability and may be one of the major issues in the future.*
- *Population movements are linked to the core–periphery model.*
- *The New International Division of Labour is becoming important in global industrial development.*
- *Industrial production has been rationalised by 'Just In Time'.*
- *Regional development can be greatly influenced by NIDL and JIT.*
- *Industrial development in Eastern Europe is in a state of flux.*

Definitions

Knowledge of the size, structure and rate of growth of the population is a very important planning tool for many aspects of society. Industries and shops need to know the size of their market, health authorities need to know what facilities are likely to be in demand and education authorities need to know how many places to provide for the children in the area.

In the United Kingdom, this information is provided by the census. The modern census is not merely a head count; it also provides information on a wide range of aspects which will be useful to the future development of the country. Questions on health and long-term illness, employment, journey to work and ethnic origin are included. It is illegal to refuse to participate in the census and most people willingly complete the census form. However, it has not always been so.

In the past people have been very suspicious of the census. It might have meant paying more tax or been taken by the enemies of the country to indicate its strength or weaknesses. Some people even claimed that it was against the will of God. The first census in England was the Domesday survey of 1086 although the Babylonians held their own censuses 5000 years ago. In Britain the Census Act was passed in 1800 and the first 'modern' census was held in 1801. It has been held every decade since, with the exception of 1941. Since 1961 the compilation of statistics has been computerised, although the individual forms are strictly confidential and are locked away for 100 years after completion.

The study of population dynamics is known as demography and the world situation has been dealt with in Chapter 1. Important information can be gained by analysing the structure of the population. This can be done by dividing the population into cohorts and constructing population pyramids. The shape of the pyramid gives valuable insight into trends in the population (see pp. 98–9).

Using Population Pyramids

A population pyramid is a convenient way of showing the *structure* of the population. Pyramids can be drawn for units of most sizes from small villages to continents. The one on the right is for the United Kingdom in 1988 and is annotated to show the features of population structure which can be read from such a diagram.

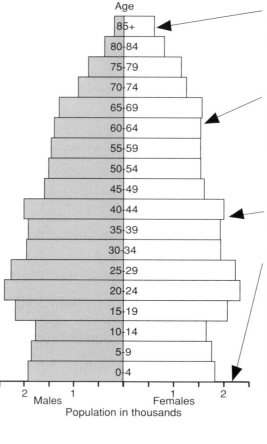

Age

Females tend to live longer than males.
Many males were also killed in the two world wars.

The steady slope of the pyramid side shows well developed medical care and a good economic situation. Diet is therefore adequate and the death rate is low.

The post war 'baby boom' is reflected in a bulge in the pyramid.

There has been a recent trend in developed countries, and in the UK in particular, to lower birth rates for economic and social reasons. The birth rate is shown by the width of the base bar. Indentations in the shape of the pyramid above sometimes reflect birth rate changes and sometimes reflect death rate fluctuations. In some cases (see below) there can be other reasons.

Males   Females
Population in thousands

Generalised population pyramids

Instead of drawing individual bars, generalised population pyramids can be constructed by evening out the shape using one continuous line. The shapes below illustrate particular features of population structure.

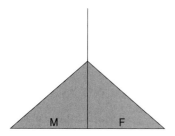

Wide base = high birth rate
Low point = low age expectancy
Shallow angle = high death rate
e.g. developing country (Algeria)

Narrow base = low birth rate
High point = high age expectancy
Steep angle = low death rate
e.g. developed country (France)

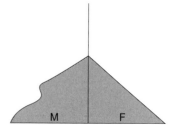

Indentation on male side shows either war in developing country or rural–urban migration of males (N.E. India)

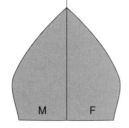

Declining birth rate in developed country
Ageing population (Japan)

Retirement town in southern UK (Bournemouth)

Construct generalised population pyramids using the actual pyramids for Japan and Kenya as a base. Label the pyramids to show the main features of the population.

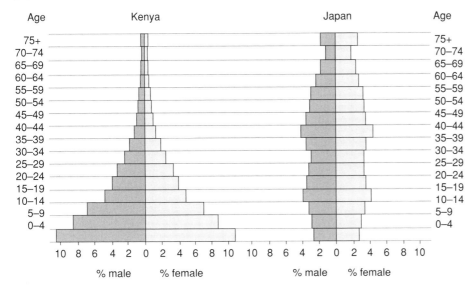

Population pyramids for Japan and Kenya

Population statistics for selected countries

Country	1990			2010		
	% under 15	% 15–64	% over 65	% under 15	% 15–64	% over 65
Australia	22.2	66.8	11.0	19.5	67.7	12.8
Romania	23.4	66.3	10.3	19.8	67.0	13.2
Gabon	42.3	51.9	5.8	43.0	51.9	5.1
UK	18.9	65.6	15.5	17.7	66.2	16.1

Population statistics for Bracknell, Berkshire, April 1987

Age	Males	Females
All ages	45676	45284
0– 4	3500	3326
5– 9	3367	3130
10–14	3111	2946
15–19	3250	3218
20–24	3969	3835
25–29	4461	4317
30–34	4110	3775
35–39	4051	3739
40–44	3477	3257
45–49	2595	2357
50–54	2279	2163
55–59	2051	2077
60–64	1875	1889
65–69	1396	1554
70–74	1044	1332
75–79	685	1073
80–84	329	807
85+	126	489

QUESTIONS

1 Construct accurate population pyramids to illustrate the statistics for one of the four countries shown in the table for 1990 and 2010. Annotate them using some of the ideas in this section.

2 Draw carefully labelled generalised population pyramids to illustrate the following scenarios:
   (a) A recently completed New Town in the UK.
   (b) A developing country in which there has been a large-scale recent famine.
   (c) A city in the developing world into which there is much migration in search of work.
   (d) A declining rural community in N.W. Scotland.

3 Population pyramids are used as a basis for planning the future demand for facilities.
   (a) Construct a population pyramid for Bracknell.
   (b) Comment on the following points:
      (i) It is likely that some infant schools will close in the near future.
      (ii) In six years time, two major secondary schools will need to combine.
      (iii) A new community centre with a day unit for retired people is being planned.

4 Critically evaluate the need for the following services: a new geriatric ward in the local hospital; a new technical college; a new housing development with 'starter' homes.

Population migration

People move for a number of reasons. Although many movements are voluntary people may be forced to move by a government or as a result of government actions. The transmigration policy of Indonesia is an example of how government action has been used to influence population movement. The Indonesian government is following a policy of redistributing population from overcrowded islands to islands with low densities, to take advantage of the agricultural potential of all parts of the country. The Ethiopian government has also followed such policies by trying to move people away from areas of low agricultural potential and thus avoid the consequences of future droughts.

Groups of people will try to flee disasters such as flooding and volcanic activity. They may flee from war zones, as when the Kurds moved from northern Iraq and attempted to enter Turkey to avoid genocide at the hands of the Iraqi leader, Saddam Hussein. The 'boat people' of Vietnam are well known for their attempts to get away from their home country, many for economic reasons but also due to persecution.

Migrants are frequently in the news as they are often the subject of attacks by politicians. Many of the boat people got to Hong Kong by 1988 but by 1992 were still in detention camps awaiting repatriation. Algerians and Moroccans who have moved to France are often the subject of abuse and political controversy, not least because they take billions of francs out of the country, sending the money home to families on the African shores of the Mediterranean sea. At present the governments of the European Community are bracing themselves to receive a large number of migrants, particularly from developing countries. Some of these people will be 'economic migrants' seeking a better standard of living, but many of them will claim to be refugees seeking asylum. Europe could become a net importer of people like Australia and the USA. Laws are being introduced in many EC countries in anticipation of such a volume of immigration. Figure 3.2 shows the likely origins of immigrants into the UK.

Fig. 3.1 Displaced Kurds in Iraq, 1991

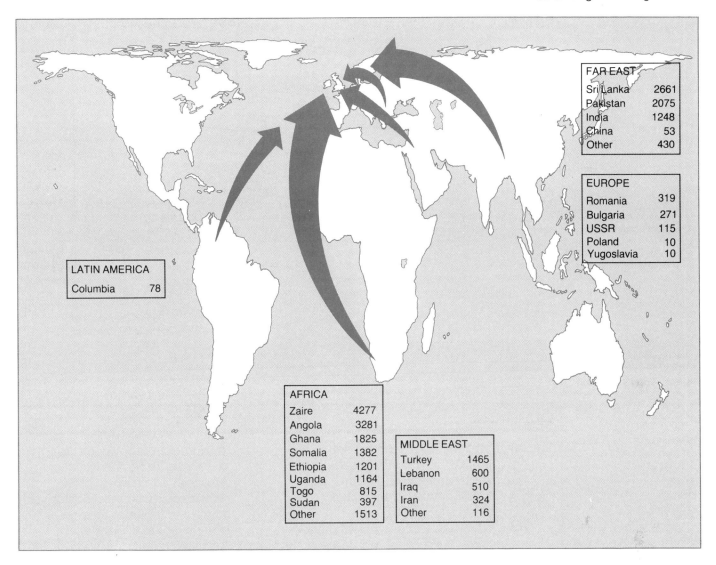

Fig. 3.2 A map showing the origins of people seeking political asylum in the UK (numbers show asylum applications for January–June 1991)

Despite the fact that international migration is often viewed negatively, migrants are often a considerable force for change. For example, the large-scale movements of people from the countries of Eastern Europe were a contributory factor towards the removal of the 'iron curtain' in Europe.

The scale of migration is vast. A recent survey estimated that there are between 10 and 15 million refugees in the world, half of them children. Of these, 80% have fled disasters in the South or the developing world.

Most people move hoping for a better quality of life. They move to improve their standard of living, to gain employment, or to gain access to health facilities and education for their children. This movement may be from one urban area to another, but is usually a rural–urban migration. Later, movement may be away from the urban area for retirement. This may be back to the home village or to a new environment altogether. People may move around the urban area or seek the environment of the suburbs. Some of these moves have been identified in Fig. 3.3.

Studies of rural–urban migration in South America and New Zealand suggest that migration is often stepped. The migrant may make an intermediate move before moving into the city from the rural area.

These studies have also found that moves are rarely made in a haphazard and ill-thought out way. Moves are often made to the home of a relative or someone known to the family. Subsequent moves may be made to new areas. The migrant may then be a 'jumping off' point for other members of the family. The family may consider very carefully which person should migrate, so that the most useful representative is chosen to go to the city. Migrants take not only the good wishes of the family: they may take some of the scant wealth of the family. If they are successful then others may follow.

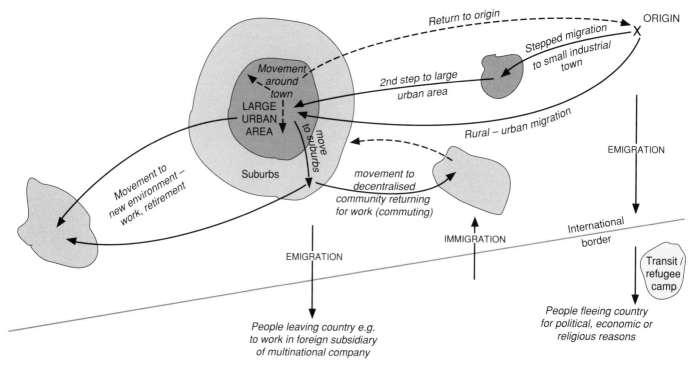

Fig. 3.3 Types of migration

QUESTIONS

3.1 (a) Using the migration model (Fig. 3.3) as a guide, research the literature to find examples of all the types of migration shown.

(b) Draw up a table to classify the types of migration, using the grid shown below. Transfer the examples you found in **(a)** to the table.

	Long term	Short term
Local (within country)		
International		

3.2 (a) Carry out an investigation amongst adult friends and family members to find out information to test the hypothesis that migration has become more common in the recent past.

Construct a questionnaire to collect information on the following:
● gender
● age group
● home origin, i.e. where brought up

● number of moves made
● reason for moves.

Arrange with the rest of the class to collect a representative sample to include a range of age groups and gender.

(b) Analyse the information collected to test the hypothesis using a variety of descriptive and statistical techniques. Make a wall display of your analysis.

(c) What are the factors affecting migration in your sample?

3.3 Make a list of information you would need to know about a region or city before you moved there. You may like to consider this in relation to the choice of an institute of higher education if you are thinking about that.

3.4 Apply the push–pull model (see pp. 104–5) to your own situation and list the obstacles to your migration to another named region or country.

Migration to and within France

France is a country which has a long colonial history and many parts of the world have embraced French culture and language. Figure 3.4 is a detailed list of the countries of origin of the migrants to France. The following exercise is the type carried out by planners in order to assess the current state of population and movement before allocating funds for regional development.

Country	Number of immigrants
Algeria	1 439 820
Cameroon	19 400
Congo	14 080
Côte d'Ivoire	20 180
Egypt	18 900
Madagascar	53 200
Mali	23 580
Mauritius	16 980
Morocco	548 500
Réunion	74 200
Senegal	54 440
Tunisia	35 820
Canada	12 220
Guadeloupe	87 320
Martinique	94 940
USA	24 240
Cambodia	43 460
India	10 940
Iran	12 200
Laos	40 500
Lebanon	20 600
Turkey	125 860
Vietnam	102 680
Austria	12 420
Belgium	129 900
Czechoslovakia	14 620
Germany	204 840
Greece	16 620
Hungary	14 140
Italy	604 680
Luxembourg	10 540

Fig. 3.4 Origin of immigrants to France in 1989

Age	All	Males	Females
65+	876 260	373 040	503 220
55–64	698 660	361 760	336 900
45–54	855 660	486 640	369 020
35–44	1 087 820	632 740	455 080
25–34	1 267 800	667 760	600 040
20–24	484 720	238 040	246 680
15–19	291 020	150 940	140 080
10–14	232 320	121 160	111 160
5–9	151 740	76 080	75 660
1–4	55 360	28 080	27 280

Fig. 3.6 Population structure of the immigrant population in France

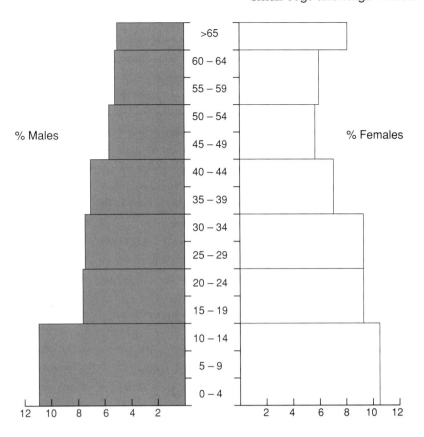

Fig. 3.5 Population pyramid of France

QUESTIONS

3.5 Draw a series of flow lines and locate them around a map of France. The flow lines should be drawn to scale so that you can see the relative numbers of people coming from different destinations. You may have to group some of them together as the list is rather long.

3.6 Describe the pattern shown by the flow-line graph.

3.7 Try to work out the push–pull factors which have led people to migrate to France.

3.8 Figure 3.5 shows the population pyramid for the whole of the French population and Fig. 3.6 gives the figures for the population structure of the immigrant population. Draw a population pyramid for the migrant population, using the same scale, on tracing paper, and compare the two population structures. This may help to confirm part of your answer to question 3.7.

Migration in Europe

A model of migration

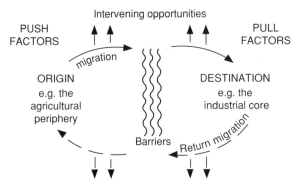

PUSH FACTORS

Intervening opportunities

PULL FACTORS

migration

ORIGIN
e.g. the agricultural periphery

DESTINATION
e.g. the industrial core

Barriers

Return migration

Application of model – the UK

1. Net inter-regional movements: by age, 1988

Thousands

	0–4	5–14	15–24	25–44	Males 45–64 Females 45–59	Males 65–74 Females 60–74	75 and over	All ages
North	—	—	−5	−2	1	1	—	−4
Yorkshire & Humberside	1	1	−1	1	2	2	—	7
East Midlands	2	2	—	7	4	2	1	17
East Anglia	1	2	2	5	3	1	1	15
South East	−8	−13	28	−13	−25	−18	−5	−55
Greater London	−10	−13	21	−33	−20	−15	−7	−75
Rest of South East	2	−1	6	20	−6	−3	2	20
South West	2	5	—	11	9	5	2	35
West Midlands	—	—	−5	−2	−1	—	—	−8
North West	1	1	−6	—	1	1	—	−2
Wales	1	3	−2	5	5	3	1	16
Scotland	−1	—	−7	−8	1	1	—	−14
Northern Ireland	—	—	−5	−2	—	—	—	−7

© Crown copyright

2. International migration, 1988; inflow (I) and outflow (O)

Thousands

| | *Country of last residence* | | | | | | | | | | | | | |
| | All countries | | Old Common- wealth | | New Commonwealth and Pakistan — India, Bangladesh and Pakistan | | Other | | European Community | | USA | | Rest of the world | |
	I	O	I	O	I	O	I	O	I	O	I	O	I	O
Region of next residence														
United Kingdom	216.0	237.2	35.6	61.8	19.1	8.0	30.3	29.9	52.1	58.6	23.1	30.3	55.7	48.6
North	5.3	7.6	1.0	1.8	0.2	0.9	0.8	1.0	1.4	1.7	0.2	0.4	1.8	1.8
Yorkshire & Humberside	13.5	11.1	1.5	2.6	2.3	1.2	1.5	1.0	4.1	4.1	1.5	0.5	2.6	1.7
East Midlands	9.8	8.6	1.3	1.4	0.8	0.4	2.4	0.8	2.3	2.9	0.1	1.0	2.9	2.2
East Anglia	9.9	11.2	0.7	1.0	0.2	0.1	0.9	0.5	2.6	2.2	3.3	5.8	2.3	1.5
South East	120.7	109.0	23.3	29.0	9.5	3.3	16.1	15.2	31.6	22.3	12.5	14.0	27.7	24.2
Greater London	77.5	53.8	18.0	14.5	6.8	2.2	10.4	9.6	18.4	10.3	6.4	5.6	17.4	11.6
Rest of South East	43.2	55.2	5.3	15.1	2.7	1.1	5.7	5.6	13.2	11.9	6.1	8.9	10.3	12.5
South West	11.7	25.3	2.1	7.1	0.5	0.1	2.0	1.9	2.4	10.9	1.7	2.6	3.0	2.7
West Midlands	12.3	15.2	1.0	3.3	2.9	0.1	1.1	3.0	3.0	4.7	1.1	1.1	3.2	2.9
North West	16.1	17.7	2.0	4.9	1.7	0.7	1.9	3.2	4.2	2.7	0.3	0.9	6.0	5.3
England	199.4	205.8	32.9	51.7	18.3	6.8	26.7	26.6	51.5	51.4	20.5	26.9	49.5	42.3
Wales	2.8	7.2	0.5	2.0	0.2	0.4	0.6	0.7	—	2.0	0.3	0.7	1.1	1.4
Scotland	13.1	21.1	2.2	7.9	0.6	0.8	2.7	2.4	0.6	2.8	2.2	2.7	5.0	4.5
Northern Ireland	0.6	3.1	—	0.2	0.1	—	0.4	0.1	—	2.4	—	—	0.1	0.4

© Crown copyright

QUESTIONS
International migration

5 From which world regions did the UK receive most immigrants in 1988?

6 To which regions of the UK did most immigrants move? Why? Add to your list of **push** and **pull** factors.

7 To which world regions did most UK emigrants move? Was there a regional pattern of their origin?

8 What intervening opportunities might there be for an agricultural worker moving from N.W. Scotland to Leeds?

9 What barriers might be experienced by a Pakistani family moving from Karachi to London?

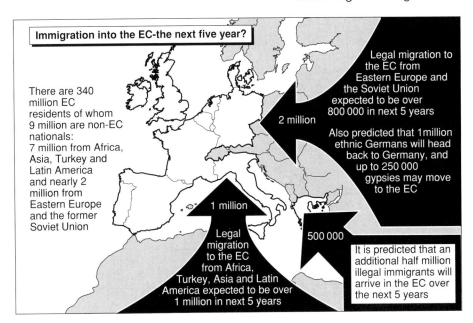

Immigration into the EC-the next five year?

There are 340 million EC residents of whom 9 million are non-EC nationals: 7 million from Africa, Asia, Turkey and Latin America and nearly 2 million from Eastern Europe and the former Soviet Union

2 million

1 million

Legal migration to the EC from Africa, Turkey, Asia and Latin America expected to be over 1 million in next 5 years

500 000

Legal migration to the EC from Eastern Europe and the Soviet Union expected to be over 800 000 in next 5 years

Also predicted that 1 million ethnic Germans will head back to Germany, and up to 250 000 gypsies may move to the EC

It is predicted that an additional half million illegal immigrants will arrive in the EC over the next 5 years

Source: The *Independent on Sunday* 27-10-91

Africa's population explosion spurs exodus of youth to Europe

Jean-Claude Chesnais

THERE are three main areas of imbalance on our planet. The American zone, bounded by the Rio Grande, separates wealthy, Anglo-Saxon America from poor and prolific Latin America, and the Pacific zone where a prosperous Japan for several decades has been able to control population growth unlike those vast lands of poverty and overpopulation, China and the Indian subcontinent.

The third area is the Mediterranean which divides Europe, with its welfare states and static populations, from Africa, whose political and economic stability is fragile, and threatened by an extraordinary population expansion. Of these imbalances, the Mediterranean is by far the greatest.

The fertility gap is twice as large as on either side of the Rio Grande or between Japan and the rest of Asia. This gap could lead to massive population movements.

On the northern side of the Mediterranean, the lack of population renewal is worsening annually, and there is a risk of underpopulation. On the other side of the sea, the fertility rates range between four and seven children per family.

The population of Europe outside Russia is about 500 million. Africa, which in 1950 had half the population of Europe now has 650 million inhabitants. According to UN forecasts, Africa may have a billion extra people in less than 40 years.

This population divide is much more marked than the divide between the two Americas. Latin America has already reduced its rate of population growth. But in

Africa, women have an average of six children, against 1.5 in the EC. However, a perceptible change is occurring north of the Sahara.

The economic imbalance is also much greater than the one separating the United States from Latin America. The average American has a purchasing power four times greater than his Latin American counterpart. Someone living in the EC has a purchasing power seven or eight times greater than the average African. This divide is now aggravated by the changes of 1989. Now that the peoples of central and eastern Europe have experienced revolutions and a subsequent return to democracy, the authoritarian regimes in the South, accentuate the frustrations of the younger generations in those countries.

The conjunction of demographic, economic and political imbalances is liable to produce migration on an unprecedented scale.

Over the past 15 years, the increase in population of people aged 15–24, those most likely to emigrate, was five times greater in Africa than in Latin America. While in Latin America the pressure for migration is unlikely to increase, in Africa it has just begun and could dominate the next half century.

While in Latin America, there were 39 million people in the 15–24 age group in 1960, and 74 million in 1980 there will be 101 million in the year 2000 and 120 million in 2020. In Africa, there were 52 million in 1960 and 91 million in 1980. But from the year 2000, the corresponding figures will be 170 million and 300 million.

The contrast in age distribution between the two shores of the Mediterranean is obvious. On one

shore, the number of elderly people increases in relation to financing for social welfare systems; on the other a glut of young people prevents their absorption into the labour market. These imbalances will only be countered by massive transfers of young people, reducing the burden of demographic aging in the North and unemployment in the South.

Thus the population structures of Europe and Africa complement each other and the inevitable migration will play its part as a demographic and economic regulator, and facilitating access to development for the nations supplying labour (through worker remittances and re-export of skills). Europe must therefore prepare for the Africanisation and Islam-isation of its population.

The European Community as a whole needs 1.2 million births a year to replace preceding generations. In Africa, the annual excess is about 15 million. So migration can only be a marginal element in the development of the South, just as it cannot cure the demographic anaemia in the North.

Will Europe remain introverted, incapable of seizing the opportunity? This is an unprecedented migration. Naturally, it carries risks but also unexpected opportunities. It requires active and insightful regulation of the flow of migrants. In the North, there must be a linkage between policies encouraging large families and open immigration. The South needs to implement regional development policies with effective intercontinental co-operation.

Jean-Claude Chesnais, National Institute of Demographic Studies in Paris

QUESTIONS
10 Read the article opposite and make brief notes to summarise the main argument.

11 Define the terms 'fertility rate' and 'under-population'.

12 How can migration from Africa to Europe be seen as 'an opportunity'? Who will benefit from this migration?

13 What are the risks referred to in the article?

14 What do you think will be the obstacles which may prevent the envisaged migration?

15 Many of the reactions to large-scale immigration to Western Europe will be emotive and racist in nature. Much of this will be a result of poor information. Using the information given and any you have collected, write a speech outlining the main issues and pointing out the consequences for not accepting the migrants into Western Europe.

There is a considerable amount of migration within France. Figure 3.7 gives the figures for the number of moves between 1975 and 1982.

Recent studies of the industrial base of France have indicated that much of the development of industry in the peripheral regions has been through the tertiary sector. Only Brittany has shown an increase in the manufacturing sector, with growth in the food processing industry. Some of the developments in the south and south-west are based on low-skilled assembly work. Wage rates are relatively low but these jobs are attractive to redundant agricultural workers. Many of the factories established are branch factories with the headquarters still located in Paris. A generalised regional analysis is shown in Fig. 3.11.

Fig. 3.7 Migration between the regions of France (1975–82 averages)

from \ to	Ile-de-France	Champagne-Ardenne	Picardie	Haute-Normandie	Centre	Basse-Normandie	Bourgogne	Nord-Pas-de-Calais	Lorraine	Alsace	Franche-Comté	Pays de la Loire
Ile-de-France	—	3 786	13 249	7 129	19 069	6 357	8 849	4 337	2 700	2 249	2 046	10 731
Champagne-Ardenne	4 057	—	1 569	397	669	251	1 189	957	2 231	417	617	523
Picardie	7 414	1 826	—	1 609	731	403	417	3 389	526	177	231	617
Haute-Normandie	5 377	251	1 517	—	1 246	1 766	297	1 000	274	177	63	1 094
Centre	8 566	454	460	1 060	—	814	1 294	434	383	320	134	2 974
Basse-Normandie	4 960	177	260	1989	963	—	249	226	229	174	74	2 566
Bourgogne	4 769	857	246	320	1 466	149	—	334	694	320	1 594	477
Nord-Pas-de-Calais	8 977	1 191	4 454	1 420	1 229	614	634	—	1 220	540	503	1 014
Lorraine	4 980	2 254	569	391	817	251	1 014	991	—	3 134	1 369	720
Alsace	1 597	357	114	251	346	149	320	374	2 197	—	1003	314
Franche-Comté	2 106	423	157	117	466	109	1 763	203	1 006	1 226	—	194
Pays de la Loire	6 737	317	374	789	3 040	1 606	354	471	374	274	146	—
Bretagne	7 837	163	214	803	980	1 589	226	491	366	200	97	4 614
Poitou-Charentes	4 134	174	160	234	1 837	249	266	220	294	166	100	2 897
Aquitaine	5 811	283	280	371	1 060	249	351	314	494	294	223	746
Midi-Pyrénées	4 891	214	234	251	586	143	211	417	266	249	146	466
Limousin	1 877	49	29	60	734	83	91	111	60	29	43	226
Rhône-Alpes	7 249	483	386	643	1 014	434	3 209	743	934	660	1 231	1 057
Auvergne	3 071	120	146	120	1 140	143	837	186	257	111	186	451
Languedoc-Roussillon	3 709	220	151	197	457	149	489	257	340	243	166	251
Provence-Alpes-Côte d'Azur	8 363	426	577	549	1 006	374	754	774	929	609	500	717
Corse	391	46	11	17	54	37	51	29	20	20	23	37
Total	**106 874**	**14 071**	**25 157**	**18 717**	**38 909**	**15 917**	**22 866**	**16 260**	**15 794**	**11 589**	**10 494**	**32 689**

from \ to	Bretagne	Poitou-Charentes	Aquitaine	Midi-Pyrénées	Limousin	Rhône-Alpes	Auvergne	Languedoc-Roussillon	Provence-Alpes-Côte d'Azur	Corse	Total	Balance
Ile-de-France	11 877	6 506	11 557	9 003	3 894	11 643	4 209	9 251	20 626	1 157	**170 223**	−63 349
Champagne-Ardenne	463	357	754	503	114	1 343	323	634	1 491	54	**18 914**	−4 843
Picardie	649	374	1 000	563	257	1 323	260	803	1 471	91	**24 131**	1 026
Haute-Normandie	1 237	426	931	583	131	1 049	140	617	1 411	51	**19 640**	−923
Centre	1 403	2 166	1 523	1 086	840	1 274	991	1 234	2 089	69	**29 569**	9 340
Basse-Normandie	2 243	317	530	329	114	737	154	363	837	14	**17 494**	−1 577
Bourgogne	420	271	6 69	406	186	4 186	1 046	700	1 946	80	**21 134**	1 731
Nord-Pas-de-Calais	891	620	1 309	1 003	229	2 740	511	1 540	3 986	83	**34 709**	−18 449
Lorraine	694	720	1 400	974	237	2 474	346	1 231	3 854	109	**28 531**	−12 737
Alsace	280	271	746	357	83	1 017	114	474	1 234	80	**11 680**	−91
Franche-Comté	180	171	314	217	89	2 149	146	466	1 249	40	**12 789**	−2 294
Pays de la Loire	5 437	2 463	1 043	694	194	1 346	291	697	1 274	26	**27 949**	4 740
Bretagne	—	591	789	403	160	969	151	540	1 591	71	**22 846**	7 891
Poitou-Charentes	886	—	3 437	777	760	603	246	517	931	97	**18 986**	1 817
Aquitaine	631	2 480	—	4 477	1 169	1 331	349	1 263	2 169	66	**24 411**	12 414
Midi-Pyrénées	426	591	4 566	—	671	1 283	529	4 060	2 400	143	**22 743**	7 251
Limousin	186	760	1 074	829	—	371	780	329	271	57	**8 049**	2 780
Rhône-Alpes	960	569	1 531	1 574	463	—	3 426	4 551	9 629	360	**41 106**	6 446
Auvergne	243	331	500	831	829	2 960	—	703	1 366	66	**14 597**	723
Languedoc-Roussillon	369	197	1 040	3 077	183	2 437	526	—	4 917	140	**19 514**	17 463
Provence-Alpes-Côte d'Azur	1 251	583	2 003	2 183	217	6 229	743	6 771	—	1 366	**36 923**	28 940
Corse	11	37	120	126	9	89	40	231	1 120	—	**2 520**	1 700
Total	**30 737**	**20 803**	**36 826**	**29 994**	**10 829**	**47 551**	**15 320**	**36 977**	**65 863**	**4 220**	**628 457**	—

Fig. 3.8 The regions of France

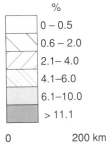

%	
	0 – 0.5
	0.6 – 2.0
	2.1 – 4.0
	4.1 – 6.0
	6.1 – 10.0
	> 11.1

0   200 km

(figure in brackets is GDP for the region)

Fig. 3.9 Percentage of European Community investment and per capita GDP (Fr) by region

QUESTIONS

3.9 Make a tracing of the regions of France using Fig. 3.8 and indicate the regions which have a net gain in population and those which have a net loss of population.

3.10 Test the hypothesis that areas gaining population are furthest away from Paris. To do this draw a series of concentric circles on a copy of Fig. 3.8 with radii of 150, 300, 450 and 600 km and with the cross as the centre (Paris). For each zone between two circles decide whether there has been more population loss than gain and shade the zone accordingly.

3.11 Test the relationship between the figures for the net population change for each area (Fig. 3.7) with the figures for gross domestic product (Fig. 3.9). To do this, you may draw a scattergraph and/or a Spearman's rank correlation. Is there any evidence that people are moving to areas of greater wealth?

3.12 Describe the pattern of population movement and use an atlas and reference books to try to account for the pattern of movement.

	MALES								FEMALES			
	Total	<15	15–24	25–34	35–44	45–54	55–64	≥65	Total	<15	15–24	25–34
FRANCE	**2 694 800**	**597 260**	**434 020**	**423 650**	**376 000**	**302 210**	**282 730**	**278 950**	**2 833 040**	**567 950**	**421 910**	**421 510**
Ile-de-France	**494 340**	**106 630**	**77 680**	**85 980**	**79 070**	**59 240**	**46 350**	**39 390**	**525 630**	**100 700**	**79 110**	**88 500**
Bassin parisien	**497 420**	**115 430**	**80 780**	**77 780**	**66 070**	**53 320**	**51 460**	**52 590**	**515 990**	**109 800**	**77 790**	**76 600**
Champagne-Ardenne	67 240	15 810	11 430	10 570	8 860	7 240	6 760	6 570	68 850	14 990	10 820	10 420
Picardie	87 550	21 380	14 510	13 960	11 750	9 250	8 660	8 020	89 820	20 330	13 960	13 960
Haute-Normandie	82 700	20 070	13 920	13 450	11 350	8 830	7 750	7 330	86 370	19 230	13 510	13 340
Centre	113 880	25 080	17 450	17 420	15 340	12 280	12 090	14 210	118 370	23 930	17 070	17 150
Basse-Normandie	67 390	16 010	11 260	10 610	8 460	7 210	7 240	6 600	70 420	15 210	10 820	10 150
Bourgogne	78 650	17 080	12 200	11 750	10 310	8 510	8 940	9 860	82 160	16 120	11 600	11 580
Nord-Pas-de-Calais	**191 200**	**48 740**	**33 270**	**30 320**	**24 120**	**20 290**	**19 180**	**15 270**	**201 830**	**46 690**	**32 030**	**29 940**
Est	**247 370**	**56 460**	**42 500**	**39 800**	**34 180**	**28 130**	**24 830**	**21 480**	**255 350**	**53 850**	**41 060**	**39 120**
Lorraine	115 460	26 580	20 000	18 370	15 470	13 200	12 160	9 690	118 460	25 180	19 370	18 060
Alsace	78 150	17 140	13 670	13 190	11 180	9 120	7 220	6 620	81 700	16 440	13 310	12 900
Franche-Comté	53 760	12 750	8 820	8 240	7 530	5 800	5 450	5 170	55 180	12 220	8 380	8 150
Ouest	**359 160**	**83 980**	**58 600**	**54 560**	**45 410**	**38 320**	**39 110**	**39 170**	**377 280**	**80 030**	**55 680**	**53 280**
Pays de la Loire	147 830	36 630	24 450	22 790	18 640	15 300	15 240	14 780	154 650	34 820	23 370	22 510
Bretagne	133 590	30 730	22 070	20 390	16 990	14 590	14 800	14 010	141 610	29 490	20 740	19 410
Poitou-Charentes	77 740	16 620	12 080	11 380	9 780	8 420	9 080	10 380	81 030	15 720	11 570	11 370
Sud-Ouest	**281 980**	**54 770**	**43 650**	**41 650**	**36 900**	**32 070**	**34 030**	**38 900**	**299 340**	**52 380**	**41 900**	**40 920**
Aquitaine	131 110	26 480	20 290	19 680	17 280	14 740	15 570	17 060	140 230	25 150	19 790	19 490
Midi-Pyrénées	115 570	21 980	18 230	16 890	15 130	13 170	14 180	15 990	121 130	21 090	17 290	16 430
Limousin	35 300	6 300	5 120	5 090	4 490	4 160	4 290	5 850	37 970	6 150	4 820	5 000
Centre-Est	**316 690**	**70 240**	**50 300**	**48 800**	**46 330**	**35 850**	**33 400**	**31 760**	**331 070**	**66 750**	**49 060**	**48 630**
Rhône-Alpes	251 340	56 960	40 270	39 080	37 540	28 310	25 540	23 650	262 990	5 4180	39 560	39 330
Auvergne	6 5350	13 280	10 030	9 730	8 790	7 540	7 860	8 110	68 080	12 570	9 500	9 300
Méditerranée	**306 650**	**61 010**	**47 240**	**44 750**	**43 920**	**34 980**	**34 370**	**40 380**	**326 540**	**57 740**	**45 280**	**44 530**
Languedoc-Roussillon	97 950	19 630	15 300	13 980	12 930	10 750	11 580	13 790	104 200	18 330	14 680	13 920
Provence-Alpes-Côte d'Azur	196 370	39 160	30 200	28 760	29 020	22 740	21 440	25 040	210 230	37 230	29 030	28 920
Corse	12 330	2 220	1 730	20 100	1 970	1 490	1 350	1 550	12 110	2 180	1 570	1 690

Fig. 3.10 The population structure of France by region (1988)

QUESTIONS

3.13 Select a representative sample of net gaining regions and net losing regions and construct the population pyramids for these regions from Fig. 3.10. For each area identify the origin of the newcomers. You may wish to draw a flow diagram for your chosen region. To save time you could share these out around the class and produce a wall display of your results.

3.14 Use this information to see if there is evidence to support your answer to question 3.12. For example, do some of the regions have ageing population structures? Are some of the regions dominated by a large number of people in the working age group?

3.15 Investigate the French regional policy of decentralisation (pp. 148–55) and relate this to your population information. Is there any evidence that people are moving to the peripheral regions following the establishment of new industries?

5–44	45–54	55–64	≥65	
3 070	301 600	312 740	444 270	**FRANCE**
6 720	57 180	51 970	71 460	**Ile-de-France**
2 610	52 950	55 310	80 920	**Bassin parisien**
8 300	7 100	7 030	10 180	Champagne-Ardenne
0 950	8 980	9 050	12 600	Picardie
0 830	8 770	8 680	12 010	Haute-Normandie
4 630	12 200	13 090	20 300	Centre
8 140	7 450	7 900	10 770	Basse-Normandie
9 770	8 460	9 570	15 060	Bourgogne
3 190	21 070	21 470	27 430	**Nord-Pas-de-Calais**
1 530	27 190	26 640	35 960	**Est**
4 450	12 930	12 380	16 080	Lorraine
0 080	8 660	8 430	11 890	Alsace
7 010	5 600	5 830	7 990	Franche-Comté
4 140	39 610	43 360	61 180	**Ouest**
8 280	15 910	16 590	23 170	Pays de la Loire
6 340	15 050	17 140	23 440	Bretagne
9 520	8 640	9 630	14 570	Poitou-Charentes
6 680	33 060	37 540	56 850	**Sud-Ouest**
7 300	15 340	17 390	25 780	Aquitaine
5 160	13 500	15 140	22 530	Midi-Pyrénées
4 230	4 220	5 010	8 540	Limousin
4 640	35 210	35 870	50 920	**Centre-Est**
6 280	27 730	27 600	38 310	Rhône-Alpes
8 360	7 470	8 270	12 610	Auvergne
3 550	35 330	40 570	59 540	**Méditerranée**
3 020	11 370	13 530	19 340	Languedoc-Roussillon
8 930	22 720	25 490	37 920	Provence-Alpes-Côte d'Azur
1 600	1 240	1 550	2 280	Corse

Fig. 3.11 A generalised regional map of France

1. The Paris region
Remaining dominant with renewed population growth. Provides nearly one-third of the French GDP. 80% of French companies have their headquarters here. Centre of high order services

4. Declining industries of the north and east
Collapse of traditional mining and heavy manufacturing. Even car assembly plants have been forced to rationalise. High unemployment and areas of poor housing leave a depressing picture

2. The prosperous regions of Rhône-Alpes, Alsace and Provence-Alpes-Côte d'Azur
Highly prosperous areas based on dynamic urban development. Benefited from 'sun-belt' location which has been attractive to high-tech industries and laboratories. Some pockets of high unemployment — e.g. shipbuilding at Fos.

5. The rural deserts
Areas dependent on seasonal tourism characterised by outward migration

3. 'France's new fertile crescent'
Containing industries which have gained from decentralisation. But most development from growth of branch factories. Low wage rates – much low skilled assembly work

0   20 km

N

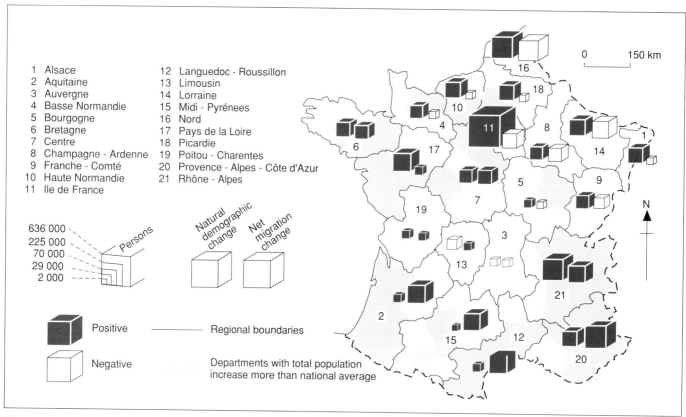

Fig. 3.12 Regional population changes in France, 1982–90

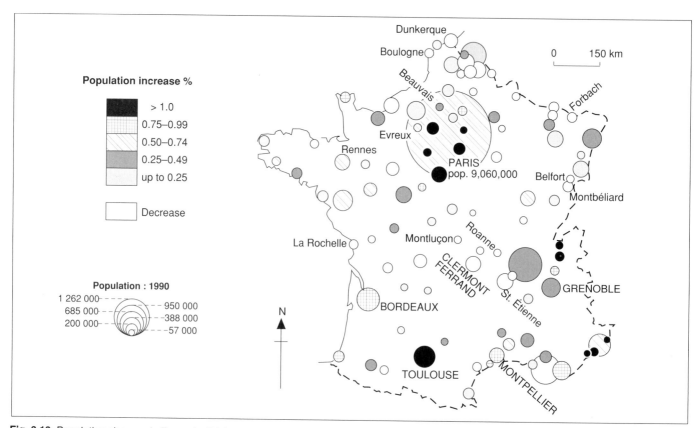

Fig. 3.13 Population changes in France's 100 largest urban areas, 1982–90

The French census of 1990 showed that the trends of the previous decade have continued. The population of France is now 56 556 000 and it has grown at 0.5% per annum. The overall picture is represented in Fig. 3.12 which shows the natural population change component alongside the migration component. The movement to the south is still evident, with out-migration from the northern regions. The increase in the population of Paris is very significant, caused by young people moving from the older industrial areas. Figure 3.13 shows the population changes in the largest urban areas. This indicates that high rates of population growth in the regions are taking place around the nuclei of large urban areas.

The core–periphery model

The relationship between population movement and industrial development is represented by the *core–periphery model* (Fig. 3.14). The model shows that as an industrial core develops it will attract resources from the surrounding area. The core region will develop by the process of *cumulative causation*, where one development leads to the additional development of related activities. People living in the adjacent area may well be encouraged to move to the core area to participate in some of its perceived benefits. The model of cumulative causation is shown in Fig. 3.15.

The surrounding area or periphery will develop as spread or backwash effects take place. The core will spread out, agricultural products will be required and eventually parts of the successful core may be decentralised to the periphery to form *growth poles*. These growth poles will stimulate the economy of the periphery and act as counter attractions to the core. Over time the area will become a fully integrated economic system where the entire population will have access to the benefits of the development.

The development of an economic region may not directly follow this path. The jobs available in the core area may be mainly for the unskilled, and because of the large pool of labour the wages will be low. In the first phase of development many of the jobs will be in construction and unskilled labour will be required. After the construction phase higher skills will be in demand. Local people may be forced to work for small service industries, many of them part of the 'informal sector'.

Stage 1. The development of the core and the periphery

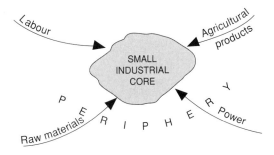

Stage 2. The core starts to spread into the periphery

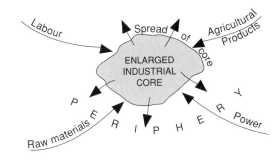

Stage 3. Fully integrated region with growth poles

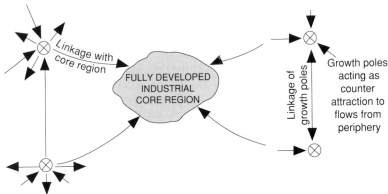

Fig. 3.14 The core–periphery model

These may include working in petrol stations, light engineering, taxi hire and working as gardeners and domestics.

Accommodation in the core area will be in short supply and this, combined with the low level of pay, may lead to the development of shanty housing. Even in the most basic of shanty developments, shanty landlords will be preying on the low-paid workers. This may mean that the original intention of bringing the family to the town at a later stage will not materialise as the wages barely pay for the basic necessities. Observation of developing core areas suggests that new migrant workers do not have access to the newly developed facilities and the culture of the migrant areas may be dominated by prostitution, drunkenness and disease.

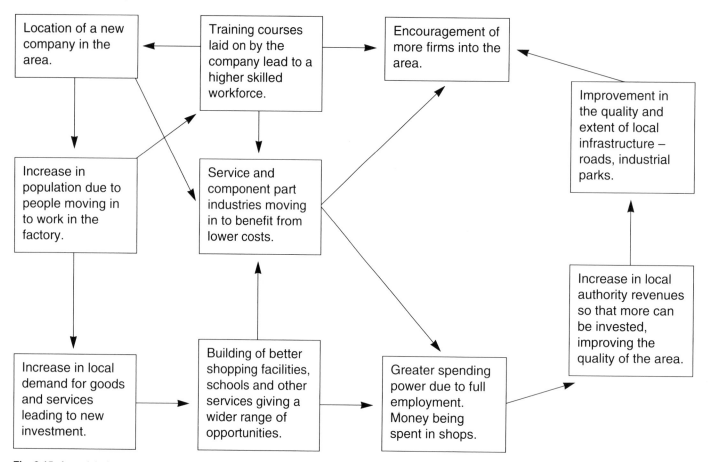

Fig. 3.15 A model of cumulative causation

In the model there are backwash or spread effects into the periphery, leading to the development of the area. In reality, the remaining population may be unable to provide enough labour to maintain the inflow of agricultural products for sale in the core area. The periphery areas may suffer from *negative causation*

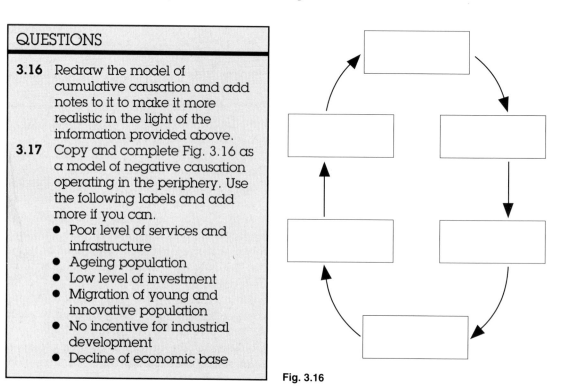

QUESTIONS

3.16 Redraw the model of cumulative causation and add notes to it to make it more realistic in the light of the information provided above.

3.17 Copy and complete Fig. 3.16 as a model of negative causation operating in the periphery. Use the following labels and add more if you can.
- Poor level of services and infrastructure
- Ageing population
- Low level of investment
- Migration of young and innovative population
- No incentive for industrial development
- Decline of economic base

Fig. 3.16

Multinational companies and the New International Division of Labour

Recent research has investigated the behaviour of multinational companies in relation to the core–periphery model. This research has not been finalised but it has led to the development of the New International Division of Labour model (NIDL). The basis of this model is that the structure of many large multinational companies has three levels or tiers. At the top of the hierarchy is the research and development section where highly paid employees work. The next tier involves high-skill production and the lowest tier deals with low-skilled standardised production. It is suggested by the model that in times of economic recession where there is the need for cost minimisation, the lowest tier of production may be moved to a developing country where wage rates are low and union structures are poorly developed. It is argued that large multinational companies have the flexibility to move to advantageous low-cost locations. Figure 3.17 shows this model in diagrammatic form.

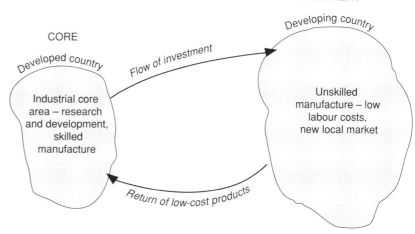

Fig. 3.17 The New International Division of Labour

Nike

Nike is a company known to many people as a producer of sportswear. They sell in excess of 40 million pairs of shoes per year with 63% of their revenue coming from the US market. All of the production is now subcontracted to countries in the Far East.

The original company was known as BRS and from 1964 they were importing shoes made by Nihon-Koyo and Nippon Rubber in Japan into the USA. The research and development centre for BRS was in Oregon in the USA. In 1973 production was moved to Taiwan and South Korea and in 1974 BRS moved the research and development centre to an area of New Hampshire, famous for making shoes. The intention was to gain from the local expertise of shoe manufacture. By 1978 the company was renamed Nike and was selling to Europe and Latin America. The industry really took off in the 1980s as the world became much more health conscious and sports clothes and shoes became part of the fashion industry.

The structure of Nike's subcontracting is shown in Fig. 3.19. The production process is shared between three sources. The developed partners in Taiwan and South Korea produce the high quality, 'statement' products.

Fig. 3.18 A sample of Nike's product range

Fig. 3.19 Nike
subcontracting structure

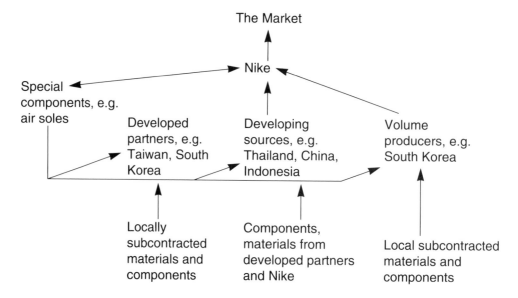

Fig. 3.20 Maps showing
Nike production sites

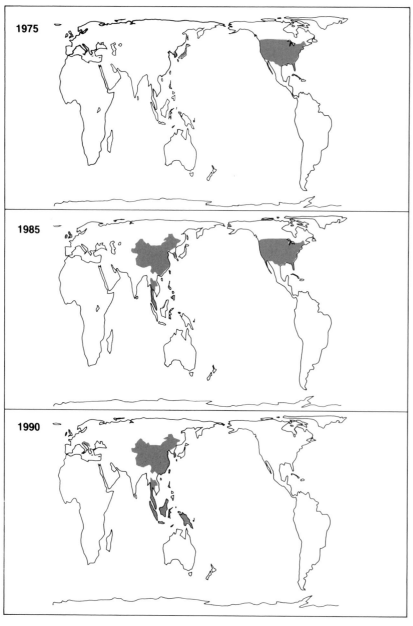

1975

1985

1990

Between 10 000 and 25 000 pairs of shoes are produced per day in these factories. The bulk of production comes from the volume producers who make 70 000 pairs of shoes per day. They also produce goods for other manufacturers but these are lower quality and lower price than the 'statement' products. The third type of subcontractor is the 'developing source'. This is an area which has recently opened up production and is on some form of trial basis. New factories in Thailand, China and Indonesia come into this category.

Special products such as the air soles are imported from the USA to these factories but the remaining materials and products are generally subcontracted locally. Nike regard the subcontractors as partners who are responsible for the quality of the products leaving the factory. They also involve the local companies in research and development. They maintain continuity of standards by sending highly skilled expatriate workers to work in the subcontracting factories. They also ensure that production is fairly consistent in the subcontracting companies by making sure that orders do not vary by more than 20% per month, giving them some security.

Figure 3.20 shows how Nike have moved production around to gain financial advantages from various locations, although the Taiwan and South Korea bases have remained consistent.

Another reason for the movement of production is to maximise the market in which the goods are sold. This is not really the case in the Nike example, but has been shown to be the case with other industries. It is a way around

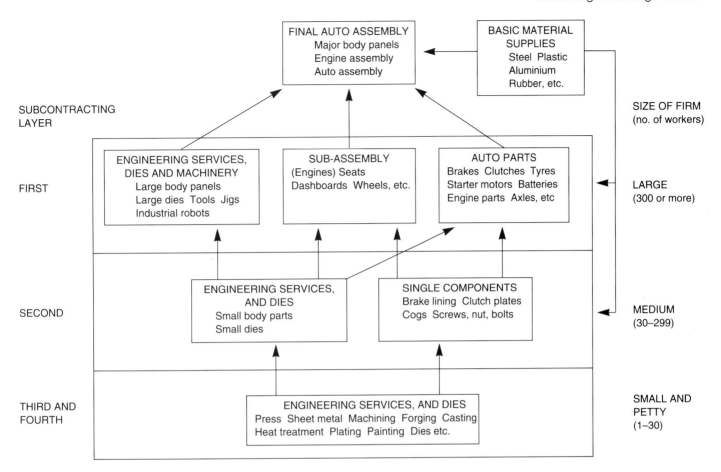

Fig. 3.21 Car subcontracting system in Japan

the protective quota system employed by economic groups such as the European Community. Hence it explains why the Japanese have invested heavily in production sites within the EC.

Just In Time

A further refinement of the NIDL model is the system of production known as 'Just In Time' (JIT). This system of production works on the basis that necessary components will be made ready for the next stage of production as and when they are required and stockpiling of components will be eradicated. This system was pioneered by the Japanese car companies as they sought ways of reducing costs to compete with the American multinational companies. The success of this system can be seen in that the Japanese now require 35% less time to build a car than competitors in the USA.

Since the end of the Second World War Toyota and Nissan have grown to be the second and third largest car companies in the world. They use a subcontracting system for their production, similar to the one used by Nike. Figure 3.21 shows the system for the car industry. Here the subcontractors form a hierarchy, with the 'bottom' contractors

producing very few components, often in a very small workshop. In fact 80% of the subcontractors in the lowest tier have less than 20 workers. The relationship between the contractors and the level above is very paternalistic and checks on quality are made at each stage of production. Hence only 30% of the production process is owned by the parent company. The JIT system means that the subcontractors and the main company have to be spatially very close. This has led to agglomeration of industries. In Japan the Tokaido megalopolises of Tokyo and Nagoya have 29% of the land, 62% of the population and produce 72% of the industrial products of the country.

To break into North American markets and to find a way around the import restrictions the Japanese car companies have established component plants in other countries of South-East Asia. These produce components which can be imported into the USA for assembly and avoid the tariff barriers erected against products made in Japan.

Another development in maximising the market potential for these companies is to make links with companies in the home market.

Fig. 3.22 Linkage between Japanese, American and Korean car manufacturers

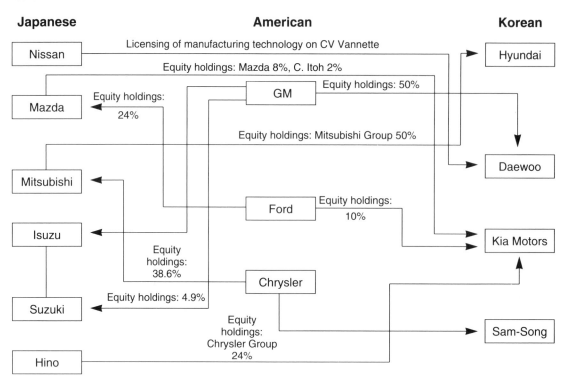

Figure 3.22 shows some of the relationships between Japanese, US and Korean car manufacturers.

In order to maximise car production in Western Europe and still use the JIT principle, the Nissan company has established a similar hierarchy of subcontractors in the UK to input into the Nissan car plant at Sunderland, Tyne and Wear. The first car was produced in 1986 and there were plans for the development to employ 3500 workers by 1992. By the early 1990s the cars coming from the plant had 80% locally produced components. The encouragement of other Japanese companies to invest in the area has greatly increased job creation in the area. These companies are part of the subcontracting hierarchy of Nissan and are shown on Fig. 3.23.

Applying the Just in Time philosophy to the NIDL model may mean that in future whole parts of the core area are transplanted to the periphery. The important aspect of JIT is the efficiency of linkage, and when these links spread over half the globe, disruption in the flow of components could be disastrous to production. JIT will move manufacturers back to gaining from agglomeration economies in the periphery and this will have the effect of focusing the developers' mind on the redevelopment of the old core region. Figure 3.25 summarises some of these developments.

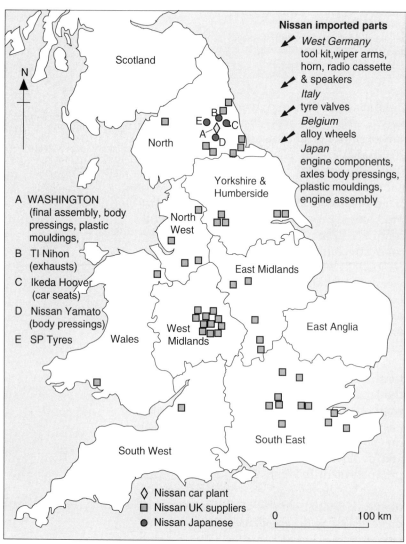

Fig. 3.23 The location of Nissan's principal suppliers in the UK

Fig. 3.24 The Nissan factory in Sunderland, Tyne and Wear

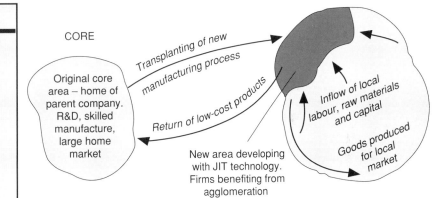

Fig. 3.25 JIT and NIDL

QUESTIONS

3.18 Define the following terms: New International Division of Labour (NIDL), Just in Time (JIT), core, periphery, backwash, agglomeration of industry.

3.19 What are the forces at work in the concentration of industrial development in the Tokyo and Nagoya regions of Japan?

3.20 What are the major consequences for developing countries of the growth and development of NIDL and JIT?

3.21 Investigate industrial linkage in some local companies. Find out if they are the parent company or, if not, where the parent company is.

Where does the manufacturing and final assembly take place?

Have they moved the manufacturing sites? If so, why have they moved them?

Have these moves involved moving people?

Try to find out if they fit into the NIDL model and see if they employ JIT philosophy. You should try to work as a class group and work out the questions you need to ask to find out the information required. This could form the basis of an individual study or project.

3.22 Using the model of cumulative causation explain how the north-east of England may benefit from the Nissan car plant.

3.23 Using the information on the map showing Nissan's principal supplier locations (Fig. 3.23) and the ideas in Fig. 3.26, describe the likely impact of Nissan on the industrial geography of the north-east of England and identify the factors which lead to sustained industrial growth.

117

From a virtuous to vicious circle

GEOGRAPHICAL clusters of self-supporting firms which reinforce virtuous circles of growth are behind the success of the Italian ceramic tile industry, centred around Emilia Romagna; the Japanese robotics industry around Mt Fuji; and the German printing press industry around Heidelberg.

They are celebrated as an integral part of Professor Michael Porter's theory of economic growth in his book on the rise and fall of industrial economies. Along with long-term banking institutions, discerning consumers and intense competition, they are part of his "diamond" of elements that generate growth. The idea is that clustered companies locate the physical and intellectual factors that reinforce their growth near them.

That the valleys of the North-east used to boast their own industrial clusters in ship-building, marine and power engineering is less well known.

Ship-building was a classic cluster; ships on the Tyne having rudders added here, an engine there and gun systems on top — the linkages feeding back into the local economy. There were forges, steel mills, and pits all producing the raw industrial material; and then machine tool builders to create the machines to bash the metal into pumps, chains, and gun barrels.

Even as late as the early 1970s, the Wear Valley still boasted an integrated ship-building industry; but its owners were quoted companies and the government — far removed from the industrial sites and even further away from under-standing their logic. Takeover and the vagaries of life in public ownership has since seen them disappear.

Now, plants and factories are outliers of larger combines or self-standing units with declining local markets. Yet, surprisingly, around Nissan a cluster of car components makers is growing. And while critics attack its dependent nature supporters applaud the emergence of any kind of logical industrial base. Elsewhere the picture is bleaker.

One study on the foreign microwave makers, notably Samsung and Sanyo, notes the brittle linkages with the local economy, arguing it is mainly low-tech assembly work. And Dr Frank Peck, author of a survey on local linkages, says despite all the disparities between industries there is one common theme; sub-contractors' and suppliers' performance is being scrutinised much more closely. The accent is on quality and the pressure to upgrade is constant. But this requires finance and skills; and with no locally controlled banks and no local stock market, the companies who engage in investment are on their own.

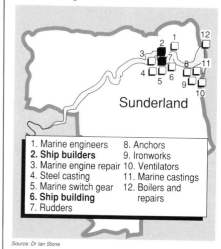

Shipbuilding in the 70's

Sunderland

1. Marine engineers
2. **Ship builders**
3. Marine engine repair
4. Steel casting
5. Marine switch gear
6. **Ship building**
7. Rudders
8. Anchors
9. Ironworks
10. Ventilators
11. Marine castings
12. Boilers and repairs

Source: Dr Ian Stone

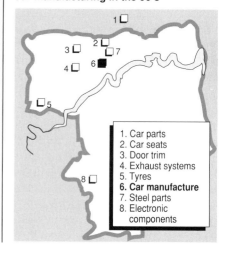

Car manufacturing in the 90's

1. Car parts
2. Car seats
3. Door trim
4. Exhaust systems
5. Tyres
6. **Car manufacture**
7. Steel parts
8. Electronic components

Fig. 3.26 An example of location based on NIDL and JIT (*Guardian* 27.5.91)

A further example: regional development in Japan

As new investment is being directed towards the areas of the periphery to maximise market opportunities and circumvent restrictions on trade, areas adjacent to the original core areas may need to develop to attract new investment. The core regions will remain as strong as they were but disparities of wealth may start to appear in areas just beyond the core areas. These 'local peripheral' areas may require investment in infrastructure to make them attractive to new development to pre-vent this happening. This development has been observed in Japan.

Post-war development

Japan has been going through a period of rapid urban and industrial growth since the end of the Second World War. This development has produced a very strong core region along the Tokyo–Nagoya–Osaka axis. The Japanese government has been trying to decentralise this core region to develop other areas and decrease regional disparities. They have done this by using a series of development plans. The first plan in 1962 established

15 growth poles in the periphery. These are shown on Fig. 3.27. These growth poles are new industrial cities (or NICs). To these were added six special areas for industrial development. There are now 96 NICs and to this programme the 4th Development Plan has added a new development called a technopolis.

Technopolis growth

The technopolis development is intended to be a growth pole specialising in research and development in the semiconductor, new materials and biotechnology industries. These industries are good choices for development in the periphery as they are footloose (not tied to a major locating factor) and give a high return for the weight of goods transported. The technopolis principle is being developed alongside developments of new towns. The planners are concerned about providing a high quality working environment to entice highly qualified workers away from the core industrial region.

The locations of the technopolis sites are shown in Fig. 3.28. However, they had to meet stringent criteria before being accepted for technopolis status. The areas chosen had to be not excessively industrial, but had to have a local population in excess of 150 000. They had to have a local university specialising in high-technology courses and have sufficient local businesses to provide a base of local entrepreneurial skills. There also had to be plans to develop the air and railway communications so that the area would be highly accessible, before it was accepted for technopolis status. Figure 3.28 shows that many of the sites chosen are on the east coast so that they could take advantage of the existing railway facilities.

Support infrastructure

One of the strong underlying concepts of the technopolis scheme was that they should build on local expertise. They should mobilise local resources and build on the existing industrial base. Other initiatives were put in place to assist the project. The Japanese government was very concerned that these areas should have modern integrated IT communication systems installed. These again should be local to the area. In February 1986 they initiated the Intelligent Cities programme to build up the level of infrastructure specification to a higher level so that the new industries could gain from the benefits of optical fibre technology.

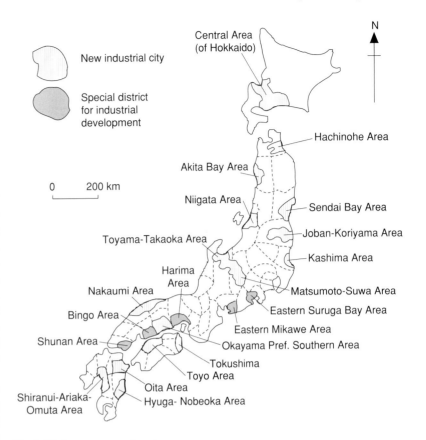

Fig. 3.27 Japanese growth poles

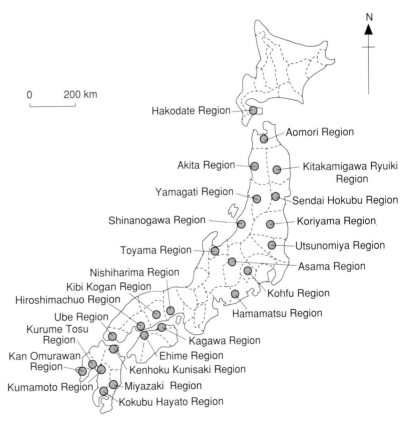

Fig. 3.28 Technopolis sites in Japan

119

Fig. 3.29 Key features of some technopolis sites

Area	Main city	Number of cities/town villages in technopolis (not including main city)	Population (technopolis area: main city)	Features of industrial complex	Features of R & D concept
Hakodate	Hakodate	3 towns	380 517	Marine industries, resources utilisation industries	Integrated regional marine research centre, resource utilisation research
Aomori	Aomori	4 cities 2 towns 2 villages	604 325 287 597	Mechatronics–biotech-nology industries	Local industry research, modern technology research laboratory, institutes of industry and technology etc.
Akita	Akita	2 towns	304 823 284 863	New materials, resource energy development, electronics, biotechnology related industries, etc.	Metal frontier centre, local technology centre, medical centre for the elderly, etc.
Utsunomiya	Utsunomiya	1 city	469 944	Electronics, fine chemicals, new materials etc.	Regional industrial institutes of physics/technology, etc.
Shinanogawa	Nagaoka	7 cities 6 towns 1 village	638 509 183 756	High-dimension systems, new materials processing, urban business, fine industry, fashion	Development Education Research Promotion Centre of Nagaoka Technical University (established), Technopolis Development Centre, Kashiwazaki Softpark
Toyama	Toyama Takaoka	3 towns	568 291 480 110	Biotechnology, new materials etc.	Toyama Technical Development Corporation Bioscience Research Centre, Modern Technology Interchange Centre
Hamamatsu	Hamamatsu	2 cities 2 towns	619 621 490 824	Photo-industry, musical instruments, information communication system, etc.	Photo-information Technology Integrated Research Centre, Electronics Centre, etc.
Kurume Tosu	Kurume	1 city 5 towns	332 487 216 974	High-system industry (information-associated industry, community development), new materials, biotechnology, etc.	R & D park, integrated information centre, etc.
Kumamoto	Kumamoto	1 city 12 towns 2 villages	738 558 525 662	Applied machine industry, biotechnology, computers, information systems, etc.	Research park, electronics applications, machine technology, research labs, etc.
Kan-Omurawan	Sasebo	2 cities 1 town	440 778 251 188	Ocean development associated instruments, resources and energy development, etc.	Research Park, labs for research in electronics applications for machine technology and for semi-conductor applications.
Kenhoku Kunisaki	Oita Beppu	4 cities 13 towns 2 villages	281 513 496 963	IC, LSI, new materials, soft engineering, techno-green industry, regional resources utilisation, etc.	Regional economy information centre, industry-university-government co-operation system, etc.

Area	Main city	Number of cities/town villages in technopolis (not including main city)	Population (technopolis area: main city)	Features of industrial complex	Features of R & D concept
Miyazaki	Miyazaki	6 towns	356 876 264 855	Electronics, new materials, biotechnology (fine chemical, biomass, etc.)	Co-operative Research Development Centre, IC laboratory, etc.
Kokubu-Hayato	Kagoshima	1 city 12 towns	691 909 505 077	Advanced equipment (electronics), new materials (fine ceramics), regional industry (modern fishing and agroindustry), biotechnology etc.	Technology promotion organisation material resources research centre, regional industry promotion associations, etc.

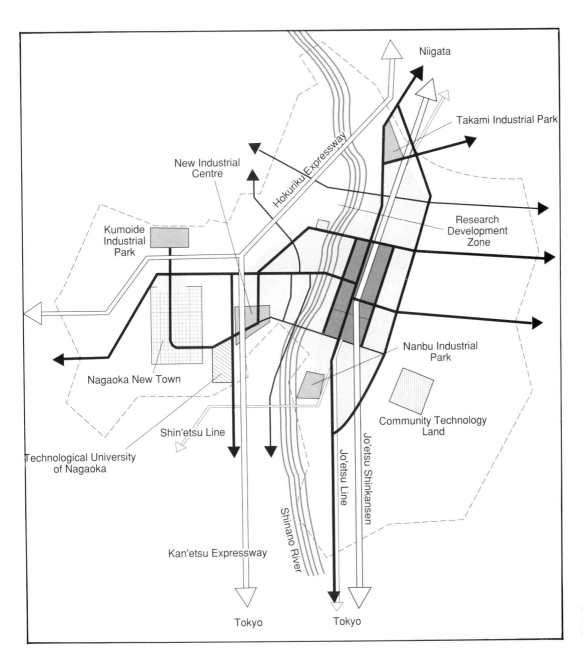

Fig. 3.30 The Shinanogawa/Nagaoka technopolis

Funding

The government, through the Ministry of International Trade and Industry (MITI), provided about 33% of the funds while the rest was paid for locally.

Shinanogawa/Nagaoka

One example of a technopolis is the Shinanogawa/Nagaoka technopolis (Fig. 3.30). Before the development this area was a 5-hour train journey from Tokyo. It is now linked by a high speed track and the journey has been reduced to 1.5 hours. From 1985 the Kanetsu Su expressway reduced the road journey from 5 hours to 3.

The old industrial base was largely agricultural with rice being the main crop. Oil had been exploited in small quantities but had given rise to a chemical industry, and a metal and machinery industry completed the picture. It was the home of the Nihou Seiki company, producing about 80% of the world's speedometers. It fitted the population criterion, with a local population of some 180 000.

The development of the Shinanogawa/ Nagaoka technopolis started in 1975 on a 1083 km^2 site on the west bank of the Shinano river. At the time it was the largest development of the Japanese Regional Development Corporation. The original plan was to build accommodation for 40 000 people by 1990 and to make allowance for ample space for parkland and recreation. A new experimental technological university was part of the plan. This university provides only technological courses and most of the work is at postgraduate level with strong links with the local community.

Since the start of this development over 40 new companies have been moved to the area. They have been encouraged by the highly qualified workforce and the low interest loans which have been paid to firms investing in state-of-the-art technology. Many of the companies have built on the original economic base, such as the biotechnology industry, using the agricultural base.

The success of this technopolis has encouraged MITI to revise their investment plans and the development area has been increased by 260 km^2. The population criterion has been revised so that 631 000 people now live within the technopolis area.

QUESTIONS

3.24 What was the status of the 'local periphery' areas (now chosen for technopolis sites) before development? Use the push–pull model to help structure your answer.

3.25 What were the main reasons for the development of technopolis sites in Japan?

3.26 What elements of the infrastructure did the Japanese government consider necessary before technopolis sites were developed?

3.27 Use all the information provided to construct an annotated map showing the regional policies of Japan.

3.28 Amongst UK examples of high-tech developments are industrial parks such as Winnersh Triangle (Berkshire), the Cambridge Science Park (Cambridge) and Aztec West (Bristol). These are smaller in scale than the Japanese technopolis sites and have been largely funded by private enterprise rather than through government action.

(a) Obtain information on one of the UK high-tech developments. Suitable sources would be the broadsheet newspapers, the New Town Development Corporations or recent industrial geography textbooks.

(b) In about 500 words compare the Japanese approach to the high-tech development in the 'local periphery' with that adopted in the UK. Which do you think will be more successful and why?

Problem-Solving Exercise

Industrial development in Eastern Europe

It is possible to apply the core–periphery model to the countries of the European Community. The core has recently been called the 'hot banana' (Fig. 3.31). Some places in the UK are preparing to benefit from their location and see this as bringing them considerable benefit. Figure 3.32 is an advertisement by the Port of Felixstowe. The map projection used in the advertisement appears to give the port a central position to support the claim that it is in an 'ideal position'. This may not be the case in the future, even if it is now.

The article (Fig. 3.31) points to some of the political changes which have recently taken place in Europe with the removal of the 'iron curtain'. These changes may affect the shape and position of the 'banana', explaining the use of the adjective 'hot'.

Many of the industries of the countries of Eastern Europe are in poor shape to compete with the industries of the West. Many of them pollute their environment and are poorly equipped with new technology. Will these countries become the periphery of the EC? How will they develop? Will the NIDL model operate and the people of Eastern Europe become workers in the subcontracting factories to compete with the factories of South East Asia? Read pp. 126–7.

Your task is to prepare a report on the future development of the industrial base of Eastern Europe. You will be expected to analyse information and define the problem, and then to make recommendations which will benefit the people and the environment of Eastern Europe. You should follow the structure given in questions 3.29 to 3.35.

Planners plot the course of Europe's 'hot banana'

Fig. 3.31 *Independent* 14.6.91

By Nicholas Schoon,

Environment Correspondent

EUROPE is dominated by a "hot banana". A huge zone curving from the British Midlands down to North Italy embraces the greatest concentration of population, economic muscle and propensity to travel on the continent — and possibly in the world.

With Gallic elegance the French call it the *dorsale*, or backbone. The few British planning experts who know about it have chosen the more vulgar title to describe its vigour and shape.

The question for Europe's planners is: which way is the hot banana moving? Is it shifting to the south-west, because of the rapid industrialisation of the recent EC entrants Spain and Portugal?

Or will it march off to the north-east, when rickety communist economies in former Warsaw Pact nations are transformed into high growth capitalist ones?

David Lock, a leading private sector planner, showed the shape on a slide during a lecture at the Royal Town Planning Institute's conference in Newcastle upon Tyne this week. Some call it the "European megalopolis".

"The hot banana is a very useful concept, but not many people in Britain know about it," Mr Lock said, "We have to ask: what does it mean for us? Can we get a larger part of its tip in Britain?"

The bent shape bestriding the continent illustrated the kind of pan-European vision which Britain's local council and government planners usually lacked, he said. Such concepts were essential for the UK to plan infrastructure, transport links and new development in an integrated Europe.

The hot banana first appeared in 1989 in the *Livre Blanc*, a document setting out strategic plans for the central Ile de France region. It was drawn up by Datar, a French national planning body which is more high-powered and better resourced than its regional British equivalents.

Not all centres of high population and intensive economic activity are within the shape. Paris and the Ile de France lie a little outside, which causes the French planners some unease. But it purports to show where the bulk of the action is. London, the

continued

Europe's hot banana

"Hot banana" regions

Peripheral regions

London ▪
Paris ▪
Frankurt ⊙
Milan ⊙

200 miles

Fig. 3.31 (*cont.*)

South-east, the Midlands and East Anglia can count themselves in.

Mr Lock also showed a map of North-west Europe tipped on its side, which revealed that the most direct line from Britain's heart to the centre of the banana is not south-east across the Straits of Dover, but almost directly east through East Anglian and Humberside ports.

Planners should not become fixated on the Channel and the Channel Tunnel, which would only carry out one-tenth of the freight passing between Britain and Europe, he said.

There would be a shift away from road and rail links radiating out from London to the provinces "to a pattern that ties us to the European mainland from the Midlands across East Anglia". Yet Midlands planners showed little sign of understanding that, he said.

The fastest way to the heart of Europe?

Fig. 3.32

QUESTIONS

3.29 Figure 3.33 gives information about the current state of gross national product, the levels of industrial output and the growth rates in the economies of the countries of Europe. Construct a series of choropleths to show the information for 1986 and draw suitable graphs to show the changes over the periods shown in the tables.

3.30 Use the photographs on pp. 128–30 and any other information you have been able to collect to describe the environmental situation in the Eastern European countries. Refer to Chapter 2 (p. 94) and use the environmental impact grid to analyse one or more of the photographs.

3.31 Write a summary of the problem as you see it, using all the information available to you.

A. Comparative changes in industrial output in East-Central Europe and the European Community, 1960–86

Fig. 3.33 Economic statistics for Europe

East-Central Europe				European Community		
	1960–69	1970–79	1980–86		1960–69	1970–79	1980–86
Albania	4.9	NA	NA	Belgium	5.1	2.2	0.7
Bulgaria	11.4	7.4	4.4	Denmark	5.7	2.1	4.1
Czechoslovakia	6.0	5.8	2.8	France	5.8	3.1	0.2
GDR	6.2	5.8	4.1	FRG	5.7	1.8	0.6
Hungary	7.0	5.0	1.9	Greece	8.6	6.9	1.4
Poland	8.6	7.4	−0.2	Ireland	6.7	4.7	4.9
Romania	12.8	11.4	4.2	Italy	7.2	3.5	−0.7
Yugoslavia	8.3	7.2	2.7	Netherlands	7.3	3.2	1.0
				Portugal	4.9	6.6	2.1
				Spain	11.7	5.0	0.8
				UK	2.9	0.7	1.3

B. Comparative changes in real gross domestic product in East-Central Europe and the European Community, 1960–86

East-Central Europe				European Community		
	1960–69	1970–79	1980–86		1960–69	1970–79	1980–86
Albania	NA	NA	NA	Belgium	4.9	3.2	0.4
Bulgaria	7.7	7.0	3.7	Denmark	4.8	2.4	2.1
Czechoslovakia	4.7	4.5	1.6	France	5.8	3.6	1.2
GDR	4.3	4.8	4.5	FRG	4.9	2.7	1.3
Hungary	5.5	5.0	1.8	Greece	7.6	4.7	1.0
Poland	7.3	5.4	−0.8	Ireland	4.3	4.5	1.8
Romania	8.4	9.2	4.4	Italy	5.5	3.1	0.9
Yugoslavia	6.7	5.7	0.2	Netherlands	6.0	2.9	0.7
				Portugal	NA	4.8	0.5
				Spain	7.5	3.7	1.5
				UK	2.7	1.9	1.9

C. Levels of economic development: gross domestic product (GDP) per capita in East-Central Europe and the European Community, 1974 and 1986 (US $) – country rankings in 1986

East-Central Europe		1986/1974	European Community			1986/1974
	1974	1986			1974	1986	
East-Central Europe				**European Community 12**			
Total GDP ($billion)	271.3	447.5	1.65	Total GDP ($billion)	1 240.0	2 461.8	1.99
Average GDP per capita ($)	2 102	3 242	1.54	Average GDP per capita ($)	3 982	7 644	1.92
Czechoslovakia	3 199	5 998	1.87	Luxembourg	5 854	11 374	1.94
GDR	3 487	5 401	1.55	Denmark	6 020	11 337	1.88
Bulgaria	1 728	3 200	1.85	FRG	6 198	10 245	1.65
Romania	1 331	2 687	2.0	France	5 067	9 276	1.83
Hungary	2 347	1 937	0.825	Netherlands	5 109	8 631	1.69
Poland	2 107	1 900	0.9	Belgium	5 467	8 219	1.50
Yugoslavia	1 182	1 850	1.59	UK	3 386	8 050	2.38
Albania	702	860	1.23	Italy	2 706	6 283	2.32
				Ireland	1 744	5 165	2.96
				Spain	1 959	4 430	2.26
				Greece	2 149	3 295	1.53
				Portugal	1 480	2 021	1.37

Eastern Europe

Diary of major events in Eastern Europe 1989–92

1989

April	POLAND	Legalisation of trade union Solidarity.
June	POLAND	Solidarity wins partly free elections.
	HUNGARY	Condemnation of Soviet invasion 1956.
July	HUNGARY	Border with Austria opened – thousands of East German 'tourists' flee to Austria.
August	POLAND	First non-communist Prime Minister for 40 years.
September	POLAND	New government with very small number of communists.
	HUNGARY	Communist Party abolished.
October	EAST GERMANY	Fall of old hard-line leadership.
	CZECHOSLOVAKIA	10 000 people demand reform on streets of Prague.
November	EAST GERMANY	1 million people march for reform in East Berlin. Berlin Wall opened and then demolished. Government resigns.
	BULGARIA	Communist leader resigns. 100 000 people demonstrate in Sofia. Citizens allowed to travel abroad.
	CZECHOSLOVAKIA	50 000 people demand free elections. Government resigns.
December	End of the Cold War between USA and USSR. Nuclear arms limitation treaty.	
	CZECHOSLOVAKIA	New non-communist government appointed.
	ROMANIA	Revolution in which dictator Ceausescu executed. New government from National Salvation Front.

1990

January	YUGOSLAVIA	Communist government gives up monopoly of power.
February	EAST GERMANY	Multiparty elections – defeat for communists.
March	HUNGARY	First free elections since 1945 – defeat for communists.
April	YUGOSLAVIA	Communists defeated in elections in Croatia and Slovenia.
May	ROMANIA	Victory to National Salvation Front in elections.
June	BULGARIA	Free elections lead to win for communists.
	CZECHOSLOVAKIA	Anti-communist alliance wins election.
October	EAST GERMANY	Reunification with West Germany.
November	POLAND	Leader of Solidarity made President.
December	ALBANIA	People demonstrate for reform.
	BULGARIA	Fall of communist Government following demonstrations.

1991

January	Trade between Eastern bloc countries based on US $ rather than rouble.	
	ALBANIA	Government introduces some reforms.
	BULGARIA	New government with some non-communists.
Febuary	ALBANIA	President dismisses communist Government.
	USSR	End of communist block in Eastern Europe – end of Comecon.
	YUGOSLAVIA	Civil war between Croats and Serbs.
December	USSR	Commonwealth of Independent States. President resigns.

1992

	YUGOSLAVIA	Civil war continues between component states
	CZECHOSLOVAKIA	Potential break-up

QUESTIONS

1 Draw choropleth maps to illustrate the indicators in the table on p. 127. Make a wall display to show the overall pattern.
2 Find out the appropriate comparative figures for countries from Western Europe.
3 Start a file of newspaper cuttings to log developments in Eastern Europe.

Indicator \ Country	Albania	Bulgaria	Czechoslovakia	East Germany	Hungary	Poland	Romania	Yugoslavia
Area (000 km²)	28.7	111	128	108	93.4	313	238	256
Population (millions)	3.3	9	15.6	16.6	10.6	38.0	23.1	23.6
GDP per capita ($)	860	5633	7603	9361	6491	5453	4117	3534
Industrial output (% change 1989–90)	NA	−6.0	−3.5	−0.9	−9.0	−20.0	−20.0	−11.0
Agricultural output (% change 1989–90)	NA	−5.1	−0.8	−4.0	−4.5	−4.4	−6.8	−3.5
Exports ($m)	500	1965	5982	3205	6465	9802	6037	11 485
Imports ($m)	NA	2176	6283	3112	5543	6571	7176	15 190
Trade balance ($m)	NA	−211	−301	+93	+1374	+3213	−1139	−5920
Gross debt ($m)	NA	11 053	7300	19 900	20 272	42 100	3550	15 687
% workforce in agriculture	51	19.5	12.1	10.2	18.4	28.2	28.5	25.1
Cars per 1000	NA	127	182	206	153	74	11	124
Telephones per 1000	NA	248	246	233	152	122	111	152

Western investment in car industry

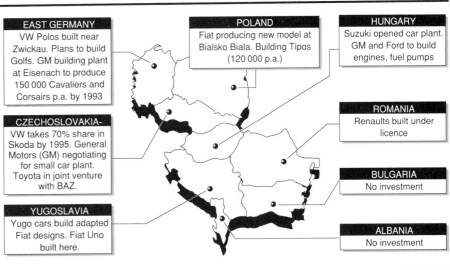

EAST GERMANY
VW Polos built near Zwickau. Plans to build Golfs. GM building plant at Eisenach to produce 150 000 Cavaliers and Corsairs p.a. by 1993

CZECHOSLOVAKIA-
VW takes 70% share in Skoda by 1995. General Motors (GM) negotiating for small car plant. Toyota in joint venture with BAZ.

YUGOSLAVIA
Yugo cars build adapted Fiat designs. Fiat Uno built here.

POLAND
Fiat producing new model at Bialsko Biala. Building Tipos (120 000 p.a.)

HUNGARY
Suzuki opened car plant. GM and Ford to build engines, fuel pumps

ROMANIA
Renaults built under licence

BULGARIA
No investment

ALBANIA
No investment

Growing links between East and West Europe

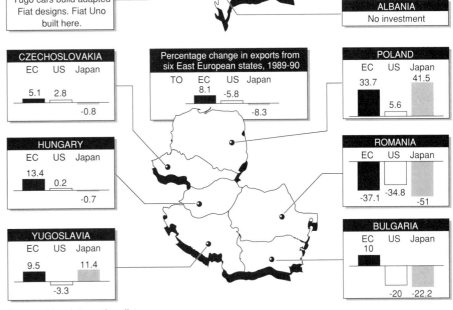

CZECHOSLOVAKIA
EC 5.1 US 2.8 Japan −0.8

HUNGARY
EC 13.4 US 0.2 Japan −0.7

YUGOSLAVIA
EC 9.5 US Japan 11.4 −3.3

Percentage change in exports from six East European states, 1989-90
TO EC 8.1 US −5.8 Japan −8.3

POLAND
EC 33.7 US 5.6 Japan 41.5

ROMANIA
EC −37.1 US −34.8 Japan −51

BULGARIA
EC 10 US −20 Japan −22.2

Migration

- 45 000 Bulgarians left Bulgaria (Jan–June 1990)
- 100 000 Romanian Germans returned to Germany
- 400 000 ethnic Germans returned to Germany from Eastern Europe

Source: *New Internationalist*

There are a number of options available to the countries of Eastern Europe. These include:

1. *The development of Open Sectors.* Continue with the economic structure as at present but establish sectors of the economy, e.g. electrical goods, which will be free from bureaucratic control, to allow firms to work for profit. Further freeing of the economic system could then follow over a longer period of time.

2. *The establishment of Free Economic Zones.* These would be areas which would allow foreign capital to invest in new factories and would manufacture products for export. There would be tax and customs exemptions and some home-based industries from the Eastern European countries would be allowed to establish themselves in these areas. Encouragement would be given to high-tech companies.

3. *Privatisation of the current economic structure.* Allow free market forces to operate throughout the economy and allow competition with all other companies on an equal basis.

4. *Decentralisation of the economy.* This would allow local authorities to make decisions on the local economy and develop and encourage the factories the local people think would be beneficial.

There are other issues which need to be considered in the development of these areas. Figure 3.35 gives a series of tables showing the public response to certain issues in selected towns in Poland. Tables A and B refer to the popular perception of existing local industry and table C gives the perception of the effects of further growth of local industry.

QUESTIONS

3.32 Analyse the four options, trying to work out the advantages and disadvantages of each option for
  (a) the economy of the country,
  (b) the people of the country,
  (c) the other countries of Europe.

3.33 Use the information from the tables to determine the nature of the industry you would encourage, taking the perceptions of the people into consideration.

3.34 Select one of the plans or a combination of plans and write an evaluation of it.

3.35 Construct a questionnaire which could be used to check on changes in environmental quality following the implementation of your plan.
  Suggest how this questionnaire could be used as part of an Environmental Impact Assessment as described in Chapter 2 (p.94).

Fig. 3.34 In Eastern Europe, industry was often central to urban development under communism

Fig. 3.35 Public responses to issues in Poland

A. Most important perceived effects of existing local industry

Nowy Sącz	% of responses
1. Health deterioration	46.8
2. Immigrants, it's more difficult to find a flat	46.8
3. GREATER NUMBER OF JOBS	35.8
4. Water supply difficulties	30.3
5. It's dirty	29.4
6. Hooliganism	27.5
7. Nature devastation	26.6
8. Worse quality or supply of food	23.9
9. NO NEED TO COMMUTE	22.9
10. Unpleasant odours	22.0

Kraków	% of responses
1. Health deterioration	81.7
2. Nature devastation	55.4
3. Worse quality or supply of food	50.2
4. Historical building devastation	45.8
5. Hooliganism	40.2
6. Immigrants, it's more difficult to find a flat	35.4
7. Water supply difficulties	31.2
8. It's dirty	29.9
9. GREATER NUMBER OF JOBS	19.9
10. EDUCATION PROSPECTS	17.5

B.(i) Rzeszów – most important effects of existing local industry

	% of responses
1. GREATER NUMBER OF JOBS	55.9
2. EDUCATION PROSPECTS	47.0
3. Immigrants, it's more difficult to find a flat	41.7
4. BETTER WAGE PROSPECTS	36.0
5. NO NEED TO COMMUTE	32.0
6. RAPID DEVELOPMENT OF THE CITY	28.7
7. BETTER TRANSPORTATION SERVICE	27.9
8. Health deterioration	27.1
9. THE CITY IS WELL-KNOWN	24.7
10. Hooliganism	21.1

(ii) Rzeszów – most important effects of further growth of local industry

	% of responses
1. GREATER NUMBER OF JOBS	42.8
2. Health deterioration	41.4
3. BETTER WAGE PROSPECTS	35.8
4. RAPID DEVELOPMENT OF THE CITY	34.4
5. Immigrants, it's more difficult to find a flat	28.3
6. EDUCATION PROSPECTS	28.8
7. Hooliganism	26.5
8. Less quiet life	23.7
9. Nature devastation	22.8
10. Worse quality or supply of food	20.9

C. Most important effects of further growth of local industry

Kolbuszowa	% of responses
1. RAPID DEVELOPMENT OF THE CITY	52.9
2. GREATER NUMBER OF JOBS	41.2
3. BETTER WAGE PROSPECTS	37.3
4. EDUCATION PROSPECTS	33.3
5. BETTER SHOPPING PROSPECTS	31.4
6. BETTER TRANSPORTATION SERVICE	31.4
7. Water supply difficulties	29.4
8. THE CITY IS WELL-KNOWN	21.6
9. Immigrants, it's more difficult to find a flat	21.6
10. Health deterioration	17.6

Tarnów	% of responses
1. Health deterioration	51.0
2. Nature devastation	36.4
3. GREATER NUMBER OF JOBS	34.0
4. Immigrants, it's more difficult to find a flat	33.0
5. BETTER WAGE PROSPECTS	29.6
6. Less quiet life	26.2
7. EDUCATION PROSPECTS	24.8
8. BETTER TRANSPORTATION SERVICE	23.3
9. Worse quality or supply of food	22.8
10. Unpleasant odours	21.8

Percentages show the proportion of respondents mentioning the given effect among the five most important consequences of local industrialisation.

Fig. 3.36 Advertising mirrors the political changes in East Berlin

Fig. 3.37 Much of communist East European architecture is the same – concrete blocks in Czechoslovakia

Fig. 3.38 A street scene in Dresden (former East Germany)

Information and communications

- *Ideas spread through an area in recognisable patterns.*
- *When an idea becomes practicable, its adoption can affect spatial patterns.*
- *Work patterns are changing under the influence of new technology.*
- *New ideas of shopping are influencing patterns of retail location and development.*
- *The footloose location of high-tech firms is an ideal basis for regional development.*

Is there a predictable pattern in the adoption of a new idea?

It takes a long time for new ideas to filter into the system and become generally accepted and used. A number of things need to come together in order to facilitate such changes. One of the most influential innovations of the late nineteenth and early twentieth centuries was the introduction and development of motorised transport and especially that driven by the internal combustion engine. It eventually revolutionised the layout of cities and the way people organised their private lives, but in the first instance it struggled to achieve acceptance. Any radical change in the way people have operated as a society is adopted in a series of 'easy steps'.

In the case of the automobile, the 'easy steps' involved not only the development of the vehicle itself, but also the improvement of the road and supply systems. These developed over a very long time. In the early stages, steam, electric and internal combustion systems vied for prominence and vehicles closely resembled the horse-drawn carriages or cycles from which they had developed. Such vehicles were the preserve of the rich and were used as amusing playthings. The best that was hoped of the innovation was that it would reduce the serious problem of manure on city streets. In fact there were some people at this stage predicting that cities could grow no larger because they were limited by the amount of manure they generated and by methane emissions which posed a serious problem! The idea of the internal combustion engine solving pollution is perhaps a difficult one for us to understand now!

Stages in adoption

Early adopters of the new 'horseless carriage' were those who substituted it for the original form of transport (horse and carriage or horse-drawn omnibus) for short journeys. The infrastructure would not have supported them in movements greater than that (the roads were not good enough for long journeys, and the availability of fuel and specialist mechanical help was restricted). Over longer journeys they would still have used either horsedrawn transport, or, if available, the railway. In other words, at this time they used the innovation in parallel with the original medium.

Gradually, however, machinery became more reliable and the infrastructure developed to enable the wider use of automobiles for transport. In the 1910s mass production of the 'Model T' by Henry Ford and developments in road paving brought with them a clearer understanding of what personal automobile transport would do for the future. Suddenly the idea of owning a car was matched by the possibility of owning one and the perceived benefits of ownership. A model of this sequence is shown in Fig. 4.1.

131

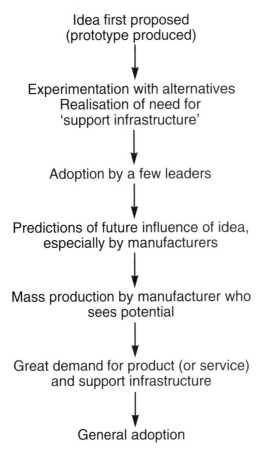

Idea first proposed
(prototype produced)

↓

Experimentation with alternatives
Realisation of need for
'support infrastructure'

↓

Adoption by a few leaders

↓

Predictions of future influence of idea,
especially by manufacturers

↓

Mass production by manufacturer who
sees potential

↓

Great demand for product (or service)
and support infrastructure

↓

General adoption

Fig. 4.1 Stages in the adoption of an idea

Fig. 4.2 The path of a raindrop through a drainage basin – the deterministic view of the spread of an idea

Organisation of time

The development of time-conscious systems of work set the pattern for industrial society. It has been argued that it was the ways in which communications companies (and the railways in particular) organised themselves that set the standard that we still use to run the whole of industry and commerce. Major strides in mass transport over large distances required new company structures and close adherence to time schedules, which had been less important before. In particular, branches of the company in widely separated locations had to communicate effectively with one another. It could be said, therefore, that communications innovations have been responsible not only for settlement structure and size but also for the organisation of industry and the regime of individuals working within it.

The spatial spread of ideas

The stages in the adoption of an idea (Fig. 4.1) might explain the sequence through which an idea passes in time (what we might call its 'life cycle'), but it does not explain how it is adopted spatially. Various attempts have been made to explain the spatial spread of ideas. The earliest were what we might call 'determinist' ideas, since proponents were quite sure that spread would occur in a predictable direction once the underlying factors were known. One way to understand this is to compare it with the passage of a raindrop through a drainage basin. Figure 4.2 shows how the drop would pass from the point where it falls to its destination. If we ignore the possibility that it might evaporate, percolate through the soil or be drunk and removed from this particular system, the passage shown in Fig. 4.2 is determined from the very time the raindrop hits the ground. Determinists said that an idea or new development would spread following similar well defined rules.

In reality, of course, we cannot ignore other possibilities. There is a good chance that the water will evaporate again, so we should recognise this fact. This is what the 'probabilists' did. They allocated chance factors to the direction an idea was likely to move from its starting point. Figure 4.3, showing the actual spread of agrarian riots in southern England in late 1830, shows a clear pattern of spread along main roads (particularly those used by stagecoaches). These roads often follow river valleys. As can be seen from a close inspection, however, they do not completely explain the pattern. It is obvious that, after the start on 15 November near Chichester, they spread outwards from that point, but also 'jumped' to the Winchester and Andover areas before spreading from those points as well. This is a very common pattern in the spread of ideas across an area.

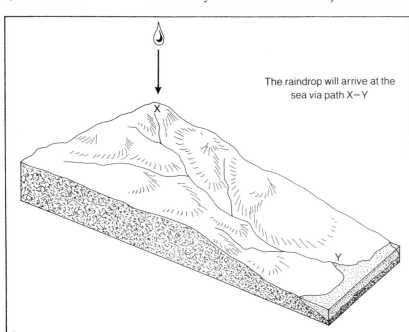

The raindrop will arrive at the sea via path X–Y

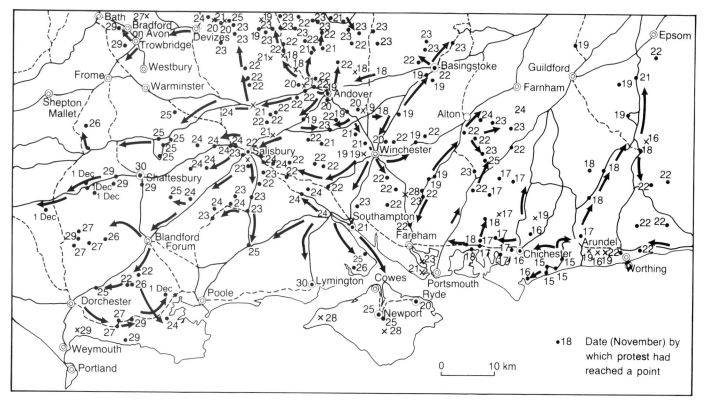

Fig. 4.3 The spread of agrarian protest and rioting in southern England between 15 November and 1 December 1830

- •18 Date (November) by which protest had reached a point

Diffusion

The geographer whose name is most often linked with the study of the spread, or diffusion, of ideas, is Torsten Hägerstrand, who worked in Sweden. He noticed clusters or 'neighbourhood effects' (like the secondary clusters around Winchester and Andover) and set out to explain them. Using computer simulation and probability matrices, he was able to provide fairly straightforward models to explain the diffusion of ideas. Computer programs derived from his spatial diffusion work are now able to copy and therefore explain patterns which have been observed. They are also able to predict the likely effects of future innovations.

Fig. 4.4 The progress of administrative reforms in Sierra Leone, 1939–47

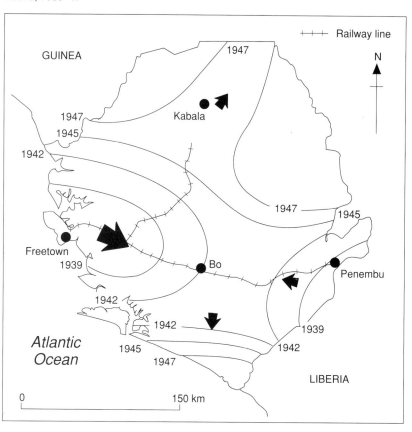

QUESTIONS

4.1 (a) Describe the pattern of diffusion of administrative reforms in Sierra Leone between 1939 and 1947 as shown in Fig. 4.4.

(b) From the information supplied in Fig. 4.4, attempt to explain the diffusion.

4.2 Look at an atlas map of Sierra Leone. Are there any other factors that might explain the pattern of diffusion shown in Fig. 4.4?

Transport and Urban Structure – the Practical Translation of New Ideas

The graph shows how population changed within the Leeds City boundary between 1700 and 1990. The rapid growth after 1820 was due to industrial expansion and migration to the city. The death rate was still high at the time but as housing conditions improved and medical facilities were made accessible to the masses, high birth rates, low death rates and continued migration led to increasing population pressure. This meant that the built-up area of Leeds expanded. It was possible for people to live in the newer areas, further away from the work places, only because means of transport also changed over the same period.

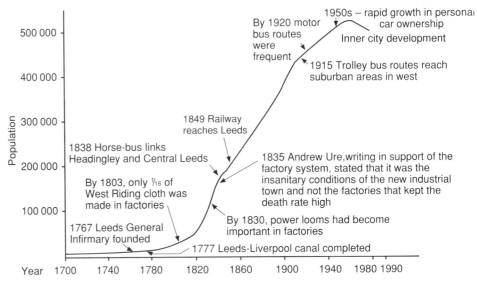

1950s – rapid growth in personal car ownership
Inner city development

By 1920 motor bus routes were frequent

1915 Trolley bus routes reach suburban areas in west

1849 Railway reaches Leeds

1838 Horse-bus links Headingley and Central Leeds

1835 Andrew Ure, writing in support of the factory system, stated that it was the insanitary conditions of the new industrial town and not the factories that kept the death rate high

By 1803, only 1/16 of West Riding cloth was made in factories

By 1830, power looms had become important in factories

1767 Leeds General Infirmary founded

1777 Leeds-Liverpool canal completed

The changing population of Leeds, 1700–1990

QUESTIONS
1 What was the approximate date by which motorised road transport become available for commuting in Leeds?
2 What factors might explain the decline in the population inside the city boundary after 1960?

(*left*) Horsforth, a residential area of Leeds

(*below left*) Leeds city centre

(*below*) Industrial redevelopment – the new Asda building, Leeds

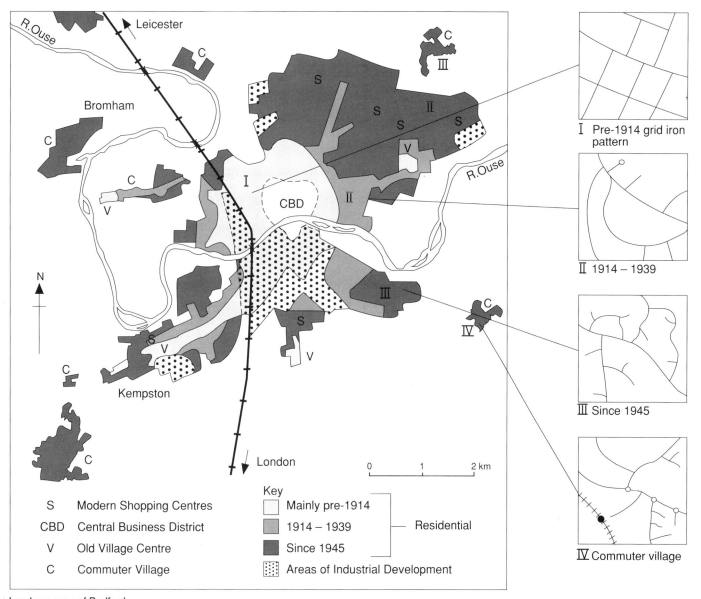

Land use map of Bedford

The growth of urban settlements in the United Kingdom progressed in phases which were linked with the type of growth shown in Leeds. Each place had its characteristics which can be identified on a map. The map of Bedford has been divided into land use zones, each of which has a distinctive road pattern associated with it. Some of these are illustrated next to the main map.

QUESTIONS

3   For each of the areas marked I to IV, describe the main type of transport used at the time of its initial growth by people living there.
4   Identify two different locations for industrial development. For each, explain its location in terms of accessibility and transport development.
5   Describe and explain the location of the modern shopping centres.
6   There are three main theories explaining the structure of British cities. These are the Concentric theory, the Sector theory and the Multiple Nuclei theory. Look up each of these in a good A-level textbook. Which theory seems best to explain the pattern of land use in Bedford?
7   Critically evaluate the statement that urban structure in the UK is governed by the spread of ideas and the practicality of transport as a result of these ideas taking hold.

Fig. 4.5 Village Christmas

New patterns of work

Today the basic organisation of industry and commerce is again being challenged by communications innovation. This time it is the 'Information Revolution' which is responsible. Computer network systems, which can allow someone at home to communicate with others almost as if he or she were in the office, have made it less important to travel to the office every day. Working at home, but being in constant contact with another part of the organisation and commuting when necessary, is known as 'telecommuting'. Fax machines and modems, which enable information to be transmitted electronically, also aid this method of working. Newer innovations such as electronic mail and video phones make daily travel even less necessary.

The 1990s is the same sort of period as when the introduction of the automobile was perceived by some as the solution to the pollution problem and by others as an irrelevance. Different views are held of the changes that are likely as a result of 'telecommuting'. Some say that it may simply support current work patterns, some that it will be complementary and others that it will largely take the place of existing patterns of work.

Support of rural communities

It is possible that technological developments might revive rural communities. Since the 1960s, many small rural settlements throughout the British Isles have become 'weekend villages' where those who have been successful in business in the city have bought houses. They live in them relatively infrequently, perhaps even to the extent suggested in Fig. 4.5. The local people, who may only have the option of agricultural work, commuting long distances or moving out altogether, have tended to do the latter. If they work locally, wages are often too low for them to afford housing. One way in which telecommuting could be used to support them and increase their options is indicated on pp. 138–9. This shows how an idea (in this case, remote working, made possible by a whole string of new developments) can affect the life of entire communities once it takes hold.

A further study – shopping in Reading

Geographical distributions are the outward expression of decisions that have been made about an idea or concept. In the case of the location, arrangement and size of shopping facilities, the type of outlet at a particular date reflects the prevailing thinking about shopping. The earliest shops were looked on as providers of necessities that could not be produced by the shopper. They grew out of the market stalls where goods had first been exchanged, then bought and sold. Allied to the fact that movement was largely by foot, the resultant spatial expression of the prevailing idea was a scattering of general stores which dealt with the vending of everyday requirements. This applied both to urban and rural areas.

The elements in shopping patterns

This very brief history shows how ideas and practice are interrelated, but the prevailing transport (and hence the ease of reaching the market or shop) dictated whether the idea could be translated into reality. The *accessibility* of a retail centre defines how many people can reach it within a reasonable time. The area within which people look towards a particular retail centre for their needs is called its *sphere of influence*. Within that sphere of influence live a number of people. It needs a certain number of people within easy reach of a retail site in order for it to be used for a particular purpose. This is called the *threshold population* and it differs for different retail establishments; for example:

	Threshold population
Marks & Spencer	20 000
Kingfisher	7 000
Burtons Tailors	10 000
Local insurance office	1 500

Both spheres of influence and threshold population change over time, reflecting different trading and transport conditions. The sphere of influence can also be constructed for entire retail centres (Fig. 4.6).

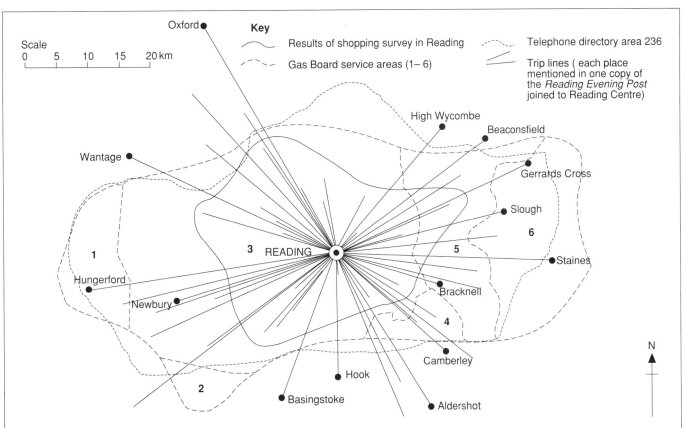

Fig. 4.6 The sphere of influence of Reading

New Patterns of Work
Telecommuting and Telecottages

Definition: TELECOMMUTING is when most of a person's work is completed at home through the use of new technology. This keeps the worker in touch with a main centre to which that worker may need to travel at regular or irregular intervals.

Possible advantages and disadvantages of telecommuting

Advantages

- Work can be task oriented.
- Progress of tasks can be measured.
- Personal supervision is unnecessary.
- Face-to-face interraction is unnecessary.
- Reduction of journey to work.
- More hours can be spent working efficiently.
- Savings in office space and therefore overheads of company.
- Better quality of life.

Disadvantages

- Some managers are reluctant to relinquish the control that personal supervision permits.
- Difficult to measure the amount of effort put in by workers.
- Management by electronics can create fear and is subject to manipulation by workers.
- Resentment of using house space on company business.
- Interference with family life.
- Loss of training possibilities and reduced promotion opportunities.

Possible effects of telecommuting

Scenario A   Small modification
The rules in place to deter home work (especially tax regulations) and the negative aspects of home work (lack of contact, less chance of promotion, etc.) deter any major shift to telecommuting. Only those jobs which easily transfer to home working do so with any enthusiasm (service sector, computer programming, writing technical literature). Most home working is still only part time. Minor reductions in commuting on a daily basis.

Scenario B   Major modification
Working at home catches on, but is dominated by large corporations setting up regional centres within easy reach of the home workers. This decentralisation offers the chance of cutting down on commuter traffic around the previous centre, but may increase it at the new regional locations. Workers are still in direct contact with Head Office from their satellite positions. If this were to be the case in the USA, there would be about 1.5 million fewer commuters on the roads every day of the week by 1995 (compared with 1990) and about 12 million would be commuting about half the distance.

Scenario C   Radical change
The idea is widely adopted by all possible acceptors. Regional centres are set up by major corporations, which encourage many specialists working from home to supply them with particular services. Much greater use is made of computer networks, modems and other electronic information systems to support workers at home. There will be several million fewer people commuting to the cities every working day.

Full time regional centre office
Part time home – regional centre
Part time regional centre – CBD
Full time home
Part time home – CBD office

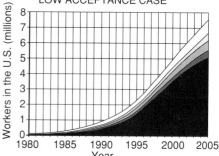

A TELECOMMUTING IN THE UNITED STATES LOW ACCEPTANCE CASE

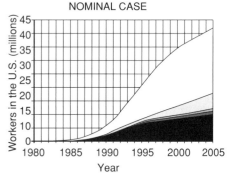

B TELECOMMUTING IN THE UNITED STATES NOMINAL CASE

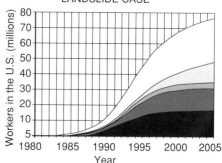

C TELECOMMUTING IN THE UNITED STATES LANDSLIDE CASE

Telecommuting in the USA – three possible scenarios

Merest whiff of the 20th century

Putting small firms on the map in rural Wessex

TELECOTTAGE is a term that conjures up a bucolic vision – a small, rural, antiquated and probably straw-thatched building, containing an array of the latest telecomms equipment.

The second part is certainly true; the first not necessarily, and probably unlikely. At Mere in West Wiltshire, the telecottage is, in fact, a back room in the splendid Victorian public library.

Mere is, it seems, appropriately named. It is right on the borders of Wiltshire, Somerset and Dorset , and its 5,000 inhabitants find themselves travelling in different directions for different services.

'Years of being treated as a mere outpost have created a high level of community spirit in Mere,' says John Lakeman of Wiltshire Community Council, who runs the county youth enterprise service.

'It was an ideal place to launch the first telecottage in Wessex. The community is involved, with a 14-person support group already set up before the formal opening on 10 April, and backing from Acre – Action for Communities in Rural England.

'BT has kindly provided the computing and telecomms equipment. We have also had help from BY staff, and advice from Alan Denbigh, the Acre teleworking adviser, who is funded by BT.'

The idea of telecottages is imported from Scandinavia, where the provision of IT equipment in a rural centre has successfully enabled people to learn skills and work in new industries without having to move towns. But it could also be used in deprived urban areas.

Gail Powell is manager of the Mere centre, a job which fits in well with her secretarial services and teaching activities.

A number of other local small businesses are participating, including an electrical shop, a firm making model soldiers and a linen supply enterprise.

'We already have projects that will help the centre earn its own income. And it is being used by the community. We are running beginners' courses in computing, and are planning one for mothers returning to work,' says Gail Powell.

'While it is useful for businesses to be able to use the fax and avoid having to travel to Wincanton to get enlarged or reduced photocopies, it is also exciting that it is being used by private individuals.

'We plan to open some evenings so that people can see what we can do for them.'

John Lakeman believes the role of telecottages is 'to educate people to the possibilities of working for themselves' – as well as fostering the development of new businesses.

But if it is only half as successful as the county enterprise scheme, where 120 new businesses have been started by the 18 to 25 year-olds in the last six years – 'with only two going bust' – he'll be a happy man.

From BT Business News, Spring 1991

Mere in Wiltshire has established a Telecottage in the Public Library. Mere is a small rural settlement, set in rich farming land, but with little alternative employment to that based on agriculture and retail.

Your communications needs.

	HOME BASE		HOME BUSINESS		TELEWORKER	
	Your basic set up	Your ideal set up	Your basic set up	Your ideal set up	Your basic set up	Your ideal set up
Facility Telephone	✓	✓	✓	✓	✓	✓
Answering Machine	✓	✓	✓	✓	✓	✓
Pager			✓		✓	
Mobile Phone		✓		✓		✓
Fax			✓	✓	✓	✓
Voicebank		✓	✓	✓		
Chargecard	✓	✓	✓	✓		✓
Phonecard					✓	
Star Services		✓		✓		✓
P.C.		✓				
P.C. & Modem				✓	✓	✓
Phone system		✓		✓		✓

From BT: *A Guide to Working from Home*

QUESTIONS

1 What is your personal opinion of telecommuting? Would you like to work at home for the majority of your life? Explain your answer.

2 The following are all ways which have been suggested to stop the 'rush hours' that occur at the moment. Research each one and suggest how likely it is to become an important part of the work pattern in your home area.

(a) job sharing
(b) car share schemes
(c) term-time contracts (females)
(d) flex-time (or flexitime)
(e) park- and-ride schemes

3 The magazine article gives further information on the idea of 'telecottages'. Use it, together with the other data on telecommuting, to write an essay entitled 'Telecommuting could be the saviour of village life in the British Isles'. Discuss.

QUESTION

4.3 With reference to an O.S. 1:50 000 map or a good atlas map, explain why Reading's sphere of influence is elongated from west to east. (You should look for relief, communications and competition reasons.)

It is very important for shop owners and town planners to understand changes in the patterns of shopping. They can then use this information to improve facilities for the public. In order to facilitate this, they need to keep up with the new ideas on shopping and adjust to the likelihood of consequent changes in spatial patterns resulting from the uptake of these ideas.

An example of diffusion

Shopping itself involves a decision-making sequence. It involves the perception of a need by an individual, the decision on what type of outlet to use, the collection of information to satisfy the need, the evaluation of that information and some action based on all this information (Fig. 4.7).

The types of outlet in which people could shop have changed over time in response to new ideas and the possibility of putting them into practice. This possibility involved increased accessibility and the availability of transport in particular. The following case illustrates this through a study of shopping in Reading, Berkshire.

Fig. 4.7 The shopping decision-making sequence

Figure 4.8 shows how ideas about shopping have changed since 1800, resulting in new types of outlet. It also shows how communications have allowed the new ideas to be translated into reality.

QUESTION

4.4 Figure 4.9 is a photograph of a shopping location in Reading.

(a) Identify one function that has probably been there for a long time and one which is a new function.

(b) Which of the following types of shopper will probably use this area, and why? commuters, local shop workers, specialist shoppers, passing vehicular traffic.

(c) Using Fig. 4.8, suggest when the particular shopping area shown in Fig. 4.9 was first developed.

(d) What do the changes shown in Fig. 4.8 mean for
(i) the size of the built-up area in Reading,
(ii) the shape of the built-up area,
(iii) the concentration of shopping in one main location?

New developments

In the same way as telecommuting is influencing patterns of work, shopping is increasingly being affected by electronic media. The first televised 'catalogue' shows in the UK were broadcast on satellite TV in the late 1980s. Catalogue shopping (where householders have a printed book containing a wide range of items that they can order by post) had been popular for many years. In France, such choices can now be made on the national 'Minitel' system. Similar systems exist in the USA and are already available for business purposes in the UK.

In the 1960s, town centre redevelopment in many British towns, Reading included, led to the building of shopping malls, on the American model. These were covered concourses which housed supermarkets, specialist shops and services, usually had a car park attached to increase access and were managed by a

Approx. date	Idea about shopping	Prevailing transport and communications	New type of retail outlet	Location
1800	Functional: shopping a necessity	Pedestrian Horsedrawn vehicles 'Word of mouth'	General stores Some specialist, e.g. butchers	Village/town centres and road junctions
1850	Functional, but increasing choice	Pedestrian Horsedrawn buses Trains Newspapers	Specialist stores	Major communication junctions
1920	Growing demand for comparison	Some cars Trams Buses Trains Newspapers & magazines	Grouped specialist services, e.g. colonnades & parades	Ribbon development and suburban centres
1960	Conspicious consumption	Cars Public transport TV & radio	Supermarkets and chains Shopping malls	Existing shopping centres & redevelopment
1980	Accessibility & convenience	Cars Public transport TV Local radio Free newspapers	Hypermarkets Video stores	Accessible out-of-town centres & commuter routes
1990	Sustainable consumption	Cars Public transport Electronic & broadcast media	Teleshopping?	Anywhere in national communications network

Fig. 4.8 Changing influences on shopping in the Reading area

Fig. 4.9 Shopping in Reading, England

141

Fig. 4.10 The interior of a shopping mall – Broad Street Mall, Reading

company which oversaw the tidiness, security and design of the centre. For a while they flourished, but tended to suffer after a while from relative lack of parking space and room to expand. In some, there were problems with security in the car parks and people felt threatened going from their car to the shops, particularly late in the evening. These are some of the reasons for a complete 'facelift' and re-launch of Reading's main centre, The Butts (renamed Broad Street Mall) in 1989.

The next move for the idea of malls was to take them out of the town centre. This allowed them to use relatively cheap land both for building and parking. They could also be much bigger from the start, creating more interest from a whole range of shoppers, not mainly food shoppers as is the case with out-of-town hypermarkets. Examples of these 'supermalls' are the Brent Cross shopping centre in London and the Metro Centre in Gateshead. Reading currently has two out-of-town hypermarkets and is redeveloping part of the current town centre vacated by old manufacturing industries that have moved out. This will be called 'The Oracle Centre', and is a major new complex which will shift the centre of gravity of the town centre away from

Fig. 4.11 Do you ever out in Reading?

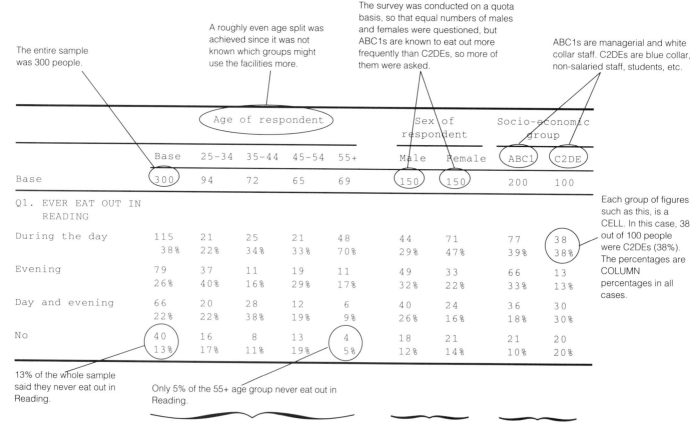

The survey was conducted on a quota basis, so that equal numbers of males and females were questioned, but ABC1s are known to eat out more frequently than C2DEs, so more of them were asked.

A roughly even age split was achieved since it was not known which groups might use the facilities more.

ABC1s are managerial and white collar staff. C2DEs are blue collar, non-salaried staff, students, etc.

The entire sample was 300 people.

		Age of respondent				Sex of respondent		Socio-economic group	
	Base	25–34	35–44	45–54	55+	Male	Female	ABC1	C2DE
Base	300	94	72	65	69	150	150	200	100
Q1. EVER EAT OUT IN READING									
During the day	115 38%	21 22%	25 34%	21 33%	48 70%	44 29%	71 47%	77 39%	38 38%
Evening	79 26%	37 40%	11 16%	19 29%	11 17%	49 32%	33 22%	66 33%	13 13%
Day and evening	66 22%	20 22%	28 38%	12 19%	6 9%	40 26%	24 16%	36 18%	30 30%
No	40 13%	16 17%	8 11%	13 19%	4 5%	18 12%	21 14%	21 10%	20 20%

Each group of figures such as this, is a CELL. In this case, 38 out of 100 people were C2DEs (38%). The percentages are COLUMN percentages in all cases.

13% of the whole sample said they never eat out in Reading.

Only 5% of the 55+ age group never eat out in Reading.

The same sample (300) is broken down in three different ways to show how age groups, sexes and socio-economic classes respond to the question.

the western end (near the Broad Street Mall) to the eastern end about two kilometres away.

A new restaurant for Reading?

On the edge of this development is Reading Station. This was redeveloped into a modern transport intersection, office and shopping complex in 1989. As part of the redevelopment, plans were drawn up to build a big new restaurant. The plans were tested on a sample of 300 respondents who either commuted from Reading Station or shopped in the main centre (about 250 metres away to the south). Because of the daytime coffee and light snack facilities planned, it was thought that it was also necessary to question the shoppers. Commuters were the target for the takeaway and restaurant facilities, whilst both sets could use the facilities in the evening. Some of the results are revealed in Figs. 4.11 to 4.13.

Using the data and the information on analysing the data set in the Appendix (p. 221), complete the following exercise.

	Age of respondent					Sex of respondent		Socio-economic group	
	Base	25–34	35–44	45–54	55+	Male	Female	ABC1	C2DE
Base	300	94	73	64	69	150	150	200	100
Q4A. FREQUENCY USE									
Once a month	79	19	24	15	21	41	38	54	25
	26%	21%	33%	23%	30%	27%	25%	27%	25%
Never	67	24	15	19	9	38	29	43	25
	22%	25%	20%	30%	13%	25%	19%	21%	25%
Less than once a month	64	13	16	18	16	29	35	43	21
	21%	14%	22%	28%	24%	20%	23%	21%	21%
Once a week	51	21	11	7	12	21	30	37	13
	17%	22%	14%	12%	17%	14%	20%	19%	13%
Several times per week	39	16	7	4	10	21	18	23	16
	13%	17%	10%	7%	15%	14%	12%	12%	16%

Fig. 4.12 How often would you use the coffee shop at the proposed site?

	Age of respondent					Sex of respondent		Socio-economic group	
	Base	25–34	35–44	45–54	55+	Male	Female	ABC1	C2DE
Base	300	94	73	64	69	150	150	200	100
Q4B. FREQUENCY USE									
Never	234	64	54	54	63	116	118	149	88
	78%	68%	74%	84%	91%	77%	79%	74%	88%
Less than once a month	25	9	7	7	1	13	12	23	0
	8%	10%	10%	12%	2%	9%	8%	12%	0%
Once a month	21	12	5	1	3	7	14	15	5
	7%	13%	6%	2%	4%	5%	9%	8%	5%
Once a week	16	6	7	1	2	10	6	12	4
	5%	6%	10%	2%	2%	7%	4%	6%	4%
Several times per year	3	3	0	0	0	3	0	0	4
	1%	3%	0%	0%	0%	2%	0%	0%	4%

Fig. 4.13 How often would you use a take-home service at the proposed site?

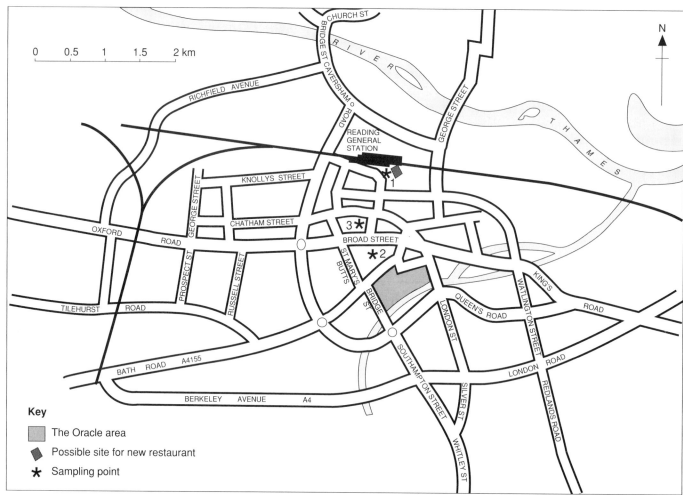

Fig. 4.14 Reading town centre

Key

The Oracle area

Possible site for new restaurant

★ Sampling point

Fig. 4.15 A town centre supermarket. Note the difficulty of parking during the weekday – late night opening allows easier access

QUESTIONS

4.5 Locate the proposed development and the sampling points on the map of central Reading (Fig. 4.14). Explain why the sampling points were selected for this exercise.

4.6 Look carefully at the annotated table showing the structure of the sample and their current eating habits (Fig. 4.11). Describe the pattern you find, referring in particular to any age groups, sex or socio-economic class that eat out more than the others. Is it an encouraging target for a new restaurant facility?

4.7 People were then asked whether they would use a coffee shop at the site or a high class take-away service provided especially for commuters. Their responses are shown in Figs. 4.12 and 4.13.

  (a) Describe the pattern of response you find.

  (b) How confident could you be that the answers reflect the true opinions of the whole community?

  (c) Would you recommend that the restaurant should be opened at Reading Station in view of the answers given to this survey?

Maintaining trade in the face of increased competition

The United Kingdom has strict rules governing days on which certain items can be sold. In the difficult trading conditions during 1990 and 1991, there was pressure put on the government by some major retailers to allow Sunday trading. The argument was that many people are themselves working all week and Saturdays, so they could only do their own shopping at lunchtimes or in the evening. Sunday opening would allow them more leisurely access to shops. On the other hand, the 'Keep Sunday Special' campaign complained that this was the one day when 'the pressure was off' and true relaxation could occur. Added to this, the shop workers' Union, USDAW, fought a campaign to protect its members from having to work on Sundays. The situation is likely to continue for some time, but with ever mounting pressure to open on Sundays. There are many stores in Reading which already open on Sundays, totally in keeping with the law. These are stores owned by people whose religion does not hold Sunday as the 'holy' day.

Another idea which has caught on in the UK is 'late night shopping'. Many stores now open until 2200 on at least one day in the week, allowing easier access to those who work all week. One aspect of late night shopping in town centres is that it allows much easier parking. In Reading, town centre stores such as Marks & Spencer and J. Sainsbury already operate such a system. Many specialist shops, such as clothes stores and record shops, operate this policy during the Christmas period.

Fig. 4.16 Asda out-of-town shopping centre, Lower Earley, Reading

Fig. 4.17 New shopping units in a shopping precinct, Reading

New Developments in Communications and Retail

The map below (Map A) shows the location of independent radio stations in Great Britain and Northern Ireland in 1981. These stations were set up to service a local need or to cater for a particular taste (jazz, light music or 'oldies' music, for example). They exist in addition to the many local BBC Radio services and are financed by their ability to attract local advertising.

Distribution on a map can be described and explained using a 'template' which can be applied to the particular map, no matter what it shows. Below are listed the points to be made in order to *describe* the distribution and then to *explain* it, followed by a completed version in answer to the question:

'Describe and explain the distribution of independent radio stations in Great Britain and Northern Ireland'.

Template

Describe
- Even or uneven distribution?
- Areas of greater or lesser density.
- Degree of concentration.
- Location of particular parts of pattern.
- Random, linear, nodal or mixed patterns?

Explain
- Correlations of observed pattern with:
  - population density
  - relief
  - urban areas
  - linear features such as main
  - transport
    - arteries and coasts
  - competition.

Complete answer

(*Describe*) Of 82 independent radio stations in 1981, about 25 were located in the area immediately around London. There was a fairly even spacing throughout the Midlands and the North West, with other minor concentrations around Gloucester, Birmingham, Manchester, Leeds, Newcastle, Glasgow and Aberdeen. Significant gaps in the distribution were found in the South West peninsula, Wales, East Anglia, Northern England (between Leeds and Newcastle), Southern Scotland, the Grampians and North West Scotland and Northern Ireland. The stations were strongly centred in the South East and around the major urban centres. Many stations were found either in coastal locations or along the main communications axes running between London and the North West. The distribution pattern had strong linear elements in it, together with particularly strong clustering in places (e.g. London and Manchester).

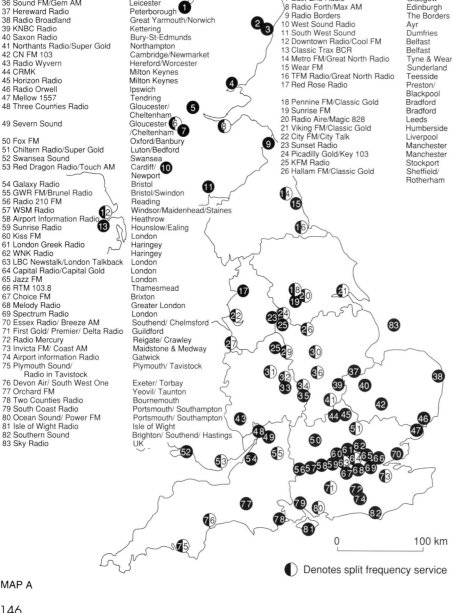

27 MFM 103.4/Marcher Sound	Wrexham/Deeside
28 UCB	Stoke-on-Trent
29 Echo/Signal Radio	Stoke-on-Trent
30 Trent FM/Gem AM	Nottingham
31 Beacon Radio/ Nice and Easy WABC	Black Country
32 BRMB Radio/Xtra AM	Birmingham
33 Buzz FM	Birmingham
34 Mercia Sound/Xtra AM	Coventry
35 Radio Harmony	Coventry
36 Sound FM/Gem AM	Leicester
37 Hereward Radio	Peterborough
38 Radio Broadland	Great Yarmouth/Norwich
39 KNBC Radio	Kettering
40 Saxon Radio	Bury-St-Edmunds
41 Northants Radio/Super Gold	Northampton
42 CN FM 103	Cambridge/Newmarket
43 Radio Wyvern	Hereford/Worcester
44 CRMK	Milton Keynes
45 Horizon Radio	Milton Keynes
46 Radio Orwell	Ipswich
47 Mellow 1557	Tendring
48 Three Counties Radio	Gloucester/ Cheltenham
49 Severn Sound	Gloucester /Cheltenham
50 Fox FM	Oxford/Banbury
51 Chiltern Radio/Super Gold	Luton/Bedford
52 Swansea Sound	Swansea
53 Red Dragon Radio/Touch AM	Cardiff/ Newport
54 Galaxy Radio	Bristol
55 GWR FM/Brunel Radio	Bristol/Swindon
56 Radio 210 FM	Reading
57 WSM Radio	Windsor/Maidenhead/Staines
58 Airport Information Radio	Heathrow
59 Sunrise Radio	Hounslow/Ealing
60 Kiss FM	London
61 London Greek Radio	Haringey
62 WNK Radio	Haringey
63 LBC Newstalk/London Talkback	London
64 Capital Radio/Capital Gold	London
65 Jazz FM	London
66 RTM 103.8	Thamesmead
67 Choice FM	Brixton
68 Melody Radio	Greater London
69 Spectrum Radio	London
70 Essex Radio/ Breeze AM	Southend/ Chelmsford
71 First Gold/ Premier/ Delta Radio	Guildford
72 Radio Mercury	Reigate/ Crawley
73 Invicta FM/ Coast AM	Maidstone & Medway
74 Airport information Radio	Gatwick
75 Plymouth Sound/ Radio in Tavistock	Plymouth/ Tavistock
76 Devon Air/ South West One	Exeter/ Torbay
77 Orchard FM	Yeovil/ Taunton
78 Two Counties Radio	Bournemouth
79 South Coast Radio	Portsmouth/ Southampton
80 Ocean Sound/ Power FM	Portsmouth/ Southampton
81 Isle of Wight Radio	Isle of Wight
82 Southern Sound	Brighton/ Southend/ Hastings
83 Sky Radio	UK

INDEPENDENT RADIO
(Radio Authority Licensees)

1 Moray Firth Radio	Inverness
2 North East Community Radio	Aberdeen
3 North Sound Radio	Aberdeen
4 Radio Tay	Dundee
5 Central FM	Stirling
6 Radio Clyde/Clyde FM	Glasgow
7 East End Radio	Glasgow
8 Radio Forth/Max AM	Edinburgh
9 Radio Borders	The Borders
10 West Sound Radio	Ayr
11 South West Sound	Dumfries
12 Downtown Radio/Cool FM	Belfast
13 Classic Trax BCR	Belfast
14 Metro FM/Great North Radio	Tyne & Wear
15 Wear FM	Sunderland
16 TFM Radio/Great North Radio	Teesside
17 Red Rose Radio	Preston/ Blackpool
18 Pennine FM/Classic Gold	Bradford
19 Sunrise FM	Bradford
20 Radio Aire/Magic 828	Leeds
21 Viking FM/Classic Gold	Humberside
22 City FM/City Talk	Liverpool
23 Sunset Radio	Manchester
24 Picadilly Gold/Key 103	Manchester
25 KFM Radio	Stockport
26 Hallam FM/Classic Gold	Sheffield/ Rotherham

0 _____ 100 km

◗ Denotes split frequency service

MAP A

(*Explain*) Most independent radio stations are found in areas with a high population density, such as the South East of England. Where densities are lower, as in Central Wales, no stations exist (though broadcasts from stations elsewhere could perhaps be heard). Where particularly high population densities occur, as in London and Manchester, duplication of stations is possible because there are enough advertisers wishing to reach the audiences and because those audiences can be further subdivided into segments (e.g. jazz and classical music lovers). Certain areas of the country are not conducive to siting radio stations because the target audience is too widespread (as in Southern Scotland) or because the high relief would necessitate either very high transmitting towers or large numbers of them. Easily accessible locations are chosen for siting stations since the 'stars' often visit them to be interviewed and need to be able to get there relatively easily. Obvious locations are chosen since there is a need for the media, and radio stations in particular, to be noticed by the users. Locations by main road intersections, near city centres and by transport termini are therefore used a great deal. This means they tend to be centrally located in major urban areas. Stations in London (64) and Liverpool (22) conform to this requirement, for example. In the same way, coastal stations, as well as being located in major population centres such as Brighton or Southampton, are in accessible and prominent sites.

Superstores

Now complete the same exercise by *describing* and *explaining* the distribution of superstores as shown in Map B. Your explanation would benefit from reviewing the text (pp. 137–42).

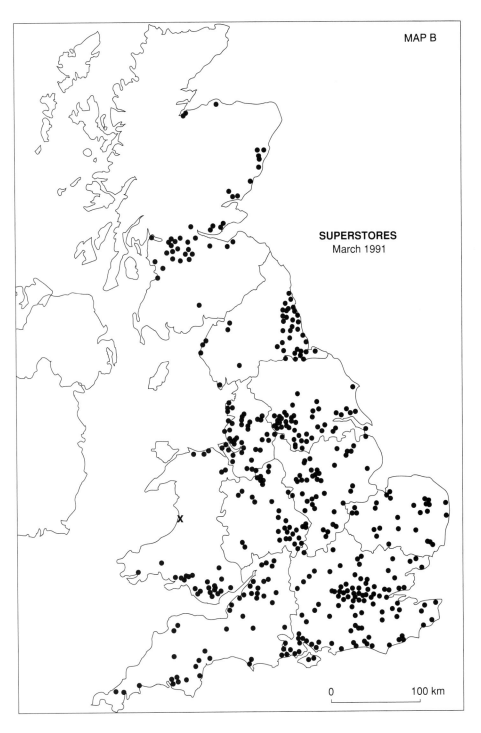

MAP B

SUPERSTORES
March 1991

0   100 km

LOCATING A NEW SUPERSTORE

A large site suitable for development as a superstore has become available at X on Map B.

(a) Collect as much information on the area around X as you can (atlas/O.S. maps, regional guides, population statistics, etc).

(b) How would you collect information on local reactions to the development? Who would you ask? (The work on the location of a new restaurant will help (pp. 143–5).)

(c) Design a questionnaire to find out where people in the area of X shop at the moment, what they think of the development and whether they would shop there.

(d) On the basis of all the information you have gathered for (a) and your feelings for (b) and (c), would you advise the company to build at X? Explain your answer.

QUESTIONS

4.8 Select one of the four main changes likely to become more important in the future (electronic shopping, 'supermalls', Sunday opening or late night opening). Suggest how it is likely to affect the shopping pattern in a major shopping centre known to you. Will it result in changes to any of the following?
- Numbers of people shopping
- Amount spent
- Range of shops
- Sphere of influence

4.9 The following new functions have become established in many towns since 1980.
(i) Video stores
(ii) Multi-screen cinemas
(iii) Fast food restaurants
For each of them:
(a) describe its location, and
(b) explain how it has affected the pattern of shopping in the town.

Problem-Solving Exercise

The location of high-tech firms in France

Background

The high-tech industry has grown rapidly since the 1960s. It is based on the manufacture, sale and servicing of computers and other electronic equipment. The most important input is not raw materials, but knowledge. For this reason, high-tech location has to a large extent broken away from the old industrial location factors of raw material supply and even market location. It tends to be sited with respect to factors such as pleasant working conditions and skilled labour supply, perhaps near universities. Such locations are known as 'footloose' locations. Examples in the United Kingdom are 'Silicon Glen' in Central Scotland and the 'M4 Corridor', which includes Reading, Swindon and Bristol.

The footloose location explanation of distribution is only partly true in the case of the French high-tech industry, however. Other factors have come into play to determine the growth and location of the industry. The following data allow you to study those factors and explain the resultant distribution. The data are for the period 1975 to 1986 and are for separate branches of the high-tech industry. The most footloose part of the industry is the high-tech consultancy branch. This involves very well qualified staff who advise often very large firms on the implementation of office automation, software development and the installation of new computer systems. The location of the French industry has been used to try to spur regional development, on account of its relative freedom to locate anywhere. The success or otherwise of this objective is the subject of this study.

Problem

How could employment be attracted to relatively less developed areas in France?

Fig. 4.18 Some statistics for the French regions

Region	Net migration 1986	Employment 1987			Unemployment rate April 1989	Doctors per 1000	Telephones per 1000
		Agriculture	Industry	Services			
Ile-de-France	−2.0	0.5	27.2	72.3	6.7	2.8	477
Bassin Parisien	−1.8	10.4	33.4	56.2	10.9	1.8	376
Nord-Pas-de-Calais	−6.4	4.2	36.2	59.6	14.7	1.9	332
Est	−6.2	4.0	38.4	57.6	8.5	2.0	355
Ouest	4.5	14.3	29.9	55.8	10.7	1.9	377
Sud-Ouest	2.5	14.1	26.9	59.1	10.5	2.4	394
Centre-Est	4.1	7.3	34.4	58.3	8.6	2.2	399
Mediterannée	12.7	6.4	22.9	70.7	12.6	2.9	447

QUESTIONS

The current situation

4.10 Figure 3.8 is a base map of the planning regions of France. Figures 4.18 and 4.19 should be used in conjunction with 3.8 to write an illustrated description of current regional differences (disparity) in France. You could draw choropleth maps using the statistics and base map and compare any patterns you find with the model (Fig. 4.19).

4.11 Figure 4.20 shows the main location factors for three branches of industry which could be contenders for development in the regions. Explain why the high-tech consultancy industry is a better contender than the others.

French assistance to industrial relocation

4.12 Figure 4.22 shows how the French government has attempted to attract industries to the currently less developed regions. Compare the pattern revealed in Fig. 4.22 with the core–periphery model as applied to France (Fig. 4.19)

and any patterns you observed in the statistics (Fig. 4.18). What is the logic behind the French government's aid to industry?

4.13 The value of the high-tech industry to France is demonstrated by Figs. 4.23 to 4.28. Use the data to describe the status of high-tech industry in the country and whether it is likely to become more or less important in the future.

Attracting industry to the regions

4.14 Changes in the distribution of high-tech industry in France are revealed in Figs. 4.29 and 4.30. Using a relevant technique, such as choropleth mapping or Lorenz curves, attempt to show that the French have been successful in attracting high-tech industry to peripheral areas. (Fig. 3.8 should be used as a base map if necessary.)

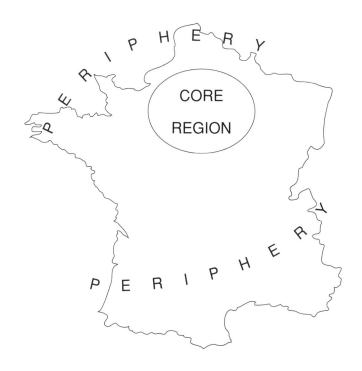

Core region
Headquarters, industrial diversity, good infrastructure, high wages, good social facilities. But also congestion, competition for housing, lack of open space.

Periphery
Branch factories, industrial specialism, weak infrastructure, lower wages and poorer social facilities. But also open space, housing availability and more pleasant way of life.

Fig. 4.19 A model of the French core and periphery

Fig. 4.20 Location factors for three types of industry

Type of industry	Example	Major location factors
Heavy industry (raw material oriented)	Boiler manufacture in Nord-Pas-de-Calais	Steel manufacture in USINOR complex at Dunkerque, power generation industries along the Channel coast, skilled work force in old-established industrial area, large factory sites required, very good road and rail links for moving finished articles.
Assembly industry (market oriented)	Renault cars at Boulogne–Billancourt west of Paris	Potential market, ease of access. Unskilled and semi-skilled labour force, large site, accessibility for import of components.
High-tech industry	Bull Computers, Toulouse	Small, high value items can be manufactured and assembled in remote locations where living and working conditions may be more favourable for the work force. Consultancy location is shown in Fig 4.21.

Fig. 4.21 The structure of French information technology consultancy

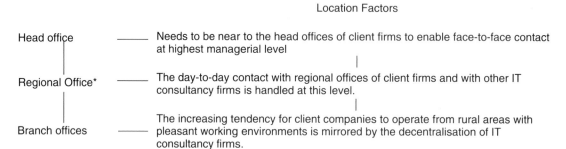

Location Factors

Head office ——— Needs to be near to the head offices of client firms to enable face-to-face contact at highest managerial level

Regional Office* ——— The day-to-day contact with regional offices of client firms and with other IT consultancy firms is handled at this level.

Branch offices ——— The increasing tendency for client companies to operate from rural areas with pleasant working environments is mirrored by the decentralisation of IT consultancy firms.

*In many cases, Regional Offices are now specialised by product and market type and are not simply a smaller version of the head office.

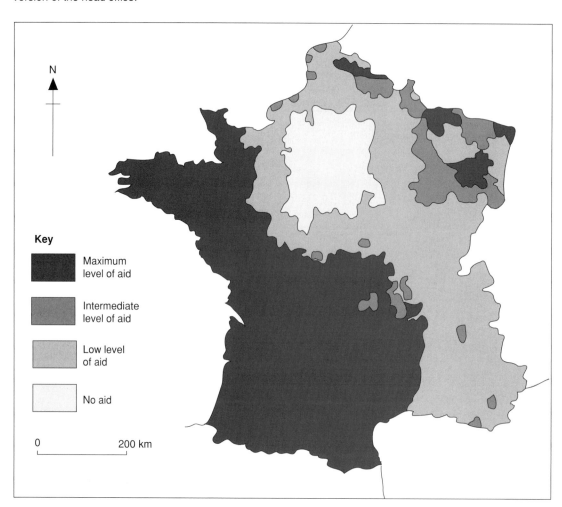

Key

- Maximum level of aid
- Intermediate level of aid
- Low level of aid
- No aid

N

0   200 km

Fig. 4.22 French government aid to industry

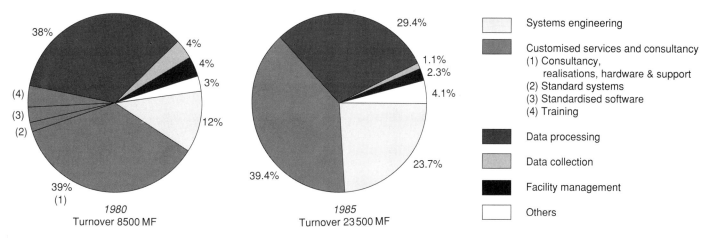

Systems engineering

Customised services and consultancy
(1) Consultancy,
    realisations, hardware & support
(2) Standard systems
(3) Standardised software
(4) Training

Data processing

Data collection

Facility management

Others

1980
Turnover 8500 MF

1985
Turnover 23 500 MF

Fig. 4.23 The turnover of the software services and consultancy sector, 1960 and 1985

		Total revenue	Processing services	Packaged software	Professional services
(1)	Cap Gemini	530.5	1.1	0.8	528.6
(7)	GSI	225.7	126.5	48.3	50.9
(8)	Sema-Metra	216.6	9.0	22.6	185.0
(10)	Sligos	193.5	120.8	17.9	54.8
(11)	CISI	184.4	39.2	—	145.2
(13)	SESA	158.5	—	25.8	132.7
(22)	CCMC	131.0	109.2	21.8	—
(24)	Telesystèmes	127.8	83.8	—	44.0
(27)	SG2	118.7	62.9	2.4	53.4
(29)	Steria	117.8	—	28.3	89.5
	Total 10 biggest French vendors	2004.5	552.5	167.9	1284.1

(*Figures in left column represent the rank number according to European market turnover.*)

Fig. 4.24 Major software and services vendors in the West European market (companies of French origin in 1987 in millions of US$)

West European market

Total	32 375 US$ million
of which:	
— Processing services	9 039
— Packaged software	12 440
— Professional services	10 896

French market

Total	7 468 US$ million

Fig. 4.25 West European and French software engineering and services market (1987)

1975	13 967	
1976	14 850	
1977	16 931	
1978	19 036	Average
1979	22 717	annual
1980	26 739	growth
1981	30 758	rate
1982	34 803	+15.60%
1983	40 639	
1984	49 790	
1985	59 469	
1986	68 722	

Fig. 4.26 Employment in information technology consultancy in France, 1975–86

Employment %	+142.36
Export %	+262.72
Turnover (taxes excluded) %	+126.65
Turnover per employee (thousand francs)	
1981	257.61
1982	284.43
1985	402.15

Fig. 4.27 Summary of economic measures in high-tech consultancy in France, 1981–85

	1981	1982	1983	1984	1985	1986	Average annual rate of growth %
V.A.* of high-tech consultancy	4 858	7 224	9 410	12 602	16 866	19 722	+32.34
(A) V.A. of total consultancy	22 077	29 103	36 293	42 666	46 436	52 639	+18.97
(B) GDP	3 164 804	3 626 031	4 006 498	4 364 893	4 692 476	5 015 867	+9.64
$\frac{A}{B}$	0.69	0.80	0.90	0.97	0.98	1.04	

* V.A. = Value Added

Fig. 4.28 High-tech consultancy compared with consultancy in general, France, 1981–86

Fig. 4.29 The distribution of high-tech manufacturing in France, by region

		Employment			Facilities		
		1976	1984	1987	1976	1984	1987
01	Nord	2.5	1.8	2.1	3.4	3.3	3.3
02	Picardie	0.7	0.8	0.9	1.7	2.0	1.7
03	Ile-de-France	56.3	52.0	43.9	46.0	40.4	37.2
04	Centre	4.6	5.0	4.2	4.3	3.8	3.4
05	Haute Normandie	3.9	2.7	2.8	2.9	2.7	2.3
06	Basse Normandie	0.9	0.9	0.7	1.4	1.2	1.1
07	Bretagne	3.7	4.3	3.2	2.7	3.6	3.2
08	Loire	3.9	4.0	3.9	3.5	4.2	3.9
09	Poitou	2.2	1.8	1.3	1.4	1.2	1.3
10	Limousin	0.1	0.1	0.6	0.9	0.9	0.8
11	Aquitaine	3.8	4.4	4.7	3.4	2.3	3.9
12	Midi	1.3	2.0	5.5	3.0	4.0	4.4
13	Champagne	0.2	0.2	0.3	1.1	0.9	1.1
14	Lorraine	0.7	1.2	1.6	2.1	2.4	3.1
15	Alsace	1.6	2.7	2.3	1.9	2.2	2.2
16	Franche-Comté	0.4	0.4	2.1	1.0	1.1	1.6
17	Bourgogne	1.3	1.2	1.3	1.7	1.6	1.7
18	Auvergne	1.1	0.7	1.3	1.2	1.3	1.5
19	Rhône-Alpes	7.6	9.8	10.9	10.0	11.6	11.6
20	Languedoc	0.4	0.4	1.2	1.3	2.5	2.8
21	Provence	2.8	3.7	5.1	5.0	6.6	7.7
22	Corse	—	—	0.1	0.1	0.2	0.2
	France (absolute sum)	303 517	336 753	466 930	2880	5139	8428

		Employment			Facilities		
		1976	1984	1987	1976	1984	1987
01	Nord	2.5	3.1	3.6	3.4	3.7	3.9
02	Picardie	0.8	0.9	1.5	1.4	1.2	1.5
03	Ile-de-France	59.1	54.5	52.9	39.4	38.3	39.8
04	Centre	2.1	2.2	2.2	3.2	2.8	2.6
05	Haute Normandie	1.7	1.6	1.6	2.2	2.0	1.7
06	Basse Normandie	0.6	0.8	1.1	1.4	1.1	1.1
07	Bretagne	1.7	2.9	1.7	3.7	2.8	2.6
08	Loire	2.4	2.7	2.9	3.4	3.4	3.2
09	Poitou	0.5	0.8	0.9	1.8	1.7	1.6
10	Limousin	0.4	0.4	0.3	0.8	0.7	0.6
11	Aquitaine	2.9	2.8	2.7	3.7	4.0	3.9
12	Midi	2.3	2.9	2.9	3.0	3.5	3.6
13	Champagne	1.0	0.9	0.8	1.5	1.4	1.3
14	Lorraine	1.6	1.5	1.6	2.8	2.3	2.3
15	Alsace	1.2	1.6	1.56	1.7	2.5	2.3
16	Franche-Comté	0.6	0.5	0.5	1.2	1.0	1.0
17	Bourgogne	1.5	0.8	0.9	2.0	1.8	1.7
18	Auvergne	0.8	0.7	0.7	1.7	1.5	1.4
19	Rhône-Alpes	10.4	10.9	10.5	11.6	11.9	11.4
20	Languedoc	1.4	1.6	1.7	2.9	2.8	3.0
21	Provence	4.5	5.7	7.3	7.0	9.1	9.2
22	Corse	—	0.1	0.1	0.2	0.3	0.4
	France (absolute sum)	131 376	210 719	252 902	8258	15 369	21 115

Fig. 4.30 The distribution of high-tech consultancy in France, by region

The case of Picardie

Recently, a number of the French Planning Regions have attempted to promote their industrial base not just by attracting footloose industries to supplement their declining heavy industrial base, but by attracting inward investment from abroad. One means of doing this has been to invite foreign firms to act as consultants whereby they can attract relocation and promote imports and exports. The following material (Figs. 4.31 to 4.35) is taken from the promotional pack for Picardie and shows what that region considers to be its advantages. Figures 4.36 and 4.37 relate to the Amiens region of Picardie.

April 27 th. 1989

RAPID RESEARCH

LYNN LAW
THE RESEARCH UNIT 15 HEADLEY ROAD
WOODLEY
BERKS RG5 4JB
ANGLETERRE

Dear Sir,

Please find enclosed an application file with a view to enable us to choose a permanent correspondent in your country.

At the initiative of the Picardy Regional Council and in collaboration with the local government partners, it has been decided to work with consulting firms like yours to help companies in the region to export to your country.

If this mission interests you the enclosed brochure on the Picardy region will give you an idea of the kind of collaboration we are looking for.

If you fulfil our requirements, we would like you to come to France in order to present your firm during a business convention to be held in October this year. You could thus have the possibility to meet about fifty companies interested in your activities.

In case your are interested in our proposal, would you kindly return the enclosed application file with a brochure concerning your activities so that we can get back to you with an invitation and program for the convention.

Thanking you in advance and awaiting your reply,

Yours sincerely.

Alain BORN

PICARDIE-ADHESION
9 rue de l'Ancienne Mairie - 92100 BOULOGNE, France
Tél:(33) 1 48 25 26 04 - Fax:(33) 1 46 03 86 26 - Télex: 631 848 F

Fig. 4.31

The population:	
Total	1 773 000
Working population	743 820
Industrial and farm products companies:	
Over 500 employees (workers)	55
200 to 500 employees	142
50 to 200 employees	499
1 to 50 employees	6 741
TOTAL	7 437

Fig. 4.32 The Picardie region in figures

1. AN INTRODUCTION TO THE PICARDIE REGION

1.1. Its principal advantages

The Picardie region is situated just north of the Parisian agglomeration, and occupies a central position in the London-Paris-Frankfurt region. Endowed with a good communications network, these three regions are within easy reach of the big population centres of northern Europe. Incidentally the Picardie region has a very long industrial tradition which is highly visible in the efficiency and professional conscience of its manpower.

Very many French and foreign groups have set up production units in this region whereas a whole lot of small and medium companies have sprung up at the same time. Their industrial activities are very diversified with a mix of traditional and modern: from textiles to electronics, from mechanical to biotechnology, from glass to para chemistry. All this goes to prove that the Picardie region is a leading contributor to industry in France as regards added value. The presence of a number of laboratories, universities and research centres public or private, have encouraged the development of high-tech activities.

1.2. Reputed know-how

The Picardie region stands third among the French industrial regions in terms of added value. A position that portrays well the ambitions of this region, the varied proof of which can be seen in the every day life of this region.

Farm products industries, like Bonduelle, Saupiquet, Panzani or Findus, but also biotechnologies and in general, high-tech industries have settled in the Picardie region. Famous perfume and cosmetic manufacturers such as Chanel, Yves Saint-Laurant or l'Oréal along with Pechiney or Orsan are also present in the region.

Fig. 4.33 An introduction to the Picardie region

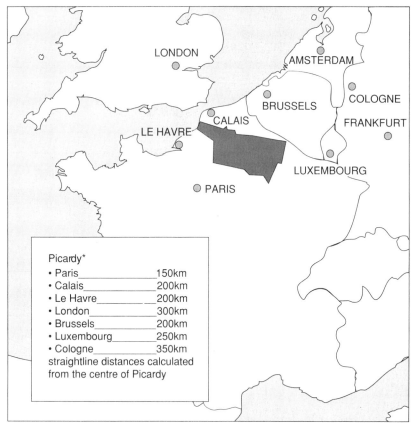

Field of activity	%
Agriculture, forestry & fishing	2.0
Farm products industry	1.5
Power (mechanical, nuclear …)	0.5
Iron and steel industry	1.2
Non-ferrous metals	1.8
Construction materials	1.0
Glass	3.5
Basic chemistry, synthetic fibres	1.7
Parachemistry	1.6
Foundry and metal works	1.7
Mechanical construction	1.6
Electric & electronic materials	0.6
Household equipment	1.5
Motor vehicle & railway materials	1.4
Naval & aeronautical construction	0.2
Textile & clothing	1.6
Leather, shoes	0.4
Wood, furniture	1.1
Paper, cardboard	1.4
Printing, press & publishing	0.5
Rubber, plastics	2.1
Construction industry, civil engineering	0.8
Wholesale business	0.8
Retail business	1.0
Car dealership & repairs	1.1
Hotels, coffee shops, restaurants	0.6
Transport	0.9
Telecommunications	0.8
Miscellaneous	4.7

Inside Fig 4.34:

Picardy*
• Paris_____150km
• Calais_____200km
• Le Havre_____200km
• London_____300km
• Brussels_____200km
• Luxembourg_____250km
• Cologne_____350km
straightline distances calculated
from the centre of Picardy

Fig. 4.34 The Picardie region

Fig. 4.35 Manpower in the private sector – Picardie

Fig. 4.36 Amiens

154

Fig. 4.37 Amiens

Fig. 4.38

QUESTIONS

4.15 Use all the material to design a newspaper advertisement particularly aimed at attracting high-tech industry to Amiens. Your advertisement should use a graphical device (a map, diagram or sketch) and about 150 words of text. An example of an attempt by a British advertiser is given as a guide (Fig. 4.38). Your advertisement could be produced using your school's desk top publishing software.

Keeping an eye on the situation

4.16 As an official in the French Department of Industry, what monitoring process would you set up to ensure that your relocation policy was working for the peripheral areas? What data would you collect and how would you present them?

Approaches to agricultural development

- *The world is growing more food today than it did 30 years ago.*
- *The problem of food supply includes the problem of distribution.*
- *Decisions on land management affect the environment. Bad decisions can cause environmental degradation and social division.*
- *Land management can be affected by political, social and commercial interests outside farming.*
- *Land ownership can affect productivity.*
- *Innovation does not always transfer to different locations.*
- *In many parts of the world, agriculture and standards of living are directly related.*
- *One method of maintaining agricultural activity in developed countries is by diversification.*

Background to farming change

Agricultural improvements happen all the time. Farmers themselves often come up with the best ideas to manage their crops and stock, but there are times when lots of changes take place at the same time, due to some other influence. Such a period in British history was known as the 'Agrarian Revolution', when such improvements as stock breeding, crop rotation, the use of 'new' crops from abroad and the invention of agricultural machinery, such as the seed drill, revolutionised farming. The benefits included the fact that food surpluses were produced which would feed the growing towns and enable the Industrial Revolution to gather pace. The disadvantages included the fact that many agricultural workers were put out of a job.

An earlier agricultural revolution had occurred somewhere in the 'Fertile Crescent' in the Middle East (roughly modern Lebanon, Syria and Iraq) where plants and animals were first domesticated about 8000BCE. Before this, hunting and gathering were the standard means of gaining a living from the land. In both these cases, a lot of different circumstances came together to allow the changes to take place.

The Green Revolution

A more recent example of major advances in agriculture is known as the Green Revolution. Just like the other examples, no exact date can be put on it, but the major impetus was in the 1960s. The Green Revolution involved many of the same elements as the earlier Agrarian Revolution, but major advances took place in plant and animal breeding. The scientific approach to selecting strains of plants for disease resistance, productivity or success in particular conditions had been used for producing flowers and vegetables for years, but it had not been applied to the sorts of crops that are grown widely in the developing world. In addition, the tremendous success of

Fig. 5.1 A short-horned bull – one of the products of the Agrarian Revolution

Fig. 5.2 Recording data on the growth of scientifically bred varieties of maize

Fig. 5.3 The Green Revolution gave rise to a lot of biotechnological improvements. Here, genetically engineered seedlings are growing in a liquid culture medium

the laboratory crossing of existing varieties to produce new hybrids proved to be the springboard to many other improvements. The new varieties of plants became known as *High Yielding Varieties* (HYVs).

The 'miracle wheat' produced in Mexico at the Centro Internacional de Mejoramiento de Maiz y Trigo (CIMMYT) doubled and tripled yields in a short period of time. Similar success was achieved by the International Rice Research Institute (IRRI) in the Philippines. Several Asian countries introduced the new seeds in 1965 and by 1970 the area growing the new crops had reached 10 million hectares.

The success can be measured by the fact that Pakistan ceased to be dependent on wheat imports from the USA, and Sri Lanka and the Philippines produced record harvests. By 1972 India had reached self-sufficiency in wheat and rice. Wheat production in India tripled between 1961 and 1980.

However, these seeds required high inputs of fertiliser and water to grow and mature fully. For this reason, the HYVs are more accurately seen as being High Response Varieties (HRVs). Yields could certainly be increased but the increase would have to come with the whole package of agricultural technology, including fertilisers, pesticides and irrigation. The problem was that the poor farmers for whom the HRVs were intended could not afford all the inputs that were required to make their introduction a success. Monoculture developed in parts of the developing world as farmers planted only one crop to maximise the use of machinery and pesticides.

Further criticism claimed that the Green Revolution methods were only effective on the most fertile land. Hybrid plants grown on substandard soil were choked out by weeds. This was because the weeds had adapted to the less favourable soils. Peasants farming in unfavourable areas could not afford the expensive irrigation equipment or pesticides required.

The success of the Green Revolution was also put in doubt by environmental side effects. Intensive use of fertilisers resulted in an excess of nitrates in the soils. Water running from the fields washed the excess away: it became fertiliser for the algae and other plants in drainage ditches, leading to eutrophication in the streams and lakes. Large amounts of pesticide such as DDT were found to be a health hazard to the local population. In addition, valuable supplies of energy were required to manufacture nitrogen-based fertilisers, and for running machinery and irrigation pumps.

The Green Revolution was also criticised for the social polarisation produced in some communities. Many of the developments suited the large landowners but some of the small farmers were forced to give up. This in turn produced a landless rural peasant class while the wealthy farmers became more wealthy. Traditional social structures such as the extended family have come under threat and the result has been a mass migration of the landless poor from the countryside to the towns and the development of urban slums. (See also pp. 160–1 on the Green Revolution.)

Food production changes

Certain areas of the world have undoubtedly benefited from the developments brought about by the Green Revolution. Global and national figures show that vast increases in food production have been achieved.

It is often assumed that all changes in the Green Revolution were introduced from outside the Third World, mainly from the USA and Europe. Whereas many innovations *were* initiated in the developed world, or at least by scientists from the developed world, many influences on the Green Revolution actually came from within developing countries themselves. By observing good farming practice, and noting which crops flourish in certain conditions and the ways in which organisation encouraged increases in output, scientists and agricultural development officers were able to evolve models to improve farming systems. This appropriate development of farming systems was an important element in increasing output, building on the crops, organisation and techniques that were already present rather than imposing totally new farming methods. One of the research organisations taking a more integrated view of agricultural practice was the International Crops Research Institute for the Semi-Arid Tropics (ICRISAT). This was established in Hyderabad, India, to cope with problems specific to the arid and semi-arid zones.

Farming 'improvement'

From what has already been said, you can see that there is a conflict between the 'improvements' promised by agricultural developments coming under the general heading of the Green Revolution and what was actually delivered. The problem with the improvements is that they have not always taken into account the political, economic, social and historical factors which are also at work in any area, be it a farming one or not.

The problems associated with the Green Revolution can be identified as follows.

- What are the 'advances'? Are they appropriate to the area for which they are suggested?
- What else needs to be considered to ensure that the appropriate changes are made?
- How can any improvements be financed?

Fig. 5.4 Going to market: Nanjing, China (see p. 162)

The Green Revolution

Some of the elements of the Green Revolution were designed to be:

- plant and animal breeding
- land improvement schemes
- irrigation development
- the use of artificial fertilisers
- better food storage and distribution schemes
- government finance to producers
- improvement of machinery
- land redistribution

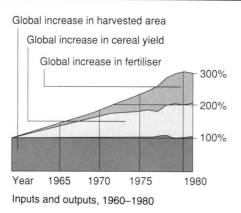

Inputs and outputs, 1960–1980

The graph shows how food production has increased since 1965. The picture is not quite what it seems, however, because food production *per head* is a much better measure of success.

Indices of food production per head

	Developed countries	Developing countries
1965	100	100
1966	104	97
1967	109	100
1968	110	101
1969	108	103
1970	107	104
1971	113	102
1972	111	99
1973	113	100
1974	115	100
1975	118	104
1976	119	105
1977	98	97
1978	101	99
1979	101	99
1980	99	100
1981	100	102
1982	103	103
1983	98	105
1984	104	106
1985	104	108
1986	105	108
1987	103	107
1988	99	108

Reindexation in 1977

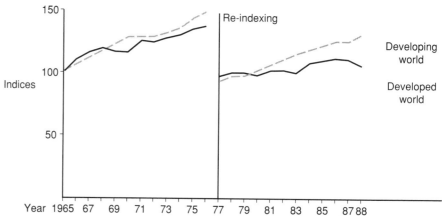

Food production indices

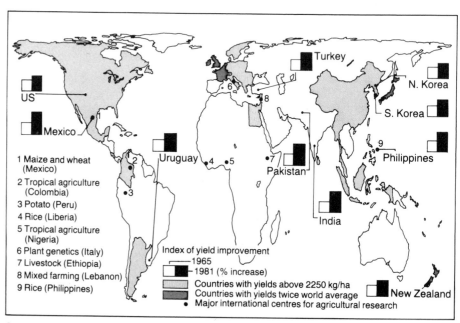

1 Maize and wheat (Mexico)
2 Tropical agriculture (Colombia)
3 Potato (Peru)
4 Rice (Liberia)
5 Tropical agriculture (Nigeria)
6 Plant genetics (Italy)
7 Livestock (Ethiopia)
8 Mixed farming (Lebanon)
9 Rice (Philippines)

Crop yield improvements

If the global average cereal harvest is taken to be 2250 kg/ha, many countries now achieve well in excess of this following Green Revolution measures.

India has doubled its wheat yield in 15 years and rice yield has risen by 75% in the same period.

This page illustrates some of the 'downside' of the improvements expected from the Green Revolution.

Chemicals and seeds

CONTROLLING COMPANIES

By the year 2000 the global seed market will probably be controlled by just 12 seed and chemical giants.

The leaders in 1986 were:

Parent firm	Industry	Seed sales (in million $)
Pioneer Hi-Bred (US)	Seed	734
Shell (Anglo-Dutch)	Petrochemicals	350
Sandoz (Swiss)	Chemicals	290
Dekalb-Pfizer (US)	Petrochemicals	201
Upjohn (US)	Chemicals	200
Limagrain (French)	Seed	172
ICI (UK)	Chemicals	160
Ciba-Geigy (Swiss)	Chemicals	152
Orsan (French)	Chemicals	119
Cargill (US)	Agribusiness	115

Source: New Internationalist

GENETIC EROSION

Of 75 types of vegetables available during the early 20th century, approximately 97% of the varieties of each type are now extinct. The table below shows a sample of US vegetable varieties that disappeared between 1903 and 1983.

Vegetable	Total varieties in 1903	% of varieties lost by 1983
Artichoke	34	94.1
Asparagus	46	97.8
Runner beans	14	92.9
Lima bean	96	91.7
Garden bean	578	94.5
Beets	288	94.1

Source: New Internationalist

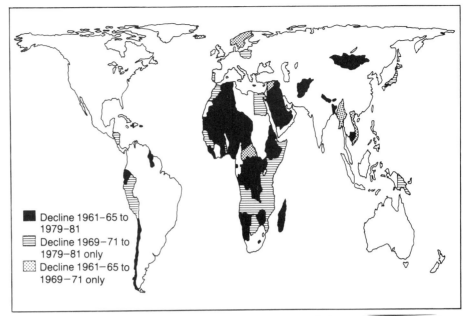

Decline in food output per capita 1961–65 to 1979–81 Source: FAO Production Yearbooks, Rome

- Decline 1961–65 to 1979–81
- Decline 1969–71 to 1979–81 only
- Decline 1961–65 to 1969–71 only

Land

WHO HAS PLENTY

Of all the land in the world which can be owned, nearly three quarters is controlled by just 2.5% of all landowners.

BIGGEST BITE:
- The New York-based International Paper Company - with its 3.7 million hectares - is reputed to be the world's biggest private landowner.
- The 9th Duke of Buccleuch - with his 140,000 hectares exceeding the Queens's 135,000 hectares - is the biggest individual landowner in the UK.
- The cattle-ranching Kidman family - with their three million hectares - are reputed to be the largest landowners in Australia.
- New Zealand Forest Products - with 528,000 hectares - is the biggest private landholder in Aotearoa (NZ).

LION'S SHARE

Percentage of land belonging to top 10% of landowners

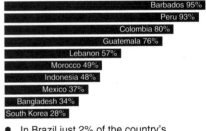

- Barbados 95%
- Peru 93%
- Colombia 80%
- Guatemala 76%
- Lebanon 57%
- Morocco 49%
- Indonesia 48%
- Mexico 37%
- Bangladesh 34%
- South Korea 28%

- In Brazil just 2% of the country's landowners hold 60% of the arable land.
- In Paraguay just 1% of landowners own 80% of the land.
- In the UK just 1% of the population owns 52% of the land.

WHO HAS NONE

More than half the rural population in the Third World are landless – and their numbers are growing.

THE LANDLESS
Rural households that have no or practically no land.

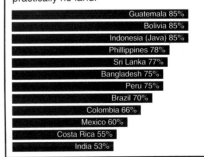

- Guatemala 85%
- Bolivia 85%
- Indonesia (Java) 85%
- Phillippines 78%
- Sri Lanka 77%
- Bangladesh 75%
- Peru 75%
- Brazil 70%
- Colombia 66%
- Mexico 60%
- Costa Rica 55%
- India 53%

QUESTIONS

4 Write down your definition of the Green Revolution.

5 What were its principal aims?

6 How successful has it been in achieving these aims?

7 Identify the countries which showed a decline in food output per capita from 1961 to 1981. In which continents were they mainly found?

8 Summarise your views on the effectiveness of the Green Revolution.

Chinese agricultural development

P China, once a model of farming failure, has now evolved some very efficient systems by the application of one variation on the Green Revolution. Recent years have seen a renaissance in Chinese agriculture. In historic times the rural areas of China were very rich but by the early years of the twentieth century they were considered to be very poor indeed in comparison with agriculture in other areas of the world.

China's rural area is larger than the rural area of the USA and is four times the size of the combined areas of the countries of the European Community. Agriculture is very important to China. In 1988 the Chinese population was over 1.1 billion and of that 750 million people were dependent upon agriculture. Of the economically active population of China, over 40% worked on the farms. If the farms fail to produce, then famine of catastrophic proportions could follow.

Fig. 5.5 The rich agricultural heritage of China

What are the 'advances'? Are they appropriate?

One major element in the Green Revolution throughout the world has been changes in the way farming is organised, not just the crops and inputs themselves. China illustrates well the search for a system which would encourage increases in output and improve the quality of life for the rural peasants. The country has been led by a communist government since 1949 and the emphasis in the management of the rural areas has reflected the ideology of the time. Figure 5.7 gives a brief history of these changes in emphasis up to the present time.

The pattern of agricultural enterprises in China is shown in Fig. 5.9. The main food crops of the country are wheat and rice. These provide much of the diet of the rural Chinese. The average consumption of the rural peasant is 206 kg of grain and 17 kg of livestock and fish. The same figures for the urban dweller are 133 kg and 41 kg respectively. The rural peasant consumes on average 2450 calories per head per day, 84% of which is in the form of grain. The encouragement of different forms of agriculture may be appropriate.

162

Fig. 5.6 Roadside stallholders in Qufu

China has been a communist country since 1949. One of the first moves of the communist government was to take the land away from the landlords and redistribute it to the poorest members of society. 40% of the arable land was redistributed in this way. The government introduced a system of co-operatives in which families shared farm tools and helped each other with harvests.

By 1958 the government of China became impatient with the progress and launched the Great Leap Forward. This meant that large irrigation projects were started which led to huge areas of land being planted with crops. By this time all the land was controlled by the People's Communes. These communes were made up of groups of villages, known as brigades. The land, draught animals and farm tools were owned by everyone in the commune. The people took all the decisions for the economic development of the area, including what to farm. They also had control of the social programme (clinics, etc.) and the schools. Overall projects were undertaken at the commune level (e.g. building new dams). Large efforts such as getting in the harvest were run at brigade level and individual jobs, such as looking after the chickens, were run at team level (perhaps two families).

However, the Great Leap Forward did not produce the results expected and the government started to encourage the farming of private plots of land. In 1966 Mao Tse Tung, the leader of China, initiated the Cultural Revolution in which people from the towns were sent to work on the land and 'learn from the wisdom of the masses'. All students had to work on farms, but the system caused massive resentment and destruction of the cultural heritage, and failed to produce enough food for the cities.

In 1979 the one-child family policy was introduced to prevent the country suffering from starvation in the next century. In the same year the government introduced the Responsibility System. In this families made contracts with the state to produce a certain amount of crops, with the remainder being sold privately. The village still owned the land, but parcelled it out to families. This led to some farmers becoming quite well off, particularly those with farms close to the edge of towns. It encouraged some farmers to specialise in sidelines such as eggs, pigs and vegetables.

The government is now looking to encourage a similar type of farming to that found in Western Europe, with large farms and machinery taking the place of people. The surplus people are being encouraged to move to the towns to take up work in services and manufacturing industry. However, it is the farmers from the unfavourable areas who are moving, leaving large amounts of land uncultivated. Now there are some wealthy farmers with many very poor farmers in unfavourable areas. Towns have grown to reduce the amount of farmland and the farms around the towns have become more intensively cropped.

Fig. 5.7 The political background as it affected agriculture

163

Fig. 5.8 Rural China today – Guishou

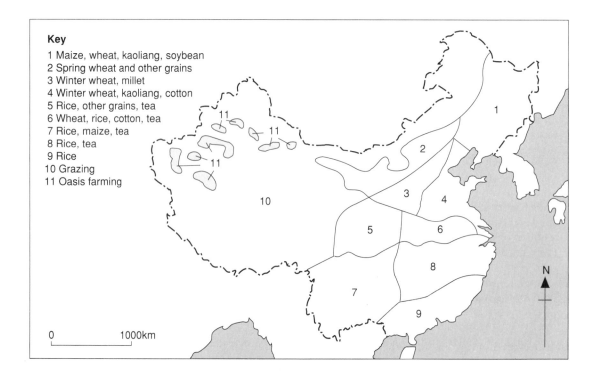

Key

1 Maize, wheat, kaoliang, soybean
2 Spring wheat and other grains
3 Winter wheat, millet
4 Winter wheat, kaoliang, cotton
5 Rice, other grains, tea
6 Wheat, rice, cotton, tea
7 Rice, maize, tea
8 Rice, tea
9 Rice
10 Grazing
11 Oasis farming

0   1000km

N

Fig. 5.9 Agricultural regions of China

Fig. 5.10 Pisciculture in China

Indeed the Chinese may look to spread the development of one of their own innovations – pisciculture (fish farming). This is a fine art in parts of China and provides a valuable source of protein. It is a highly efficient form of agriculture in which the conversion of feed to edible protein (the conversion-efficiency ratio) is far higher than is available through animal stock. In a typical pond silver and bighead carp occupy the middle and upper layers, feeding off the water plants, sugar cane leaves, cut grass, plankton and algae. Dace occupy the lower levels, living off algae. The ecosystem is sustained by public waste and the sludge provides fertiliser for farm crops. A pond can yield 4.5 tonnes of fish per hectare per year, which is five times better in terms of protein production than the best crop alternative.

What else needs to be done to ensure the appropriate advances are put in place?
The organisation of farming has been one of the problems faced by the Chinese peasant, but it was often magnified by other factors. For many farmers in China the main problem has been one of survival. The people have been caught in a vicious spiral of increasingly low productivity forcing them to grow crops on unsuitable land. In the period known as the Cultural Revolution the government insisted on farmers growing more cereal crops. In an effort to maintain living standards, more marginal land came under cultivation. This included growing cereals on slopes which were too steep. The result of this was increased evaporation of soil moisture and a breakdown in soil structure. When the heavy rains came the soil was eroded from the land and the deep loess soils of the plateau were criss-crossed with steep gullies, making farming impossible. The only alternative for the farmer was to move to new land, and so the cycle of deprivation continued.

Further pressure was placed on the farmer by the low prices for grain set by the government. This meant that the small surplus production would not bring in enough money to buy the necessary machinery. Instead, rural farmers had large families to provide labour for the farm. This also meant that more mouths needed feeding.

165

The move to a system where the farmer is allocated land for 15 to 30 years and can sell the surplus production above the quota, has brought about a number of changes. Farmers have more say in the use to which they put their land. They can therefore grow crops more suited to the area. This has led to an increase in the amount of livestock reared in the area. This will in turn improve the protein intake of the rural community. The farmers are

Production of selected crops 1963–88 (000 tonnes)

Crops	1963	1970	1975	1980	1985	1988
Wheat	22 230	31 000	41 001	59 196	85 812	87 550
Barley	14 701	NA	21 000	3 133	2 701	3 000
Rice	86 038	102 000	116 470	145 665	171 417	172 365
Maize	9 178	NA	11 040	60 720	64 056	73 820
Soya	10 683	11 430	12 062	8 266	10 521	10 918
Millet	17 126	NA	24 007	5 790	6 302	5 501
Sorghum	4	NA	22	7 034	6 835	6 115
Vegetables	46 979	NA	65 331	79 989	99 705	112 954
Fruit	3 791	NA	5 520	8 857	12 040	18 430
Tea	178	172	334	334	465	566
Cotton	1 258	1 518	2 168	2 627	4 150	4 200

Area under cultivation for selected crops 1963–88 (000 hectares)

Crops	1963	1975	1980	1988
Wheat	25 195	30 001	28 930	29 001
Barley	11 860	13 601	1 295	990
Rice	30 953	35 390	34 323	32 500
Maize	9 138	11 050	19 986	19 792
Millet	27 785	30 004	3 981	2 701
Sorghum	3	7	2 828	1 902

Yields in kg per hectare for selected crops 1963–88

Crops	1963	1975	1980	1988
Wheat	882	1 367	2 047	3 017
Barley	2 782	3 285	4 244	5 304
Rice	1 265	1 544	2 418	3 030
Maize	2 477	2 999	3 038	3 730
Millet	612	800	1 454	2 037
Sorghum	1 183	2 711	2 493	3 215

Production of pigs (000 head), and hens' eggs (tonnes)

	1963	1975	1980	1988
Pigs	196 917	238 315	313 660	334 862
Hens' eggs	2 654 715	3 630 017	2 882 415	6 685 000

Tractors, harvesters and nitrogen fertilisers (000 tonnes)

	1963	1975	1980	1988
Tractors	75 400	190 000	738 140	891 952
Harvesters	NA	NA	27 113	33 802
Fertilisers	NA	5 039	10 641	13 650

Fig. 5.11 Some agricultural statistics for China

QUESTIONS

5.1 What changes have taken place in Chinese agriculture since 1963?

(a) Convert the data in Fig. 5.11 to a series of indices, using 1963 as a base year of 100. Plot the indices on a graph against time. (See Appendix, p. 226.)

(b) Analyse the main changes shown by these indices.

(c) Do the changes support the view that a renaissance has taken place in Chinese agriculture?
Relate your graphs to the political changes described in Fig. 5.7. Annotate the graphs with the appropriate information from Fig. 5.7.

(d) Comment on the degree of success of the political policies in raising agricultural output.

5.2 In view of the population information given above and the reaction to recent moves towards a more western form of agriculture, do you consider that the changes in China prior to 1979 were *appropriate*? Explain your answer.

Fig. 5.12 Gulleying in the loess plateau

also encouraged to make appropriate improvements to the management of the land. A farmer's effort is rewarded by an increase in production. This has led many farmers to make the investment of terracing the land. Fruit trees can be grown to improve the stability of the terraces as well as providing a valuable cash crop. The increase in income can be used to buy fuel for domestic use. This has the double effect of liberating the women from the task of collecting fuelwood and keeping the trees growing on the slope instead of being cut down for fuel.

At present some 10% of the loess plateau has been managed in this way. The farmer is able to manage the land in a more sustainable way and the rural economy is more capable of coping with extreme conditions because the local economy is more diversified.

A more sympathetic management of the land on the loess plateau also bring benefits for areas in other parts of the drainage basin. The main river of the area is the Yellow River. The name comes from the amount of sediment it carries: 1.6 billion tonnes of sediment per annum, much of it from the erosion of the loess plateau. Sediment is deposited on the bed of the channel, which raises the level of the water. Over the last 40 years the bed has risen by 2 metres. Natural banks of silt are formed by further deposition. These require constant reinforcement to stop the river flooding along a length of over 500 miles and destroying the rich rice-growing land on the floodplain. By reducing the input of sediment into the river the rate of sedimentation is decreased.

This management is supplemented by the building of small check dams in the upland areas (Fig. 5.13). This slows the surface wash after a storm, and reduces the erosion of the fine top soil. The soil that is eroded is deposited behind the check dams and in time new land is reclaimed for farming. The reduction of the velocity of the surface wash reduces the chances of the river flooding in the lower reaches.

QUESTIONS

5.3 List the other factors you think should be taken into account in making any major agricultural changes.

5.4 Give examples of as many of the factors you have listed in **5.3** as you can from the case study of China.

Fig. 5.13 Small dams built of earth and stones can help to check erosion of the loess

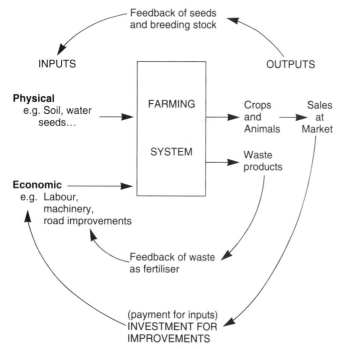

Fig. 5.14 A simple model of farming to show the relationship between production and investment

How can improvements be financed?

Agricultural improvement in any area demands some sort of added input from the farmers themselves. Sometimes this input is simply the uptake of an idea. Sometimes it is extra work. More often, however, it is the financing of changes. The way in which finances become available to the farmer is shown in Fig. 5.14. The same potential for investment can be analysed by looking at overall production changes in the area.

What is the stage of agriculture development in the provinces of China and what potential is there for investment and further development? The following table (Fig. 5.15) gives data for four factors which reflect agricultural development. They are the percentage of arable land currently irrigated, the input of fertiliser per arable hectare, the land intensity as measured by a multiple cropping index and land productivity. The last measurement is the gross value of the crops per arable hectare (yuan/ha).

Provinces	Effective irrigation (% of arable land)	Fertiliser per arable hectare	Land intensity multi-cropping	Land productivity (crop/ha)
Anhui (1)	47.4	260	184.9	3531
Beijing (2)	80.4	215	144.4	3893
Fujian (3)	73.1	458	192.1	3978
Ganzu (4)	23.7	72	100.6	1072
Guangdong (5)	63.9	408	204.1	5153
Guangxi (6)	52.7	222	177.4	2388
Guizhou (7)	28.5	176	168.2	2382
Hebei (N) (8)	53.9	175	133.1	1900
Heilongjiang (9)	8.1	54	95.4	1146
Henan (10)	45.9	212	168.9	2624
Hubei (centre) (11)	63.5	294	208	4141
Hunan (12)	83.2	304	226.2	3892
Jiangsu (13)	77.1	370	185.4	4607
Jiangxi (14)	76.1	264	230.1	2948
Jilin (15)	18	153	101.6	1780
Liaoning (16)	20.7	206	103.8	2394
Neimenggu (17)	20.6	44	93.1	823
Ningxia (18)	31.1	94	104	1273
Qinghai (19)	29.1	60	90.2	1224
Shaanxi (20)	34.7	109	130.3	1656
Shandong (21)	65.3	271	158.6	NA
Shanghai (22)	98.1	459	203.9	5054
Shanxi (23)	28.2	122	105.9	1132
Sichuan (24)	43	248	186.9	3257
Tianjiu (25)	77.3	98	132	3887
Xinjiang (26)	88.8	72	93.4	1468
Xizang (27)	54.8	23	95	1590
Yunnan (28)	34.8	248	145	1866
Zhejiang (29)	85.3	449	248.7	5758

Fig. 5.15 Agricultural potential. The numbers refer to the map below

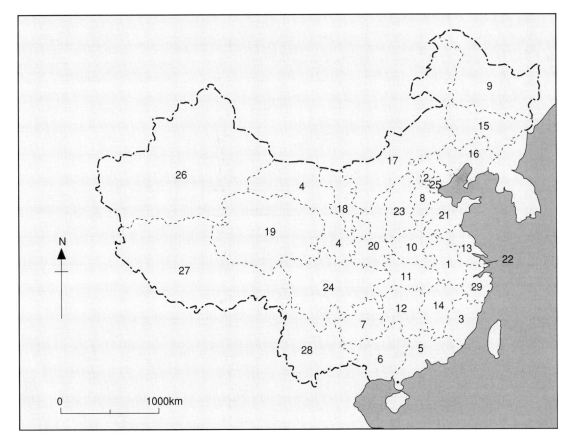

Fig. 5.16 China: provinces

5.5 (a) Construct a table showing the provinces of China and calculate the z score for each factor shown in Fig. 5.15 (see Appendix, p. 222). It would be best to divide this work up between a group of you as the calculations can be tedious. When you have the z scores for the four values, sum them and rank the totals.

(b) Construct a dispersion graph and try to classify the provinces according to the level of development.

(c) Produce a choropleth map using Fig. 5.16 and your findings and analyse the pattern of agricultural potential in China.

Fig. 5.17 Gross value of agricultural output in 1980 constant prices and agricultural population, by province, China, 1979 and 1986

	1979			1986		
	Gross value (m. yuan)	Agricultural population (m. persons)	Gross value per capita (yuan)	Gross value (m. yuan)	Agricultural population (m. persons)	Gross value per capita (yuan)
Total	187 145	814.01	230	276 307	848.19	326
North-east						
Heilongjiang	7 879	20.06	393	11 368	19.73	576
Jilin	4 482	14.84	302	7 188	14.58	493
Liaoning	6 425	22.79	282	8 408	22.17	379
North						
Beijing	1 274	3.76	339	1 876	3.88	483
Hebei	9 385	45.16	208	14 115	48.35	292
Henan	12 429	65.58	190	17 492	68.91	254
Shaanxi	5 045	23.81	212	6 399	25.01	256
Shandong	15 573	65.74	237	26 377	67.97	388
Shanxi	4 121	20.32	203	4 764	21.03	227
Tianjin	830	3.59	231	1 400	3.70	378
North-west						
Gansu	2 592	16.34	159	4 222	17.45	242
Neimenggu	3 566	13.73	260	5 129	14.44	355
Ningxia	565	3.00	189	1 040	3.33	312
Qinghai	725	2.80	259	1 018	2.93	348
Xinjiang	2 667	9.07	294	5 127	9.34	549
Centre						
Anhui	8 770	42.75	205	14 821	44.61	332
Hubei	11 061	39.14	283	15 953	39.09	408
Hunan	11 489	46.17	249	15 542	48.89	318
Jiangsu	15 599	50.69	308	22 385	51.27	437
Jiangxi	6 347	27.50	231	8 710	28.73	303
Shanghai	2 028	4.45	456	2 379	4.30	554
Zhejiang	9 415	33.33	282	11 800	34.17	345
South						
Fujian	4 323	21.33	203	6 336	22.94	276
Guangdong	9 426	47.29	199	15 880	49.75	319
Guangxi	6 045	30.83	196	7 616	34.57	220
South-west						
Guizhou	3 286	24.15	136	5 106	26.44	193
Sichuan	16 756	85.93	195	26 484	88.34	300
Xizang	485	1.55	312	616	1.77	349
Yunnan	4 557	27.97	163	6 756	30.50	221

Note:
The agricultural population in 1979 is derived from the output of grain and the output per person in agriculture.

Fig. 5.18 Percentage of agricultural population in each province

	Very poor (under 200 yuan per head)	Fairly poor (200–300 yuan per head)	Medium level (300–500 yuan per head)	Rich (over 500 yuan per head)
Heilongjiang	1.3	3.8	62.0	32.9
Jilin	none	1.5	58.1	40.4
Liaoning	6.0	14.0	43.9	36.1
Beijing	none	none	none	100.0
Hebei	11.2	12.5	45.7	30.6
Henan	28.6	32.6	37.0	1.8
Shaanxi	31.5	34.7	32.8	1.0
Shandong	none	10.8	43.7	45.4
Shanxi	6.8	29.1	53.5	10.6
Tianjin	none	none	none	100.0
Gansu	35.6	42.2	16.5	5.7
Neimenggu	38.0	21.9	32.0	8.1
Ningxia	49.9	3.5	34.1	12.5
Qinghai	1.7	48.9	44.6	4.8
Xinjiang	2.4	21.5	59.7	16.4
Anhui	2.0	24.8	67.6	5.6
Hubei	5.4	21.1	57.4	16.1
Hunan	9.4	27.7	53.0	9.9
Jiangsu	none	none	38.5	61.5
Jiangxi	6.0	47.2	41.5	5.2
Shanghai	none	none	none	100.0
Zhejiang	2.3	7.3	40.1	50.3
Fujian	5.2	40.6	40.0	14.2
Guangdong	0.9	10.5	48.6	40.0
Guangxi	19.7	15.9	63.8	0.6
Guizhou	39.0	46.7	14.1	0.2
Sichuan	21.6	40.7	34.1	3.6
Yunnan	42.4	43.4	12.5	1.7
China	13.1	23.6	42.4	20.9

QUESTIONS

5.6 Figure 5.17 gives some recent changes in the value of output for each province, with the agricultural population and the gross value of agriculture per head of the population. Use an appropriate method to show the changes from 1979 to 1986.

5.7 The present distribution of wealth is shown in Fig. 5.18. Use an appropriate spatial technique to illustrate this data.

5.8 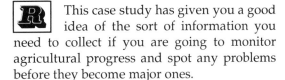 Using all the information from this set of questions, describe the pattern of agriculture in China and suggest how developments are affecting this pattern. What form of management system would you advise the Chinese to adopt to avoid making the same mistakes as in the past?

This case study has given you a good idea of the sort of information you need to collect if you are going to monitor agricultural progress and spot any problems before they become major ones.

QUESTIONS

5.9 What sort of data would you collect from Chinese farmers if you were in charge of agricultural planning?

5.10 What problems would arise in the collection of this data?

5.11 How would you use one of the types of data you have suggested collecting to plan for the future?

China – the Agricultural Context

China covers 9 597 000 km^2 and has a population in excess of 1 120 000 000 people. Although its GNP per capita at $360 US is amongst the lowest in the world, this hides the fact that most people have an adequate and improving diet, thanks to the Chinese system of agriculture.

Population

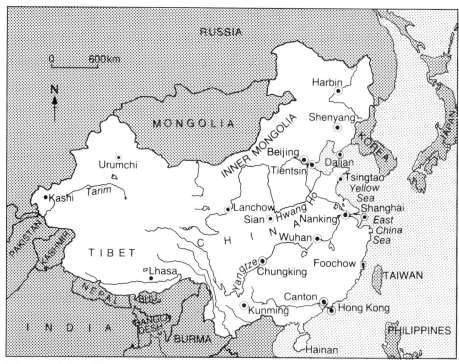

Urban population of China was 20.6% of the total population in 1985.

Most populous nations [in millions (1989)]			
1. China	1120	9. Pakistan	109
2. India	812	10. Bangladesh	107
3. USSR	286	11. Mexico	84
4. USA	250	12. Germany	79
5. Indonesia	179	13. Vietnam	66
6. Brazil	147	14. Philippines	60
7. Japan	123	15. Italy	58
8. Nigeria	109	16. UK	57

☐ Fertility rate:
number of children borne by average woman

■ Percentage of female age group in secondary education

Rice harvesting in China

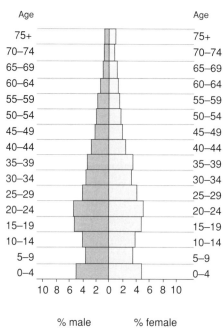

% male   % female

Population pyramid for China

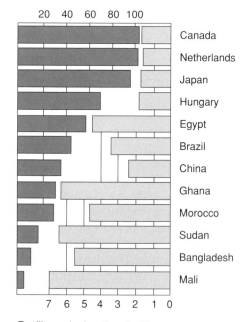

Fertility and education: fertility rates compared with female education, for selected countries, 1988 (*Source:* Philip's World Atlas 1991)

Agricultural output

The commune system of organisation has resulted in steadily rising output.

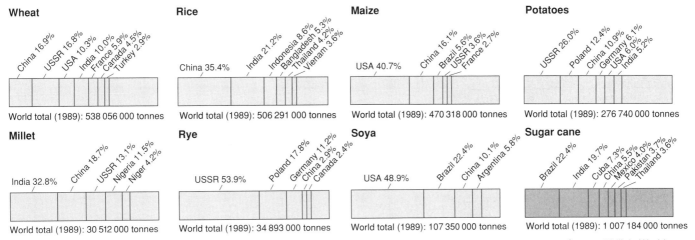

Wheat — China 16.9%, USSR 16.8%, USA 10.3%, India 10.0%, France 5.9%, Canada 4.5%, Turkey 2.9%
World total (1989): 538 056 000 tonnes

Rice — China 35.4%, India 21.2%, Indonesia 8.6%, Bangladesh 5.3%, Thailand 4.2%, Vietnam 3.6%
World total (1989): 506 291 000 tonnes

Maize — USA 40.7%, China 16.1%, Brazil 5.6%, USSR 3.6%, France 2.7%
World total (1989): 470 318 000 tonnes

Potatoes — USSR 26.0%, Poland 12.4%, China 10.9%, Germany 6.1%, USA 6.0%, India 5.2%
World total (1989): 276 740 000 tonnes

Millet — India 32.8%, China 18.7%, USSR 13.1%, Nigeria 11.5%, Niger 4.2%
World total (1989): 30 512 000 tonnes

Rye — USSR 53.9%, Poland 17.8%, Germany 11.2%, China 2.9%, Canada 2.4%
World total (1989): 34 893 000 tonnes

Soya — USA 48.9%, Brazil 22.4%, China 10.1%, Argentina 5.8%
World total (1989): 107 350 000 tonnes

Sugar cane — Brazil 22.4%, India 19.7%, Cuba 7.3%, China 5.5%, Mexico 4.0%, Pakistan 3.7%, Thailand 3.6%
World total (1989): 1 007 184 000 tonnes

Source: Philip's World Atlas 1991

Average daily intake per capita

	Calories no.	Protein (g)	Fat (g)	Calcium (mg)	Iron (mg)
China	2628	62.0	41.4	244	11.9
UK	3257	88.0	143.4	839	13.6

	Fertiliser use per ha 1986	Tractors per 10 km² 1987	Growth per head 1977–88 Agriculture	Food
China	1840	2.0	3.7	3.5
UK	3798	28.0	1.2	1.2

	Balance of trade in food ($m)	Food as % of total Exports	Imports
China	2706	–	4.3
UK	−5902	4.7	9.6

	Total land area (km²)	Arable land	% of total land area 1987 Permanent pasture	Forest and wood	Irrigated as % of arable
China	9 326 410	7.5	34.2	12.5	46.2
UK	241 600	28.9	47.9	9.6	2.2

	Labour force in agriculture	GDP from agriculture (% of total)	Pop. per km² of arable land	Output per agric. worker ($)
China	68.9	33.8	1175	228
UK	2.1	1.4	826	22 295

Source: The *Economist*, 'Vital World Statistics', 1990 (Hutchinson)

Agricultural statistics for China and the UK

Top 10 vegetable producers, 1988 '000 tonnes		Top 10 fruit producers, 1988 '000 tonnes	
1 China	112 954	1 Brazil	27 523
2 India	48 528	2 US	25 735
2 USSR	33 781	3 India	24 649
4 US	27 894	4 Italy	18 846
5 Turkey	16 889	5 China	18 430
6 Japan	15 250	6 USSR	14 503
7 Italy	13 662	7 France	11 145
8 Egypt	10 818	8 Spain	11 024
9 Spain	9 754	9 Turkey	8 890
10 South Korea	8 712	10 Mexico	7 937

> ## QUESTIONS
> 1 Explain why it is so important that Chinese agriculture is organised efficiently.
> 2 Compare the agricultural picture in China with that in the UK.
> 3 Using the agricultural statistics, discuss the potential for improvement in the Chinese situation.

Farming change in the developed world

In the developed world, farming activity has been under pressure from a number of directions. Unlike the developing world, where the necessity is to produce more food for a growing population, the drive in the developed world is to produce food more efficiently. This does not necessarily mean more food. In fact, one of the responses to the search for greater efficiency has been to take some land out of production. In addition, quotas have been set for the production of some foodstuffs, meaning that some farmers have had to pull out of the production of certain items, such as milk and beef.

Four major farming changes can be identified in Europe. These are:

1. *Intensification*, whereby more machinery, fertilisers, chemicals and greater expenditure

Fig. 5.19 Types of agricultural development in Europe

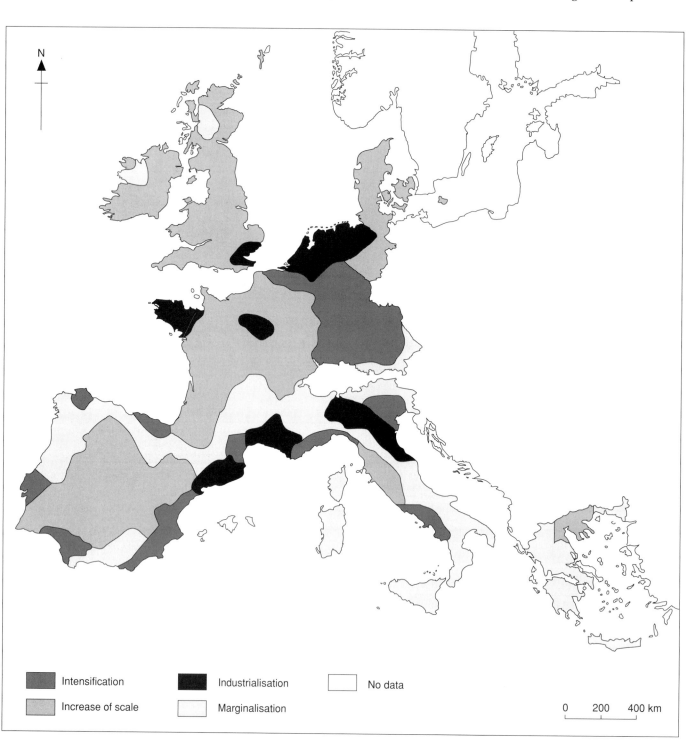

Intensification

Increase of scale

Industrialisation

Marginalisation

No data

0   200   400 km

on infrastructure are aimed at producing goods more efficiently.

2. *Industrialisation*, where the agro-industrial mix (agribusiness) is developed and production is for nearby industrial processing (frozen food, oil production or sugar refining, for instance) or for consumption in urban markets.

3. *Increase in scale*, where marginal farms are bought up by more successful units. Along with mechanisation and automation of production processes, this often leads to a rapid drift of previous agricultural workers from the land.

4. *Marginalisation*, where the modernisation process at work on all farms fails to keep agricultural wages at an acceptable level. In these cases, farms cease to operate and farm labour drifts into other areas or types of employment.

Economic pressures have forced farmers throughout Europe to reassess their situation. Many have left farming altogether, but most have achieved a more comfortable existence for themselves and their families by embracing 'pluriactivity'. This means that they have other forms of income as well as running the farm. Farms are usually run by families, not individuals, so this activity could apply to any of the family members. It might include:

- employment on other farms (e.g. hired labour)
- para-agricultural activities such as food processing (e.g. wine making for direct sale)
- other non-agricultural activities on the farm (e.g. tourist accommodation, furniture making)
- off-farm activities (wage labour).

Some of these activities would be classified as diversification of the farm itself, whilst others would take place away from the farm, although benefiting it economically. Figure 5.19 reveals the areas of Europe where each of four major changes occurs most frequently. The other data will allow you to assess the current situation and suggest ways in which pluriactivity could benefit a particular farm.

QUESTION

5.12 **(a)** Referring to Fig. 5.19, describe the location of areas of Europe which are suffering from farming marginalisation.

(b) Using an atlas map of Europe, and quoting actual examples, explain the main physical reasons for the distribution you have described in **(a)**.

(c) Another of the reasons for marginalisation is the peripheral location of the areas. Refer to Fig. 4.19 in Chapter 4 (the core–periphery model as applied to France) and explain why this should be the case.

Figure 5.20 gives some information for four countries which are members of the EC and for the ten members of the EC before Spain and Portugal joined. The four countries illustrate the situation for the four principal changes indicated in Fig. 5.19.

	EC-10	Italy	FRG	The Netherlands	UK
Farm size (ha)	17.3	7.9	16.6	16.7	58.9
Farm labour (AWU*/100 ha)	12.8	13.6	7.7	11.6	3.2
Large livestock units (% of total animals)					
>50 cows/holding	31	26	13	60	81
>200 pigs/holding	74	75	88	56	92
Nitrogen (N) balance					
Mineral fertiliser application (kg N/ha)	94	64	128	247	93
Livestock units/ha	1.12	0.82	1.66	4.27	0.97
Total N/ha (kg)	172	121	244	546	161
N-surplus (kg/ha)	—	—	167	367	—

*AWU = Annual Work Unit

Fig. 5.20 Some key data on the structure of agricultural production for selected European countries (1985)

Fig. 5.21 Proportion of households with regular* off-farm work (OFW) in the study areas

EC study areas ranked highest % regular pluriactivity to lowest	% households: with any member with OFW	% households: farmer with regular OFW	% households: spouse (not farmer) with regular OFW	% households: other family members only with regular OFW	% households: with >0.5 AWU[†] on-farm non-agricultural work
Freyung-Grafenau (FRG)	81	56	4	21	1
Agueda (Portugal)	68	29	22	17	2
Euskirchen (FRG)	65	41	4	20	1
Udine (Italy)	53	20	9	24	29
S. Lazio (Italy)	50	30	6	14	27
Asturias (Spain)	48	14	13	21	2
Languedoc (France)	48	36	8	4	2
Buckingham (UK)	44	25	14	5	14
Mass-Waal (The Netherlands)	44	27	7	10	5
Ireland (East)	43	18	6	19	3
Devon (UK)	43	20	13	10	9
Calabria (Italy)	43	30	2	11	17
Grampian (UK)	40	20	12	8	8
Fthiotis (Greece)	40	26	4	10	4
Catalunya (Spain)	39	13	8	18	4
Korinthia (Greece)	36	22	3	11	7
Andalucia (Spain)	33	18	4	11	1
Ireland (West)	33	14	5	14	4
Savoie (France)	33	15	6	12	7
Picardie (France)	27	8	13	6	1
Average (%) of EC study areas	58	24	8	13	7
Non-EC study areas					
Austria (West)	70	23	15	33	34
Austria (S.E.)	69	36	12	22	19
West Bothnia (Sweden)	72	57	11	4	3
Le Chablais (Switzerland)	44	31	6	7	8
Average (%) of non-EC study areas	64	36	11	17	17

*Regular off-farm work = full-time and part-time regular employment
[†]AWU = Annual Work Unit.

QUESTIONS

5.13 **(a)** Using the heading 'Italy – marginalisation', describe the current situation of farming in that country.
  (b) Do the same for 'FRG – intensification', 'The Netherlands – industrialisation' and 'The UK – increase of scale'.
5.14 **(a)** Figure 5.21 gives data for 20 study areas in the EC and for 4 comparative areas in non-EC countries. Compare the structure of OFW (off-farm working) in the UK and the FRG.

  (b) Compare the situation in the EC with that in other European countries. Does there appear to be any significant difference between the two groupings?
5.15 Referring to the introduction to this section and to Fig. 5.22, write a definition of pluriactivity and explain why farmers throughout Europe are tending towards this as an answer to the problem of declining agricultural income.

STRUCTURAL DIVERSIFICATION	AGRICULTURAL DIVERSIFICATION

1.Tourism
  (i) *Accommodation*
      Bed and breakfast
      Self-catering
      Camping and caravan sites
  (ii) *Recreation*
      Farmhouse teas/cafe
      Demonstrations/open days
      Farm zoo/children's farm
      Water/land-based sports
      War games
      Horticulture
      Craft centres
      Nature trails/reserves
      Country/wildlife parks
  (ii) *Combined*
      Activity holidays

2.Adding value to farm enterprises
  (i) *By direct marketing*
      Farm gate sales
      Farm shop
      Delivery round
      PYO scheme
  (ii) *By processing*
      Cheese
      Ice cream/yogurt
      Cider/wine
      Jam/preserves
      Potato packing
      Flour milling
  (ii) *By selling skins/hides/wool*

3.Passive diversification
Leasing of land
Leasing of buildings

1.Unconventional enterprises
  (i) *Crop products*
      Linseed
      Teasels
      Evening primrose
      Borage
      Triticale
      Fennel
      Durum wheat
      Vineyards
  (ii) *Animal products*
      Fish
      Deer
      Goats
      Horses
      Lamoids
      Sheep milk
  (iii) *Organic farming*

2.Farm woodland
Energy forestry
Amenity/recreation
Wildlife conservation
For timber

3.Agricultural contracting
For other farms
For non-agricultural
        organisations

1. *Adding value by direct marketing*
   Farm gate sales
   Farm shops
   PYO schemes
   Delivery rounds

2. *Accommodation*
   Bed and breakfast
   Self-catering
   Camping/caravan sites

3. *Recreation*
   Horse riding/stables
   Water sports
   Shooting
   Nature trails
   Farm tours
   Special events
   Informal recreation

4. *Adding value by processing/commercial activities*
   Farm catering
   Dairies
   Cheese making
   Ice cream/yogurt
   Craft activities
   Cattery/kennels
   Stud farm

5. *Passive*
   Dumping
   Building lets
   Land lets
   Farm woodlands

Fig. 5.23 Categories of farm diversification on the West Midlands urban fringe

Note: some of these are ways in which farms can diversify. Others are outlets for individuals in the farming family which could lead to pluriactivity

Fig. 5.22 Farm diversification and pluriactivity

A study of farms in the West Midlands has suggested that diversification measures can be classified as shown in Fig. 5.23. These activities would either enhance the present agricultural enterprise or add new forms of employment which could be taken up by family members. Nearly all the diversification that has occurred in the West Midlands has been since 1975 and nearly two-thirds of the diversifying farms are found within 5 km of either Coventry or Birmingham. Adding value activities tended to be concentrated in this inner ring, whereas farm-based recreation and accommodation tended to be further out in the rural fringe.

One hundred and twenty farmers in the West Midlands area were asked which factors affected their decision to diversify. Figure 5.24 shows that four main factors were isolated. By giving first choice a score of 3, second choice a score of 2 and third choice a score of 1, total scores were computed for the factors. (Resources refers to land, labour and capital availability.)

QUESTION

5.16 If you owned a farm 3 km from Birmingham and wished to diversify, which activities from those listed in Fig. 5.23 would you choose and why?

		Relative importance				
Factors		1st	2nd	3rd	Not listed	Total score
1.	Income	96	12	2	10	314
2.	Resources	7	46	31	36	144
3.	Location	3	47	40	30	143
4.	Personal	14	10	12	84	74
5.	Other	7	1	6	106	29

Fig. 5.24 Factors affecting the decision to diversify

QUESTIONS

5.17 **(a)** To what extent would you say that economic factors are the main reason for farmers diversifying?

(b) Make a list of what could be 'personal' factors affecting such a decision.

5.18 Figure 5.25 is a map of a farm near Coventry as it was in 1973. Since then, it has changed considerably as its owner has diversified and the family has gone in for pluriactivity. You are supplied with data on the farm in 1973 and should redraw the land-use map to predict the changes that could be made to enhance the earning potential of the family. In particular, locate on your map:

- an enterprise to attract the large potential custom along the main road;
- a leisure activity to appeal to weekenders from Coventry;
- a new farming land use which gives seasonal employment in the area;
- two other ideas.

5.19 Write an explanation of your plan for pluriactivity on the farm.

Fig. 5.25 A farm near Coventry, 1973

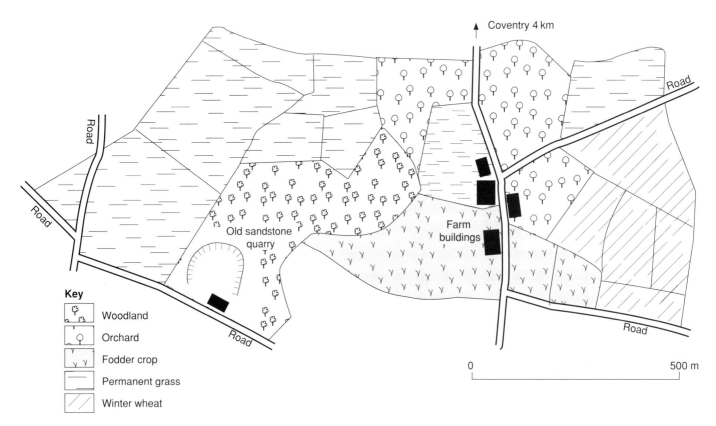

Key

🌲	Woodland
🍎	Orchard
Y Y	Fodder crop
—	Permanent grass
///	Winter wheat

0 — 500 m

MACHINERY

4 tractors
Silage trailer
Plough
Seed drill
Disc harrow
Fertiliser spreader
Pesticide tanker

LIVE STOCK

150 Friesian cattle for milking
40 Friesian calves
(for fattening for beef)

ORGANISATION

Run by family:
52- year- old farmer
53- year- old wife
23- year- old daughter
20- year- old son
4 permanent staff

LAND USE

500 ha permanent grass
50 ha woodland
100 ha winter wheat
50 ha fruit trees
50 ha fodder crops

TOTAL AREA = 750 hectares

Changes in farming are not without their effects on the environment. In the past, low input farming was the main creator and maintainer of the environment, but with intensification many changes occurred, such as:

- the ecological impoverishment of farming areas, the progressive disappearance of species and the destruction of wildlife habitats;
- the reduction in rotations and the replacement of permanent pasture by leys and arable;
- the increased pollution of ground and surface water;
- the intolerable degree of soil erosion and compaction and the overexploitation and abandonment of land;

- the high inputs of non-renewable fossil energy and of other non-renewable resources.

(*Source*: Karlheim Knickel, *Journal of Rural Studies*, Vol 6 No. 4, 1990.)

QUESTION

5.20 The situation in (West) Germany is revealed in Fig. 5.26. Describe the ecological effects of the recent changes in German farming.

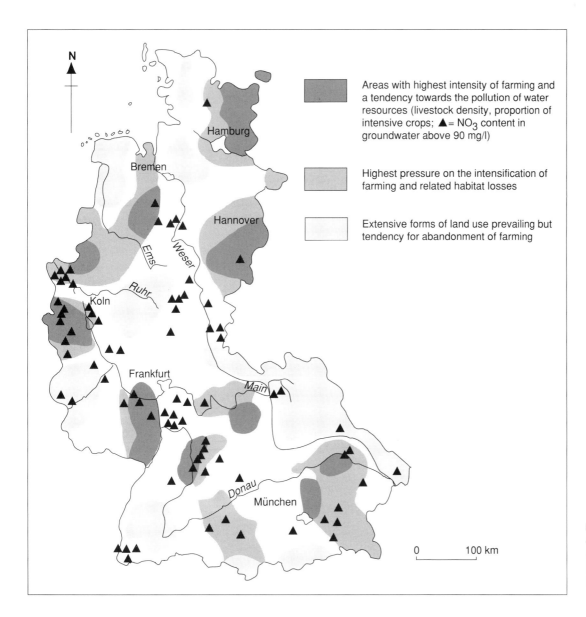

Areas with highest intensity of farming and a tendency towards the pollution of water resources (livestock density, proportion of intensive crops; ▲ = NO$_3$ content in groundwater above 90 mg/l)

Highest pressure on the intensification of farming and related habitat losses

Extensive forms of land use prevailing but tendency for abandonment of farming

Fig. 5.26 The ecological effects of recent farming changes in the Federal Republic of Germany (West Germany)

Fig. 5.27 *Financial Times* 21.11.91

QUESTIONS

5.21 Read the article 'UK "green" farming scheme extended' (Fig. 5.27). How can the environment be enhanced through the encouragement of the co-operation of farmers?

5.22 **(a)** Using the information gathered for answering question 5.20, describe the likely environmental impact of the changes you suggested for question 5.19.

(b) How would you monitor the sort of changes you have predicted and what would you do to minimise them?

UK 'green' farming scheme extended

By David Blackwell

THE LAKE District and Dartmoor have been designated "environmentally sensitive areas," or ESAs, the schemes under which the UK Agriculture Ministry rewards farmers for taking conservation measures.

Mr John Gummer, the minister of agriculture, yesterday named 12 new areas in England to join the 10 schemes launched five years ago to protect areas like the Norfolk Broads. The expansion will more than treble the amount of land under the English schemes to over 1m hectares.

Finance for the schemes, announced earlier in this month's autumn statement, is to rise to £64.5m in 1994-5 from this year's £13m.

ESAs have been at the heart of the debate over "green" farming. Mr Gummer said the schemes were a British invention that was being taken up all over Europe. The whole idea was to ensure the survival of the agriculture base that had created the landscape in the first place.

Administration costs take up about 25 per cent of the budget, Mr Gummer said. But he stressed that administration was part and parcel of the schemes, which were expensive to organise and involved monitors going out in the field.

Existing ESAs will also be expanded further in the not-too-distant future, the department said. It is also likely to lengthen the schemes' contracts to 10 years from five years.

Under the schemes farmers receive annual payments for undertaking "a prescribed form of environmentally beneficial management reflecting the character of the area", according to the department.

Payments vary: in the Pennine Dales farmers are paid £100 an acre to protect meadows, pastures and other landscape features, while in the Northern Peak, £20 a hectare is paid for managing and regenerating heather.

The grants are effectively compensation for profits lost through farming in more traditional and less intensive ways.

The National Farmers Union yesterday welcomed the new areas, which demonstrated "the principle of voluntary incentives for farmers to manage the countryside positively."

The Royal Society for the Protection of Birds said the announcement of new areas was excellent news for conservation.

"The Government now faces the difficult task of persuading our partners in the European Community that green farming schemes such as ESAs must be at the very heart of common agricultural policy reform," said the RSPB.

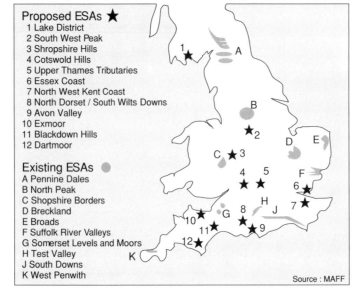

Existing and proposed ESAs in England

Proposed ESAs ★
1 Lake District
2 South West Peak
3 Shropshire Hills
4 Cotswold Hills
5 Upper Thames Tributaries
6 Essex Coast
7 North West Kent Coast
8 North Dorset / South Wilts Downs
9 Avon Valley
10 Exmoor
11 Blackdown Hills
12 Dartmoor

Existing ESAs ●
A Pennine Dales
B North Peak
C Shopshire Borders
D Breckland
E Broads
F Suffolk River Valleys
G Somerset Levels and Moors
H Test Valley
J South Downs
K West Penwith

Source : MAFF

Problem-Solving Exercise

Multinational companies and agribusiness

Background

Decisions taken by a farmer involve a complicated set of processes, whether that farmer is a peasant farmer in the developing world or part of a large business organisation. The farmer has a vast amount of knowledge, much of which has been acquired by years of experience. In recent years farming systems in developed countries have developed techniques from manufacturing industry in an attempt to maximise their output. Hence farms have increased in size by amalgamation, machinery has replaced muscle power and fertilisers have altered the character of the soil. In short, there has been a trend towards using a high level of inputs to maximise the yield. This has been supported by government policy as countries strive to increase their surpluses and their self-sufficiency.

One facet of this is that farms in Britain may be owned by large insurance companies as investments. The farmer may have been replaced by a manager taking decisions for several farms with the aid of high-tech equipment. Decisions taken to improve the investment potential of the land may conflict with the longer term husbandry of the land.

Multinational companies are large companies investing in more than one country. They are usually large companies made up of several smaller companies. Many of them have grown large with the support of the governments of the developed world and many of them have annual sales figures larger than the GNP of some middle income countries. They have developed by horizontal integration, where the company might control a number of companies in a similar stage of production, and by vertical integration, where they control a series of products from the extraction, processing, marketing and sales stages. A number of these companies are involved in agriculture and they have the resources to develop agribusiness to a sophisticated extent.

Unilever PLC is the fifteenth largest company in the world. Its annual sales are in excess of the gross national products of Ireland, Peru and Bangladesh. It has its headquarters divided between London and Rotterdam and produces a vast variety of consumer products, including dairy products, frozen foods and ice cream, tea, convenience foods, washing powder, soap, road construction machinery and textiles. Many famous brand names such as Liptons and Brooke Bond are part of the Unilever company. 304 000 people work for Unilever in 194 different companies. Nearly half of the total workforce is in Africa.

Unilever has been involved in agribusiness since 1911, when they developed oil palm plantations in the Congo, now Zaire. The oil was the basic raw material for the margarine and soap factories. Today, they control 65 000 hectares of oil palm plantations in Colombia, Cameroon, Ghana, Malaysia, Thailand and Zaire. They have smaller interests in coconut, cocoa and rubber plantations. In 1964 they took over Brooke Bond and this brought them over 16 000 hectares of tea and coffee estates in India and Africa. This acquisition of Brooke Bond also included agricultural industries such as the exporting of over 180 million carnations each year from Kenya.

There is a body of opinion which says that the activities of multinational companies such as Unilever, Tate and Lyle and Lonrho exploit people and resources, especially in the countries in which their agribusiness activities take place. A lot of the criticism is directed towards plantations. The following article, 'Planting Poverty' (Fig. 5.28), shows the strength of the feeling of one critic.

Unilever dispute a number of the points made in the article 'Planting Poverty'. In particular, they point to the fact that their maximum profit ever from their plantations was £24 million in 1974. Far from being a dirty word, 'profit' is in fact necessary to be able to invest in future developments. All the Unilever palm oil produced in Africa is currently manufactured and used in that continent. In order to cope with increasing demand, Unilever is investing in new crop varieties, better management techniques and improved distribution. None of this would be possible without producing a profit, but in fact Unilever tend to divert profits from other parts of their business to the now loss-making plantations. Without this, the plantations would fall into disrepair and disuse, or at best (as has been the case with plantations in Zaire which have been 'privatised') produce at a much less efficient level.

Planting poverty

Plantations – where the tea, coffee and vegetable oils we consume are grown – are central to Unilever's international food business. Barbara Dinham looks at the plantations which the company now controls in the Third World and argues that they do not serve the real needs of poor countries.

WORK on all oil-palm plantation is back-breaking and dangerous. Palm-oil fruits (used in making margarine and cooking oil) grow alongside thorny fronds, 12 to 15 feet above the ground. They are cut down with a long and heavy pole and the skin, head and eyes of the harvester are likely to be cut by the falling fronds. In Malaysian plantations, fruit is cut down mainly by men, while women collect and load the 40-kilogram fruit branches, and thorns can become permanently lodged in the hands, causing irritation and infection.

Only rarely is protective clothing issued to the women who spray a mixture of lethal paraquat on the ground to kill weeds. The clothes are too warm for the climate and they don't even afford much protection: as the sprayers aim for weeds the fine mist drifts and slips inside the clothing. Some people believe the chemicals cause the material to disintegrate.

Wages on plantations are low. Oil-palm plantation workers in Malaysia earn just under the industrial wage – if they are lucky.

Earning the full weekly wage usually involves long hours in the baking sun, struggling to fulfil the company's quota of palm-oil nuts. The whole family – mothers, grandparents, fathers and children usually work together. Their wages are also dependent on the world market price for palm-oil, and so fluctuate with that price.

The oil-palm harvesters work a six-day week. There is an official entitlement to 16 days leave plus ten days public holidays.

Unilever's plantations span the world's tropical belt, where the company cultivates about 92,000 hectares of oil-palm, rubber, coconut, cocoa and tea. The company operates in many countries including Cameroon, Ghana, Nigeria, Zaire, Colombia, Malaysia, Thailand and the Solomon Islands.

The history of plantation development was associated with some of the worst colonial practices. Land was annexed and the local farmers prevented by British and other colonial powers from growing food for themselves. The colonialists expanded cash crops, encouraged white settlers and mass produced foods consumed in the West.

Lever Brothers' first plantations were coconut groves in the Solomon Islands. In 1929 plantations were added in Nigeria and Cameroon. Africa became and then remained the centre of the company's plantations until 1947, when oil-palm estates were established in Malaysia.

During the period following independence of many Third World countries, foreign ownership of land became increasingly unacceptable. Africa is a continent of farmers, so it seemed logical to many statesmen and women that the foreign plantations should be taken back into local hands. Unilever responded to demands for local ownership of land, as well as to the political and economic insecurity caused by fears of its nationalization, by withdrawing from and running down its plantations.

Zaire is a classic example of the damage caused by Unilever's behaviour towards its plantations. Unilever ran down its 'risky' estates – those which it felt might be nationalized – and switched its oil-palm investments to safer regions. The consequences were devastating: the World Bank reported in 1978 that Zaire – once a massive exporter of palm-oil – would be importing it within 12 years.

But now Unilever has changed direction and is expanding its agribusiness and plantation interests again. Since taking over Brooke Bond in 1984 Unilever has acquired vast tea plantations in Kenya, Tanzania, Malawi, South Africa (about 16,000 hectares in all) and India. This makes Unilever the world's largest tea producer. In 1981 it took control, with a partner company, of an oil-palm plantation at Llanos in Colombia. In 1983 it bought a 51 per cent interest in a palm plantation business in Southern Thailand. Unilever also has interests in cattle ranching and growing carnations.

Profits from plantations amounted to $251 million in 1985, 16.5 per cent of the company's total profits of $1,518 million. About 34,000 people work on Unilever plantations, excluding the tea estates.

Unilever asserts that it is committed to improving productivity of the land as well as increasing the efficiency of crop processing. It claims to be able, using its international organisation, to transfer its experience around the world. This is done, says Unilever, by 'concentrating on a lead country to develop the best practices in these areas, and then transferring it to others, and by creating productivity groups in each country whose task will be to seek continuing improvements.'

The results are not equally good for everybody. For example the introduction of 'block picking' on tea estates could be called a transfer of so-called 'best practices'. Block picking involves making workers responsible for one patch, thereby isolating them and increasing their workload. The technique is intended to control quality and increase productivity: it is the equivalent of 'quality control circles' developed in factories. In plantations where payment is often linked to the amount picked, this policy makes working conditions worse.

Unilever also sponsors large-scale research in order to work out how many of its raw materials can be used, or grown, interchangeably. Once Unilever has acquired this knowledge, then it ceases to be dependent on any one set of growers or suppliers. It can move between the producers according to its own interests. Central to the research programme are cloning and biotechnology experiments to improve plantation yields.

These agribusiness developments mean that the company can play one country off against another. The technology for producing margarines and other oil-based products is now such that any oil can be substituted for any other. Producers of one crop who become awkward from Unilever's point of view are likely to find that the company no longer wants their crops. It also becomes impossible for independent farmers to afford the new seeds and plantation methods of agriculture, so preventing them from being able to survive in markets dominated by Unilever.

Unilever's plantations also take the attention of Third World governments away from the needs of small farmers. Not only do plantations take the best land, they also attract investment away from food crops which are grown for local consumption. Agribusiness consultants advise governments on investments in, and development of, export crops and estate, or plantation, agriculture. Unilever's experts' advice is based on a Western model of large-scale, capital-intensive agriculture, with heavy investment in seeds, fertilizers, pesticides and hormones to force growth, plus, increasingly, cloning and biotechnology techniques. Massive sums are poured into the research and development for plantation crops, using these techniques.

Aid funds are readily available for such large-scale agricultural projects. Development funds are invariably channelled towards export crops at the expense of local food production. Methods of farming too expensive for peasant farmers are researched and the improvement of rain-fed agriculture, for example, which would improve food yields, has been neglected.

Transnationals like Unilever argue that in a world of food shortages, large-scale agricultural developments are the only solution to meeting food needs. Yet plantations add to landlessness and poverty. They divert agricultural production from meeting local needs to meeting those of consumers in rich countries and in the cities. Unilever falls into the old trap of assuming that increased production is an end in itself. Yields could improve ten-fold but without increasing the means of distribution, growing the right crops and transferring wealth to the rural and urban poor, there will be no better access to food for poor people.

To increase food supplies, poor countries must increase their ability to exploit their own agricultural resources. This means controlling the research and deciding what crops to grow. While it is essential to increase production of locally consumed food crops, it is also necessary to build knowledge of the world market for cash crops in order to take informed decisions. Priority in the area of cash crops should be given to small, independent farmers. To do this, countries must increase the power of peasant farmers, to give them a stronger say and to build on their knowledge and experience. Plantation and agribusiness interests are opposed to small farmer's needs.

Fig. 5.28

UNILEVER PLANTATIONS — ECOLOGICAL CHARTER

In addition to our commercial objectives we recognise that we have responsibilities for the well-being of the communities in which our plantation companies operate. Safeguarding of the environment is one of the most important of these responsibilities.

Unilever Plantations companies therefore aim to use environmental resources in an ecologically sustainable manner. They will:

- Not destroy primary rain forest in order to plant plantation crops.
- Not consider for development areas of unique scientific or historic interest, or habitats important for endangered plant or animal species or vulnerable groups of people.
- Undertake or commission an environmental impact assessment of any proposed new development, and before any major change in land use.
- Avoid polluting water courses and the atmosphere.

- Take practical measures to prevent soil erosion and degradation.
- Plant ground cover or green manure crops, recycle waste materials, and take other practical steps to conserve soil fertility and reduce dependence on chemical fertilisers.
- Use integrated pest management techniques, including biological control where feasible.
- Use renewable energy sources wherever possible.
- Follow clearly defined and routine reporting and auditing procedures on environmental matters, and allocate responsibility for this to appropriate individuals at each management level.
- Adhere to all relevant environmental legislation of the host country, and use their best efforts to ensure that sensible environmental policies are adopted and adhered to.
- Operate with due regard for public and occupational health and safety.

Fig. 5.29

It is indicated elsewhere in this book, in particular in Chapter 6, that the well-being of workers throughout the world is inextricably tied up with the care of the environment. This is the approach followed by Unilever. Trees are the 'natural' crop to grow in tropical areas where the forest has been removed to give way to agriculture. They shade the ground, maintaining a cover for the easily eroded soil, and they allow the important recycling of minerals through leaf fall and decay. Other forms of tropical agriculture tend either to allow rapid depletion of both quality and quantity of soil or to demand enormous inputs of artificial fertilisers to maintain fertility. In order to ensure that their agribusiness activities benefit the environment, Unilever were instrumental in establishing the 'Ecological Charter' of the Tropical Growers Group. Since the final version was somewhat too tame for the company, they issued their own stronger version which has become the guideline for their tropical agriculture enterprises (Fig. 5.29).

One example of Unilever's practice of an ecological approach which has had an economic spin-off is their work with the pollination of oil palms. The following item is taken from the publication *Unilever's Plantations: Developing agriculture in the developing world* (Fig. 5.30).

Fig. 5.30

Insect pollination

Palm oil and kernels are obtained from fruit bunches, so good pollination of the female flowers is essential if high yields are to be achieved. In parts of South East Asia a few years ago, there was a great deal of perplexity as to why the efficient pollination of oil palms was not occurring naturally. In wetter parts of Malaysia, New Guinea, the Solomon Islands and elsewhere, each individual palm had to be manually dusted with pollen every three days to achieve satisfactory pollination. The costs, both in terms of expenditure and time, were enormous. It was generally thought that the problem was due to insufficient wind for circulation of the pollen, so local plantation operators assumed that poor pollination was the natural order of things and had resigned themselves to the high cost of assisted pollination. However, because Unilever operated plantations in Africa as well as Malaysia, it was in a position to challenge the theory that high rainfall in parts of South East Asia was preventing wind pollination by washing pollen out of the atmosphere. The Sabah Estate Manager who had worked in both areas drew a comparison with the African estates where rain was virtually incessant for months at a time and yet there had never been a need to pollinate the female flowers by artificial means. He was convinced that pollination in Africa was done by insects. In response to this in 1977 Unilever engaged an entomologist from the Commonwealth Institute of Biological Control to investigate whether insects played a part in the natural pollination process in West Africa. It was soon established that, contrary to the text books' assertion that the oil palm was wind-pollinated, insects (and in particular weevils of the genus *Elaeidobius*) were the principal agent involved and that wind was only a minor factor. These weevils were not present in South East Asia. The entomologist was also able to show that, in those parts of South East Asia where natural pollination did occur, a local insect (a species of thrip called *Thrips hawaiiensis*) had become adapted to the oil palm, but it was a much less efficient pollinator than the *Elaeidobius* weevils.

In retrospect it became clear that when the early pioneers brought the oil palm seeds from Africa to the Far East, they left behind not only the pests and diseases but also the beneficial insects which had developed a symbiotic relationship with the oil palm – probably over millions of years of evolution. It therefore seemed a reasonable assumption that if the *Elaeidobius* weevils could be brought over the to Far East in carefully controlled conditions, the palm's eco-sphere would be completed and an artificially-created vacuum would be filled.

Poorly-pollinated and well-pollinated oil palm bunches.

Over a three year period, and in co-operation with the Malaysian Government, an intensive series of checks was carried out to confirm that the weevils were not harmful to a wide range of other plants. This research showed that *Elaeidobius kamerunicus* was completely specific to the oil palm, and was unable to feed or breed on any other plant species. Finally, early in 1981, the weevils were released onto Unilever's Malaysian estates. The results were extremely encouraging and soon eliminated the need for assisted pollination. Apart from saving the cost of that laborious operation, yields of fruit increased by 20 to 50 per cent after the first full year. The insect was introduced throughout Malaysia wherever there are oil palms, and the Malaysian Minister of Primary Industries has estimated that in the year following its introduction, as a direct result, the country's plantations yielded an additional 400 000 tons of palm oil and 300 000 tons of palm kernels, with a total value of over US$370 million. At 10 kg per head, this represents the provision of the oils and fats requirement of 40 million people in the developing world every year.

The introduction of the insects has been of particular significance to smallholders in Malaysia and elsewhere. On the large, highly organised estates artificial pollination – although expensive – was efficiently done and a reasonable standard of pollination was thus achieved. Many smallholders, however, did not have the resources or labour required for the collection, drying and application of pollen and as a result their yields were much lower. By contrast, the weevils do not discriminate, pollinating smallholders' flowers just as efficiently as they do an estate's flowers. And it is not only

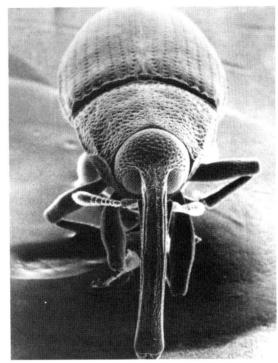

The Elaeidobius *weevils, only 4 mm long, are efficient pollinators of the oil palm*

the countries where Unilever operates which have reaped the benefit of its research and of its ability to transfer know-how internationally; the weevils have also been released by other plantation companies in Papua New Guinea, the Solomon Islands and Indonesia, where Unilever has no oil palm interests.

QUESTIONS

5.23 Read the article by Barbara Dinham (Fig. 5.28) and try to construct a model of linked boxes to summarise the reasons why she thinks that Unilever is 'planting poverty'.

5.24 Multinationals also bring benefits to developing countries. Perhaps their major role is to give these countries access to the latest ideas, technological advances and investment capital (even though World Bank finance is never made available through private companies). What other benefits do they bring? Use the following headings to structure your answer:

- Investment in technology, scientific research and expertise
- Employment and skill transfer
- Provision of development infrastructure
- The balance of payments of the developing country
- Feeding the world's population
- Ecological care in the tropics.

5.25 There is a lot of literature currently which is critical of multinationals and their role in agribusiness. Amongst these are *The Ecologist* magazine and Barbara Dinham's own book, *Agribusiness in Africa*. Less has been written in recent times on the beneficial role of multinationals in tropical agriculture, but the individual companies do have some printed material themselves. For example, Unilever issue various booklets from:

External Affairs Dept.
Unilever PLC
Unilever House
PO Box 68
Blackfriars
London
EC4P 4BQ

Using all the information in this chapter and material you have collected on agribusiness, write an essay entitled:

'Plantation agriculture is the most appropriate form of agricultural organisation for a tropical developing country. Discuss.'

You should include in your essay reference to the ways in which the activities of multinationals might be monitored in order to ensure that they play a beneficial role in the agriculture of developing countries.

A global action plan?

- *The way that people define 'resources' determines the way they are used.*

- *Resources can also be viewed as 'commodities'.*

- *The population:resource equation is a vital one for the future of the earth.*

- *The developing world is faced with real dilemmas in its search for a fairer share of world wealth and the developed world has a responsibility to help it in a sustainable development strategy.*

- *The more efficient use of energy would help greatly in the more rational use of resources.*

- *The control of resources is the control of political power.*

- *Recycling could play a significant part in the conservation of world resources.*

- *Individual action can play a major part in sensitive resource utilisation.*

Defining 'resources'

I The way that people think of resources affects the way that they are used. Historically, a country's wealth was assessed by its ability to exploit the resources that it was fortunate enough to discover. 'Resources' during this period tended to mean natural resources (minerals, water, wood, fish, etc.). Most definitions omitted any mention of people.

Gradually, the realisation began to dawn that wealth was not just the sum total of the resources a country owned, but how those resources were shared amongst the population that depended upon them. The GDP (Gross Domestic Product) describes the total value of the resources produced by a country and the value added to them by manufacturing and services. If this sum is then divided by the total population of the country, the GDP per capita figure is derived.

Figure 6.1 shows some recent statistics, including the GDP per capita figure, for a range of countries. This figure does not necessarily provide a reliable measure of the standard of living, since the wealth of a country may not be evenly divided amongst the population. Differences in the cost of living between countries also make it less reliable to use in comparisons. For this reason, the United Nations, the Organisation for Economic Co-operation and Development (OECD) and the European Commission (EC) have developed the PPP (purchasing power parity) statistic. This is an estimate of the GDP per capita adjusted for living costs, but it still does not get over possible unequal distribution of wealth within the country.

Fig. 6.1 Measures of wealth

Country	GDP ($bn)	GDP per capita 1988 ($)	PPP 1988 (US = 100)	1980–88 real GDP growth %
Australia	232.80	14 083	71.1	3.4
Hungary	27.83	2 625	31.2	1.8
Hong Kong	54.60	9 613	60.4	7.6
Papua N.G.	2.61	733	10.5	3.0
Philippines	38.90	662	10.7	1.3
China	332.79	301	12.1	11.4
Bangladesh	18.72	179	5.0	2.9
Benin	1.73	389	6.5	2.6
Ethiopia	5.45	114	1.6	1.3
South Africa	87.55	2 958	28.3	1.5
Kuwait	19.97	10 189	78.6	−1.1
United Arab Emirates	23.34	15 560	69.2	−3.7
Argentina	88.17	2 759	26.4	−0.9
Brazil	354.06	2 451	24.5	2.4
Haiti	2.43	440	4.4	−0.8
UK	826.32	14 477	66.1	2.8

QUESTIONS

6.1 **(a)** Resources are often classified as 'renewable' or 'non-renewable'. Write a short definition of each of these terms.

(b) Classify each of the following resources into the categories renewable or non-renewable: sunlight, fish, uranium, lead, wood, gold, coal, wind, iron ore, oil.

(c) Comment on any problems you found in classifying any of these resources.

6.2 There are many other ways of classifying resources. One of the more recent concepts is of 'environmentally friendly' and 'environmentally hazardous' resources. Write definitions for each of these terms, then re-classify the list of resources in 6.1(b) using these headings. Again, comment on any problems.

6.3 Research the literature to find at least two other ways of classifying resources. Descriptive classifications could be used, e.g. metals, biological, etc., or the use to which they could be put, e.g. food, energy, etc.

6.4 Comment on the methods of classifying resources. Which do you think is the most successful and why?

6.5 Draw up a table to analyse the statistics in Fig. 6.1. In the first column, rank the countries according to their GDP per capita (the highest is Rank 1). In the second column, rank the same 16 countries according to their PPP. Comment on the differences you find between the two lists. Which countries do you suspect have a low cost of living?

6.6 Devise a suitable method to check whether it is the richest countries which had the highest real growth rate in the GDP between 1980 and 1988. Explain your answer.

'Conservation' began to be an important concept in resource management in the 1960s, although at this time it was more talked about than practised. It was given added impetus as far as oil was concerned in the early 1970s with the 'oil crisis'. The Organisation of Petroleum Exporting Countries (OPEC) had for a long time played the game dictated by the large users of oil: Europe, the USA and Japan. They had supplied large quantities of low priced oil and had boosted production to match demand. In the 1970s, as a response to economic factors in producing countries, but also in an attempt to give OPEC a much more powerful voice on the world stage, production was cut, forcing prices up. For a while, petrol rationing took place in the United Kingdom and prices of manufactured goods, most of which are in some way related to oil, rocketed. Serious thought began to be given to the conservation of oil stocks and exploration for new ones. This change of emphasis also affected views on the use of other resources.

In the 1960s, astronauts orbited the earth in spacecraft and were staggered by the beauty of the planet as seen from this new perspective. Photographs were published making these images widely available. The 'blue planet' began to be recognised as something very special and the concept of 'Spaceship Earth' was born. Spurred on by this realisation, one English NASA scientist, James Lovelock, began to develop the hypothesis that the earth was in fact a functioning whole. It had a self-renewing biosphere which depended on the non-living elements in the earth itself and interrelated with the atmosphere. The earth was a living entity. In Lovelock's words, it was 'a "feedback" or "cybernetic" system which seeks an optimal physical and chemical environment for life'. Lovelock put this forward as a hypothesis to aid the understanding and sensitive occupation of an increasingly misused earth, but much evidence now supports this idea and it has revolutionised the way that many people view the earth's resources and how they are used. His theory is known as 'Gaia', taking its name from the Greek goddess of life.

Since the 1960s, resources and how they are used have taken an ever more important place on the international agenda, until at the end of the twentieth century it could be argued that this topic is the single most important one. It underlies all the other important decisions that need to be made. For example, the arms limitation talks conducted in the

Fig. 6.2 A Kayapo chief, a representative of a threatened Amazonian tribe

1990s between the USSR and the USA were spurred on by a huge budget deficit in the USA and a need to divert resources from the defence industry into restructuring industry in the USSR. Since the effective break up of the USSR, the importance of population–resource balances in the constituent states has become even more critical.

As explained earlier (p. 33), the perception of resources affects the way in which they are exploited. The examples quoted above are not the only ones which limit this exploitation, however, because the perceptions discussed so far have largely been western industrial ones. People in other areas of the world see things very differently.

Tribes in Amazonia have existed in harmony with their environment for a long time. They have lived a rich life of hunting, gathering, farming and trading and the structure of the forest has been only marginally changed by their activities. Recent estimates are that population densities in the Amazon region at the height of Indian occupancy have been much higher than previously imagined,

up to 70 people per square kilometre over the huge area. In other words, this system of usage has been a very efficient one. The Indian's idea of a resource would be one which could be harvested at a sustainable level. They have a huge fund of knowledge about how to use individual plants and animals.

Exploitation of the tropical rain forest might be far more lucrative in the long run if some account is taken of the success of the Indian approach compared with the failure of the large scale deforestations of recent years, spurred on by inappropriate agricultural developments. It could be argued that the Indian's knowledge is itself a valuable resource. In western terms, it would be classified as 'intellectual property' and carry a great deal of financial muscle. If firms such as Coca Cola can make large profits out of knowing how to make soft drinks, then perhaps the knowledge owned by native peoples such as the Amazonian Indians should command its own price. It might also be the saving of the ecosystem.

Some Gross Facts

The Amazon River is 4,000 miles long; a fifth of all the land-based water in the world is flowing in the Amazon; its outflow is twelve times that of the Mississippi and sixteen times that of the Nile; ten Amazon tributaries are larger than the Mississippi; it has more than a thousand tributaries, seventeen of which are more than a thousand miles long; more water passes out of the Amazon in a day than passes in front of the Houses of Parliament in a year; the outflow is 7 million cubic feet per second; approximately 15 per cent of all the water entering the Atlantic comes from the Amazon, measurably lowering the salinity of the ocean over an area of 2.5 million square kilometres and adding each day approximately 1.33 million tons of particulate matter; those tributaries of the Amazon which drain the interior basin (total catchment area: 6 million square kilometres) are largely nutrient free; the gradient of the Amazon is very mild, a fall of only a hundred metres over 3,000 kilometres, and the difference in river height from low to high season may be as much as thirteen metres (as in Manaus in 1953 and 1963); Amazonia contains about a tenth (500–880 thousand) of all the plant, animal and insect species of the earth; the Amazon Basin covers about 60 per cent of the eighth largest country in the world and is about the same size as continental USA; the island of Marajó in the mouth of the Amazon is the size of Switzerland (or Wales, or Denmark); Amazonia contains half the total bird species of the world; it has the largest parrots, rodents and ants, the longest snakes, and more species of bats and monkeys than any other forest; it has more species (2,500) of fish than there are in the Atlantic, including 500 species of catfish alone; the average rainfall is eighty inches, in some places 390 inches; the major Amazonian state of Pará is larger than Portugal, France, England, Italy, Belgium and Holland combined; Brazilian officials claim that 5 per cent of the forest has been cleared, World Bank researchers claim 12 per cent, and most of this has been destroyed in the past ten years; the first nine pig-iron smelters around the Serra das Carajas mine will require 1.1 million tons of charcoal each year, an amount which would fill a building 100 metres wide, 100 metres long, and fifty storeys tall; in 1985, 18 million live aquarium fish were exported from the state of Amazonas; in 1987, Brazilian scientists estimated that the amount of forest burned that summer was 77,000 square miles, an area one and half times the size of New York state; the same satellite data indicated that there were, conservatively, 170,000 individual fires (virtually all fires are illegal); the forest service has 900 wardens for an area larger than Europe; 16 per cent of the students at the University of São Paulo, one of the best, have Japanese surnames; 70 million Brazilians (i.e. half) are black or 'mixed race', but none of the governors of Brazil's twenty-three states is black and only seven of the 559 members of Congress regard themselves as black; 81 per cent of Brazil's farmland is held by 4.5 per cent of the population; Brazil's foreign debt is more than $100,000 million; gold fetches about $10 a gramme, of which the putative mine-owner receives 55 per cent; the remaining 45 per cent is divided up amongst the panners, diggers, hosers and guards such that an individual worker receives on average only 2 per cent; in Roraima, a territory in which the threatened Yanomami live, 45,000 miners produce three tons of gold each month.

An Easy Score

There are a number of reasons for the relative ease with which large-scale expropriation of Amazonian resources has been effected. Examples of these large-scale projects include the Serra do Carajás iron-ore mine, the bauxite mining on the lower Trombetas, the Tucuruí hydroelectric dam on the Tocantins River, coffee plantations and cattle ranches in Rondônia and Acre, the proposed Xingu hydroelectric project and manganese mining at Macapá. On a smaller scale but just as predatory and destructive are the various gold-mining centres as well as the numerous timber-felling and milling operations.

The first reason is that during the period of the National Security state (emerging in the years following the 1964 coup and lasting until 1985) Amazonia was effectively internationalized and made accessible to foreign and transnational capital.

Second, the suspension of political rights and a free press during the generals' reign precluded an open and critical discussion of the rationale for rapid Amazonian development.

Third, the resources on offer were most appealing to very large investors or consortia who, able to take advantage of economies of scale, could most profitably co-ordinate Amazonian extraction with their other enterprises. Small investors less capable of implementing such vertically integrated operations were squeezed out or, more typically, resorted to a strategy provided for them by the state – land speculation.

Fourth, Amazonian hyperbole (the biggest this, the longest that, like a sub-equatorial version of Texas) provides a constant background of mystification against which more discreet – and perhaps significant – factual matters appear drab and uncompelling.

Accounts of the actions of such entrepreneurial swashbucklers as Ford and Ludwig are much more easily assimilated than are accounts of the tropical forest's closed nutrient cycle, and they sell more newspapers.

Last is the fact that much as Amazonia might epitomize for Europeans the locale of 'the other', it does the same for Brazilians. Implicit in Brazil's self-image as standing resolutely at the cutting edge of Third World capitalist development is its own sense of maintaining a periphery so vast and exotic that it cannot fail to suggest unlimited potential.

QUESTIONS

6.7 Read the extract from *Big Mouth: The Amazon Speaks* by Stephen Nugent (Fig. 6.3).

(a) What resources attract people to Amazonia?

(b) Make a list of the main reasons for the 'large-scale expropriation of Amazonian resources'.

(c) How do you think the development of Amazonian resources should be controlled in future?

Commodities

Figure 6.4 shows the contribution of non-fuel primary products to the export earnings of a range of world areas. It can be seen that the developing countries depend for their wealth to a disproportionate degree on non-fuel primary products. These are what have hitherto been called 'resources'. On the other hand, the developed countries depend to a far greater degree on manufacturing for export earnings. Put simply, they import raw materials from the developing countries at as low a price as possible (so long as it is a stable price), add value to the materials through the manufacturing process, and then re-export them as finished and much more valuable goods.

As an example, tin is mined in many developing countries, amongst them Bolivia (Fig. 6.5). It is traded on the various commodity exchanges in such places as New York and London. Consumers try to obtain it at low prices so that they can make profits on the deal. When there is under-production of any commodity, or when producing countries get together to control trade, the world price can rise dramatically. Most of the time, however, more efficient mining and competition amongst producing countries keeps the price of tin low.

Another way in which commodity prices can be kept down is by users grouping together to agree on purchasing policy. The story of Jamaican bauxite graphically illustrates this point. Bauxite (the ore of aluminium) had been discovered in Jamaica in 1942. Aluminium was extremely important in the growing aerospace industry and therefore attracted United States investment in order to ensure supplies. Six North American companies gradually came to control most of the production of bauxite as the aerospace industry became even more strategically important. The Jamaican government could only look on as it received about 2% of the market value of the finished aluminium.

There were several examples of developing countries 'fighting back' over resource provision, but the one which attracted the attention of the Jamaican government was the 1973 OPEC agreement to raise oil prices. This was successful in so far as it obtained a fairer return for raw materials for the producers, even though it later led to other financial problems. The Jamaican government, under Gerald Manley, instigated discussions between a negotiating team and the bauxite mining companies with a view to increasing Jamaica's return and a 51% share of the companies' operations on the island. The companies refused these approaches and Jamaica, along with many other producer nations, set up their own price-setting body (known as a *cartel*), the International Bauxite Producers Association. Unfortunately for them,

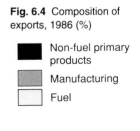

Fig. 6.4 Composition of exports, 1986 (%)

■ Non-fuel primary products

▨ Manufacturing

□ Fuel

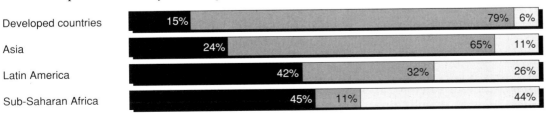

Developed countries	15%	79%	6%
Asia	24%	65%	11%
Latin America	42%	32%	26%
Sub-Saharan Africa	45%	11%	44%

Fig. 6.5 The state tin mines at Potosi, Bolivia

two of the major producers, Australia and Guinea, refused to join. In addition to joining the Association, Jamaica raised a 7.5% levy on all bauxite production, increasing the country's revenue five-fold in one year.

By the end of 1974, all but one of the companies which produced bauxite in Jamaica had agreed to these terms, but arguing against the levy, they started investing in Australian and Guinean production as well. The companies were suspicious of Jamaican state intervention and wished to control their own production. In this way, Jamaican revenue from bauxite fell and the country became unable to pay back the loans it had taken out. It had to obtain help from the International Monetary Fund in 1977. Severe repayment terms were imposed. Along with continued lack of co-operation from the bauxite-producing countries, this contributed to the overthrow of Manley's socialist government in the 1980 elections. On the other hand, Australia and Guinea could be seen as acting in their own best economic interests and they had no economic ties with Jamaica which suggested that they should 'co-operate'.

Immediately after his election, the new leader, Edward Seaga, was granted a whole range of new loans and eventually better IMF terms. The bauxite-producing companies began mining at full capacity again and resumed their control of the Jamaican bauxite industry, including production figures and pricing.

Most cartels suffer in the long run from one or more of the members deciding that their share is 'unfair'. In rocking the boat, they tend to promote price instability and this can affect both producers and consumers very badly.

In order to show the changes in commodity prices, Fig. 6.6 was compiled by making the values of the commodities in 1980 equal to 100 (an *index*). The subsequent changes in relation to this figure therefore eliminate changes in the relative value of the currencies concerned and show how the value to the producing country of the raw material changed over time. They show the results of shortages and gluts on prices, but also illustrate such factors as both buyer and seller cartels.

As well as fluctuations in commodity prices, changes occur over time in the 'terms of trade', which is defined as the average value of a unit of exports divided by the average value of a unit of the goods the country or region imports. In other words, it shows how much can be bought for the amount that is produced through export. The net result since 1980 has been a fall in the purchasing power of the developing countries. With very large debts incurred through loans taken out in the 1970s, this means that the standard of living has

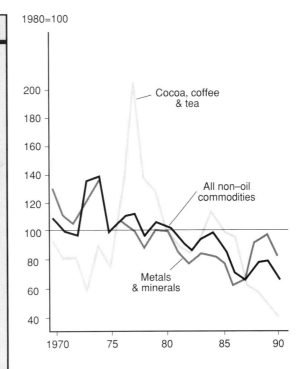

Fig. 6.6 Real non-oil commodity prices

6.8 During the 1980s, the real value of total world trade grew by an average 4.3 per cent per year. At the same time, trade in commodities grew by only 1.7 per cent per year. Explain why this situation occurred. (Think of efficiency of manufacturing and levels of demand.)

6.9 In 48 out of 55 African countries, the three leading commodity exports accounted for more than half the total exports for the period shown in Fig. 6.6. How would the following have affected these countries' terms of trade?

(a) A loss of market share as alternatives have been developed (e.g. sunflower oil replacing ground nut oil).

(b) A decline in demand (e.g. for coffee, on health grounds).

(c) A search for new markets for manufactured goods by developed countries.

6.10 A cartel is only one way in which producers can achieve stable prices for their commodities. Another way would be to set up a co-operative producing, purchasing or marketing arrangement. These have been successful both on a national basis (Danish farming, Indian textiles) and on an international level (Oxfam, Traidcraft). Research the literature to find out how a co-operative organisation works. How can it improve the price paid for a producer's raw materials?

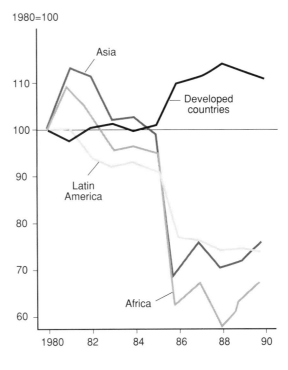

Fig. 6.7 Terms of trade

declined in these countries. Figure 6.7 shows how the terms of trade have changed from 1980 to 1990.

The basic problem in devising a global action plan to improve the standing of the developing countries would therefore seem to be that there is a different view of 'resources' in the developed and developing worlds. This may be summarised as in Fig. 6.8 (p. 196).

Unless other factors are built into the equation, manufacturers will continue to try to obtain commodities at the lowest prices possible. How can the use of resources be planned on a fairer basis?

'Resources' v. 'Commodities'

Resources

Look in any book which reviews the distribution of wealth throughout the world (such as *Philip's Geographical Digest*, the *Economist: Vital World Statistics* or most good atlases) and you will find sections on 'Resources'. There usually follows a listing of the production of minerals, agricultural products, fish, timber, etc. All these products are resources which are being exploited. The figures can, however, give a false impression.

OECD = Organisation for Economic Co-operation and Development

1. Shares of world food output (% of world total)

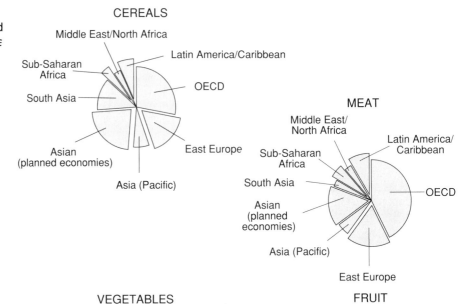

2. Energy consumption per head – Europe 1988 (coal equivalent)

	kilos
Austria	4 018
Belgium	5 560
Denmark	5 346
Finland	5 692
France	3 720
W. Germany	5 624
Greece	2 452
Ireland	3 462
Italy	3 570
Luxembourg	11 139
Netherlands	7 263
Norway	6 782
Portugal	1 329
Spain	2 106
Sweden	5 004
Switzerland	3 794
UK	5 107
Albania	1 291
Bulgaria	5 912
Czechoslovakia	6 311
E. Germany	7 891
Hungary	3 819
Poland	4 810
Romania	4 624
Yugoslavia	2 423

3. Some mineral production figures (1988)

	Top 5 Producers	('000 tonnes)	Top 5 Exporters	('000 tonnes)	Top 5 Consumers	('000 tonnes)
Paper and Board	US	69 477	Canada	11 420	US	76 394
	Japan	24 624	Finland	7 185	Japan	25 035
	Canada	16 638	Sweden	6 377	China	13 229
	China	12 645	US	4 294	W Germany	12 367
	USSR	10 750	W Germany	3 780	USSR	10 025
Tin*	Malaysia	49.9	Malaysia	48.9	US	37.6
	Brazil	42.7	Brazil	33.6	Japan	32.2
	Indonesia	28.2	Singapore	27.7	USSR	30.0
	China	24.0	Indonesia	23.1	W Germany	19.4
	USSR	17.0	UK	14.0	China	14.0
Copper*	US	1 857	Chile	976	US	2 211
	USSR	1 380	Zambia	424	Japan	1 331
	Chile	1 013	Canada	262	USSR	1 250
	Japan	955	Zaire	198	W Germany	798
	Canada	529	Peru	147	China	465

* Refined production

Commodities

This term is used in the financial markets of the world to define the raw materials that enter world trade. In other words, it is a technical term for resources, but its very use helps to colour people's attitudes towards the producers of the products. Consumers attempt to obtain 'commodities' at low prices so that they can realise profits on the subsequent manufacture. This scenario is very worrying for countries which rely heavily on one basic product.

Countries such as Burma have to exploit their natural resources, such as teak, if they are to raise enough money to develop other forms of activity. In the meantime, they are often accused of insensitive development.

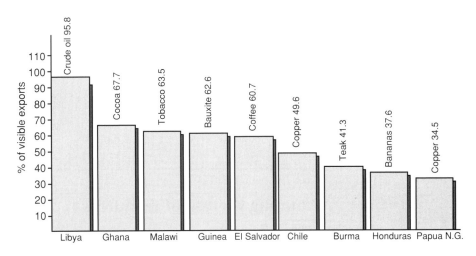

The dependence of some countries on a single export commodity

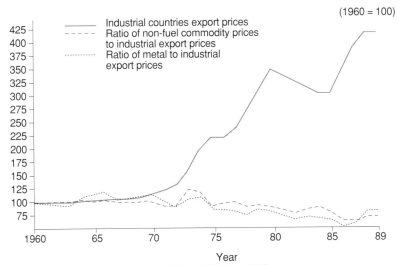

Commodity and industrial export prices 1960–89 (1960 = 100)

QUESTIONS

1 Using the energy consumption per head figures, construct a topological map of Europe (see Appendix, p. 227).

2 Describe the situation revealed by your map. Comment on any patterns revealed by it.

3 Attempt to explain the map you have drawn. How far do the following help to explain the situation?
(a) climate
(b) industrial development
(c) population density.

4 Using the agricultural output pie charts, comment on the relative positions of the OECD and Sub-Saharan Africa in all four commodity areas.

5 Using all the information on this double-page spread, comment on what might happen in an economy heavily dependent on one agricultural resource export, under the following conditions:
(a) poor harvest
(b) sudden slump in world prices
(c) sudden increased demand which is not sustained
(d) development of a substitute for the product (e.g. Nutra-sweet for sugar).

Fig. 6.8 Two views of resources

Manufacturers in Developed Countries	**Governments in Developing Countries**
Raw materials produced by developing countries are 'commodities' to be obtained as cheaply as possible. Value is added to them in the developed countries and they are re-exported at a profit. Competition amongst producers is therefore to be encouraged, although stable prices are much more important than wildly fluctuating ones, even if this means very small profits for a while.	Raw materials are the basis of the world manufacturing system. They should command higher prices than they do. If producer countries could get together to organise sales, or if the developed countries could be persuaded that fairer prices are urgently required, the system could be changed.

Planning the use of resources

One of the earliest attempts to show how population levels and economic well-being related to resources was made by the Reverend Thomas Malthus in 1798. In his view, there was a ceiling to population levels and this was determined by the availability of food resources. Population, unless checked by some factor, increases geometrically according to the series 1,2,4,8,16… . Food resources, on the other hand, increase arithmetically according to the series 1,2,3,4,5,6… . The relationship between these two rates is suggested in Fig. 6.9.

In fact, since 1798, observation has shown that a simple Malthusian view cannot explain the situation that actually arises. A Danish geographer, Ester Boserup, preferred to explain the relationship between population and food supply by suggesting that 'agricultural developments are caused by population trends rather than the other way around'. To her, population pressure acted as a stimulus to agricultural changes and new levels of production resulted from these pressures. The

Green Revolution, for example, is explained by the absolute necessity to feed people. A comparison between the Malthusian and Boserup views of the population: food resources equation is shown in Fig. 6.10. The two views might be regarded as pessimistic and optimistic extremes, with Boserup perhaps evading the vital question of whether there is a final limit to growth beyond which food resources cannot be increased.

An attempt to put the use of resources into context was made by the Club of Rome in 1972. The report had three main conclusions:

1. If population growth rates, food production changes and resource depletion continue at their present rates, the limit to population growth on earth will be reached within 100 years (Fig. 6.11).
2. It would be possible to influence this prediction to establish a relationship between production and consumption which

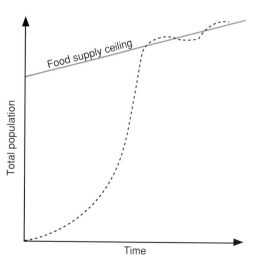

Fig. 6.9 Malthus' view of the food supply ceiling to population growth

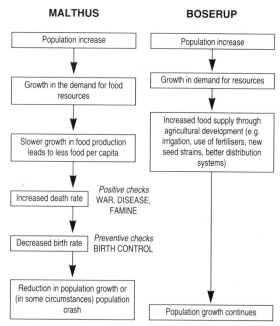

Fig. 6.10 A comparison between the Malthusian and Boserup views of the population: food resources equation

would achieve some sort of economic and ecological balance (Fig. 6.12).

3. The sooner such measures were introduced, the more chance there would be of success. An illustration of the situation as it would be if management policies were adopted in CE2000 is shown in Fig. 6.13.

A lot of discussion and little concerted international effort has taken place since 1972. Other major reports, such as the American government's 1982 study, *The Global 2000 Report to the President*, warned of the same scenario as that envisaged by the Club of Rome's worst case (Fig. 6.11) and pleaded for 'vigorous, determined new initiatives' if 'worsening poverty and human suffering, environmental degradation and international conflicts are to be prevented'. In other words, it argued for the rapid implementation of economic measures in order to avoid political problems, including wars.

Taking a more ecological view, the Brundtland Report of 1983 argued for an approach to resource usage much more balanced between economy and ecology. Mrs Gro Harlem Brundtland, the Prime Minister of Norway, reported to the Secretary General of the United Nations. Her commission was asked to investigate the major environmental problems that had begun to be noticed, such as changes in atmosphere, water supply, soil quality and numbers of plant and animal species. Her radical report showed a clear relationship between poverty in the developing world and global environmental problems. For example, peasants in Brazil were forced to add to the deforestation of Amazonia because they had few or no resources themselves. Workers in Mexico had little choice but to work in archaic and polluting factories because there were few alternative sources of employment. They could put no pressure on the management to change their conditions and had to suffer both long hours and noxious emissions. The Brundtland report argued for a change to economic systems, giving fairer treatment to raw material producers. Even more than that, it argued for a change in the management of 'global commons' (Antarctica, the oceans and space in particular). By stressing the importance of ecological balance making economic sense, it argued strongly for sustainable development policies to replace the present largely exploitative ones. It stated that there was a 'moral obligation' to use the earth's resources more wisely in future, 'to draw on

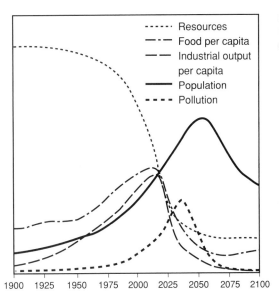

Fig. 6.11 The Club of Rome's worst case scenario

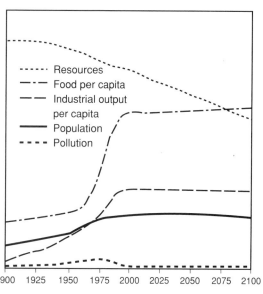

FIG 6.11   76x72 wide

Fig. 6.12 The Club of Rome's modified prediction for a stabilised situation

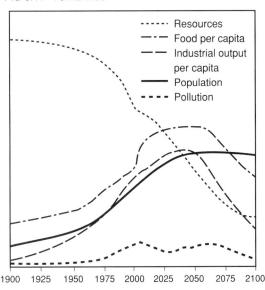

Fig. 6.13 What would happen if management measures were not taken until CE2000, according to the Club of Rome

197

the interest we can get from sustainable husbandry of its resources' rather than to use them as though they were a capital resource to be used up at will.

Despite all this, 'economic growth' remains one of the most important yardsticks by which countries are judged on the international scene. This tends to mean how effectively output is increased. 'Output' includes the value of agricultural produce, raw material, manufactured goods and services. 'Effectively' means how much paid effort is put into producing that output. In other words, economic growth is underpinned by the exploitation of resources, both in the traditional sense and on the human side of the equation. In this view, people are themselves seen as a resource and the aim is to use them as effectively as possible.

Resource dilemmas

 Many dilemmas are presented by the concept of economic growth. These are the subject of much debate and the view chosen governs the way in which resources are exploited in any area. Some of the dilemmas are illustrated below.

Dilemma One. Should the developing world copy the western industrial model of economic development?

Many countries have now passed through the 'exploitation' stage of resource utilisation. Examples would be the United Kingdom, where the widespread use of coal did so much to influence the beginnings of the Industrial Revolution, the Scandinavian countries, where coniferous timber was once used as a 'stock' resource but is now managed to provide future supplies, and Canada, where hydroelectric power is becoming much more important than that produced by the burning of fossil fuels. Such developed countries have come to see that careful resource management, not necessarily total protection, is vital both for the maintenance of supplies and the future health of the environment.

On the other hand, the efficient use of energy, the use of new forms of energy and high-technology production are both expensive and technologically demanding. Newly emerging countries, such as the North African states, have resources such as oil which they feel they have to exploit if they are to raise their living standards to those of the developed world. Between the developed nations to the north (Spain, France, Italy, etc.) and the developing nations to the south (Egypt, Libya, Tunisia, etc.) lies the Mediterranean Sea. This sea is already polluted by many years of unwise resource exploitation in Europe, yet those same countries are now attempting to control the development of resources on the other side of the sea, using the fragile ecosystem of those waters as the main bargaining plea. Needless to say, the countries of North Africa are not impressed by such arguments. Should they be allowed to go through the same stages of industrial development as the developed world, making their own mistakes, or not?

Dilemma Two. Should the developing world be more responsible in its use of resources?

The tropical rain forest has been identified as 'the green lung of the earth' by such workers as James Lovelock. It covers about 11% of the land surface of the earth, although that percentage is declining fast. The forest is currently being destroyed at a rapid rate. By the year 2000, it may well cover only 7% of the earth's surface and could have disappeared from some areas altogether.

The destruction of the forest has several causes. Some is cut down by local inhabitants for fuel wood, some to provide agricultural land. Some timber is cut down for export to industrial countries and some to make clearances for mining operations. Much forest in Brazil has been cleared to create pasture land for cattle, the carcasses of which are then processed and may end up as beefburgers in the developed world.

Despite these links between forest destruction in the developing world and industry in the developed world, a commonly held view in developed countries is that inhabitants of the developing world should know better than to destroy the forest. They should stop exploiting it and see it as a valuable resource whilst it is still growing, not as a collection of valuable commodities to be exploited. Since much of the destruction comes about as the result of necessity rather than ignorance or greed, however, should the developed world invest in tropical forest areas to remove the necessity for the local inhabitants to continue the destruction? In other words, should the forest inhabitants be paid to look after their environment rather than to exploit its constituent parts?

Fig. 6.14 A soap works in Sousse, Tunisia

Fig. 6.15 Stockpile buildings at the Trombetas bauxite mine, Brazil

Dilemma Three. Should industrial expansion be based on increased power production?

Resources which are used for creating electrical energy, such as coal, oil, natural gas, lignite and uranium, are all finite resources which are used up in order to create energy. In using them, noxious side effects are created, such as emissions from the burning of fossil fuels and radioactive waste from nuclear fuels.

Some people argue strongly that there is a clear alternative to the use of such energy sources. This is to use renewable energy sources such as sunlight, water, wind or wave power. The named resources are often claimed to be clean, non-polluting and, if used wisely, renewable. In September 1991, for example, National Wind Power (a company formed by National Power, British Aerospace and Taylor Woodrow) announced that it would build at least five new wind farms a year in the UK from 1992. This would be despite the fact that electricity generated would cost 4p per unit as opposed to 2p per unit from 'conventional' sources. It would have to depend on subsidies provided by the government's Non-Fossil Fuel Obligation (NFFO) fund in order to compete.

The dilemma over whether to produce what the industrialists see as clean, renewable energy (through hydroelectric power) or whether to put more onus on the users to be more energy efficient, is well illustrated by the La Grande hydroelectric power scheme in northern Quebec. By 1991, three stations had been build on La Grande River, producing between them 10 300 MW of electricity. These are some of the world's largest installed stations, LG2 (an underground facility) being half a kilometre long and 47 metres high.

The operating company, Hydro-Quebec, is now expanding the scheme to add a further six generating stations producing 5100 MW. On completion of these, the La Grande River will produce electricity at seven different sites. The next stage is the really contentious one. The Great Whale River 200 km to the north (see Fig. 6.17) is to be developed in a scheme which could mean that a quarter of all North America's hydroelectric power would be supplied from Quebec.

The building of three new generating stations, four new dams and the diversion of several rivers will necessitate the flooding of 3400 km^2 of land, the construction of new roads into the virgin territory presently occupied by the Inuit (Eskimo) and Cree Indians, and some drastic changes in river flow. These will affect the wildlife upon which the local inhabitants depend (salmon, char and fur-bearing animals such as the beaver). In addition, the change in water flow will lead to the leaching of mercury from the soil, a process which has already led to a total ban on fishing in the La Grande River reservoirs. Fresh, warm water flowing into Hudson Bay

Fig. 6.16 The La Grande 3 dam and hydroelectric power station

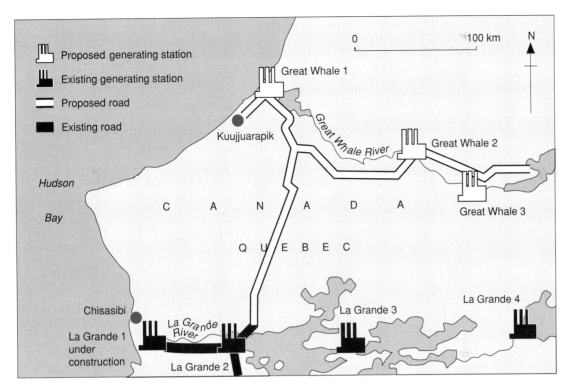

will also seriously affect winter ice formation, something which will be of serious consequence to the winter seal-hunting activities of the Inuit.

In order to make these building works economically viable, Hydro-Quebec has to sell the resulting electricity. It has entered into agreements with a number of US bodies, such as New York State, to supply them with electricity. Environmental pressure groups, however, spurred on by the recognition of some disastrous effects of the earlier La Grande scheme, have forced the prospective purchasers to think again. In New York, they have launched court cases aimed at holding up the progress of the project and have succeeded in getting the deadline for withdrawal from the 1000 MW agreement between New York Power and Hydro-Quebec extended by one year. They are pressing their case for greater energy efficiency in New York (and other potential users) which, they say, would remove the necessity for the scheme altogether.

Whereas no environmental assessment was made before the initial La Grande scheme was started, 180 people are now employed in Hydro-Quebec's environmental department. Changes have been made to the Great Whale scheme to protect the most environmentally sensitive tributaries, changes which mean that huge losses in potential revenue have been accepted.

Energy is wasted to a huge extent throughout the world. No new power generation sources would be needed for many years if conservation measures were taken. The pages on energy efficiency (pp. 202–3) include the advice recently given to householders in the UK by the Department of Energy. Should new industrial development be required to conform to higher standards of energy efficiency and should greater efforts be put into alternative energy production rather than the development of even more energy resources, even if they are 'environmentally friendly'?

The cost of producing electricity is high in the early stages of development of a resource, since research, development and installation (capital) costs have to be recovered. California currently has the largest installed capacity of wind turbine generation. It produced about 80% of the world total of 3.2bn kW h from its 15 000 wind turbines in 1990. It was able to do this because state legislation gave long-term contracts to wind farm developments and tax incentives to investors. Electricity supply companies also have to guarantee high prices to the wind generation companies who supply them, at least for the first ten years of their existence. The second highest producer, Denmark, has a different policy but is no less successful. Rural communities are encouraged to build their own generators on a co-operative basis and the installation is run for the benefit of the community.

Energy Efficiency

Some of the largest development schemes since 1970 have been those associated with the production of power. Many have involved the building of huge dams in environmentally sensitive areas and the flooding of vast areas. Most have been billed as 'multi-purpose schemes' since they also provide drinking water, improved communications, fisheries and irrigation water, but most have had the driving force of power production behind them.

Example: The Mahaweli Programme, Sri Lanka

The bare facts

- Commenced 1978.

- Three dams to be built across the Mahaweli river.

- Power stations to triple the country's production of energy.

- Irrigation of 120 000 hectares also planned.

- Required resettling of 1.5 million people.

- Financed partly by grants from the UK, Sweden and W. Germany.

- Other finance from commercial loans.

- Original estimate of cost = $8 billion.

- Last known cost = $14 billion.

The effects

To finance the spiralling costs, taxes have had to be raised, food subsidies cut and loan terms renegotiated. Profits largely went to the construction companies from the three 'donor' countries which were awarded the huge building contracts. The newly irrigated land was largely farmed on a commercial basis and brought few benefits to the local inhabitants. Indeed, many lost their land as it was flooded. They moved to small forested plots of land on the steep slopes away from the scheme, adding to the deforestation and inevitable soil erosion (which must eventually lead to silting of the lakes behind the new dams).

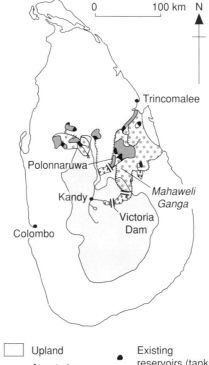

☐ Upland	● Existing reservoirs (tanks
⬚ Area to be irrigated	⊔⊔⊔ New channels
▨ Existing irrigated area	⬭ New reservoirs
	= Dams

Alternatives

There are several ways in which the necessity for large schemes could be removed.

A. ENVIRONMENTALLY SUITABLE SCHEMES

Wind power is environmentally more acceptable, but is this so from a visual perspective?

In the developing world, more appropriate energy supply could come from **biogas** development.

The waste products from animal production and human excreta are fermented in the tank, producing methane which powers lights and cookers for the village. Biogas generation is well developed throughout China. The used material goes to an outlet pit and can then be used as fertiliser. Amongst other 'appropriate' energy production schemes are mini hydro-power schemes, the growing of fuel wood and the use of solar power.

This 'wind farm' in California produces electricity without pollution – but does it improve the environment?

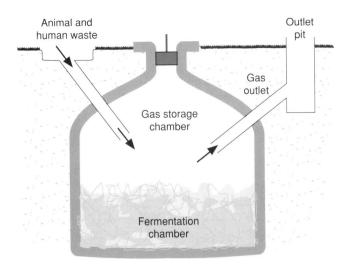

A biogas generator

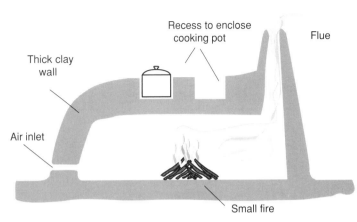

A fuel-efficient clay oven (cross section)

House A: UNINSULATED

No insulation

Boiler more than 10 years old.

Time switch

No draught-proofing and single glazing only

Total annual heating cost £497
CO_2 emissions 6300 kg/year

House B: TYPICAL

As house A except: 50mm loft insulation

25mm hot water cylinder insulation

25% double glazing

Room thermostat

Total annual heating cost £426
CO_2 emissions 5400 kg/year

House C: DESIRABLE

As house B except:

150mm loft insulation

80mm hot water cylinder insulation and thermostat

100% double glazing

Condensing boiler

Full draught-proofing

Thermostatic radiator valves

Wall insulation

Floor insulation

Total annual heating cost £150
CO_2 emissions 1900 kg/year

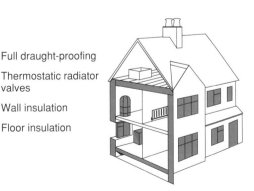

Source: HMSO

B. INSULATION

The reduction of heat and energy loss from cookers and houses, for example, would greatly reduce the necessity for the damaging 'big schemes'.

C. RECYCLING

The re-use of commodities such as aluminium would reduce the necessity to smelt new materials (see p. 210).

QUESTIONS

1 Investigate a recent large hydroelectric power development. Has it had a similar history to that of the Mahaweli scheme or was it more sensitively developed?
2 Conduct an insulation survey on a building known to you (the school or your house, for instance). To what extent could the energy efficiency be improved?
3 One of the greatest wasters of energy in the developed world is the automobile. List the ways in which more efficient use of transport could be made.
4 Write an essay entitled 'Energy efficiency begins at home'.

Fig. 6.18 These windmills in California rotate about a vertical axis

Fig. 6.19 The Akosombo Dam and power installations, Ghana

The United Kingdom is one of the windiest countries in the world, but its current target for renewable energy production is two per cent of the country's requirements by 2000 (including wave, geothermal, hydroelectric and landfill gas plants). One of the reasons for this is that there is some uncertainty over the generation of wind power from an environmental point of view. For example, an oil-fired power station occupies some 870 m² for every megawatt of electricity produced. A gas-fired station would occupy 1500 m² on the same basis, but a windpower station would need 1 700 000 m² to produce one megawatt of energy at the current level of technological knowledge. To create as much electrical energy from wind power as can be created from a large fossil fuel power station, huge areas of countryside would have to be covered with enormous windmills. These would create noise and visual pollution.

To develop the hydroelectric potential of the Volta river in Ghana, a tenth of the country was flooded. Other dams, for example in Ecuador, have necessitated the driving of roads through hitherto virgin territory. Once built, lakes have sometimes silted up very quickly (as in the case of Lake Nasser, impounded by the Aswan High Dam in Egypt) or have become breeding grounds for tropical insects and their associated diseases. Hydroelectric power schemes have even been accused of increasing the risk of earthquakes by putting extra pressure on the earth's surface in susceptible areas, such as northern India.

The counter argument is that we do not really need to produce as much electrical energy in any case, because we could save up to half our present consumption by such measures as effective double-glazing, recycling 'waste heat', the use of energy-efficient stoves, better use of public transport and many other such measures.

Dilemma Four. Should resources be used now or saved for later?

At one time, steam power was the most important motive force in industry. In order to produce steam, fossil fuels were burnt. Industry therefore flourished especially where coal was plentiful or where it could be obtained cheaply, as in south Wales.

Later, electricity took over and industry became less closely tied to coalfield locations. Now, modern assembly industries and high technology plants could be located almost anywhere. They are not tied to the resource which creates the power and are known as footloose industries. It is now more likely that computer industries will be located with respect to good climate for the work force (as in Silicon Valley, California) or high quality of life (as in Glenrothes, Scotland).

This sort of rapid change in both requirement for raw materials and location factors means that industrial development at one site can be transient. There is all the more encouragement, therefore, for countries or regions which have resources to exploit them whilst the conditions demanding those resources still exist. Countries such as Abu Dhabi and Kuwait produce vast amounts of oil which they are able to sell at relatively low prices while high levels of production occur.

Fig. 6.20 Llanwern steelworks, Newport, South Wales

Fig. 6.21 A new industrial park in 'Silicon Valley', California

205

They do so because, at any time, new producing areas might be found or new inventions lead to declining oil consumption. They are making the best of the present circumstances, even though pressure is put on them to husband their resources from an environmental or local economy point of view. On the other hand, producing countries could artificially raise prices by agreeing with others (such as members of OPEC) to cut production, a fact that would also prolong the life of the oilfields. One thing which stops this happening is the possibility that the resource being exploited might be substituted in the future. For example, Brazil already runs much of its road transport system on ethanol, made from sugar cane, instead of petrol. An even more radical threat to oil could come from electric vehicles.

Similar arguments could apply to minerals such as platinum. In 1991, the price of platinum plummeted (Fig. 6.22). Platinum, along with rhodium, is a principal constituent of catalytic converters, which help to reduce emissions from internal combustion engines. A market for it had been ensured by legislation in many countries which made catalytic converters compulsory. In May 1991, Nissan, a Japanese company, announced that it had invented a new converter which used palladium instead of platinum. Important platinum producing countries, such as South Africa and the Soviet Union, suffered badly as a result. Production of the new converters is not even certain, but the news has meant that platinum prices remain depressed, even after this fact has been realised.

There are many other examples of resources which have 'had their day': they spawned industry when in full production, but have been superseded by changes in technology or even fashion. Whaling settlements grew up all along the north-east coast of Canada to satisfy the demand for whale oil in the nineteenth century. Many are now ghost towns. The same applies to settlements in Amazonia devoted to the collection of natural rubber, tin-mining settlements around Dartmoor and coal-mining settlements in north-east France. Undoubtedly, new resources will be exploited in the future which will give life to new areas and take importance away from currently prosperous ones. This thought is one of the main drives behind the desire to get as much use from current resources as possible and acts against such things as a cut in oil production. Should short-term profit motives be allowed to govern the use of resources or should conservation measures be introduced?

QUESTION

6.11 Using all the resources provided and any case studies of resources exploitation you have studied, suggest how each of the following problems should be solved and how it could be funded.

(a) Should developing countries be free to exploit their own resources as they wish?

(b) How can peasants in developing countries be stopped from cutting down forests?

(c) Should 'alternative' power sources be used instead of fossil fuels?

(d) Should resources, which may only be in temporary demand, be exploited whilst they are valuable in world trade?

Trade v. Aid

It has been shown how the developed countries purchase raw materials at low prices, import them, often from developing countries, and then process them to create more valuable items. This is one of the contributary factors to the huge budget deficits of developing countries. They do not produce enough income to finance their required spending on the infrastructure and social services,

Fig. 6.22 Platinum – London morning price ($ an ounce)

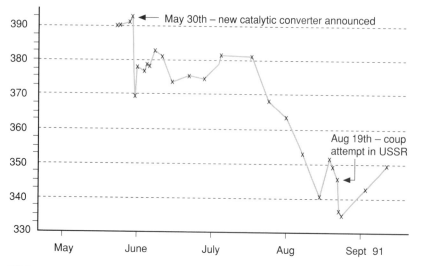

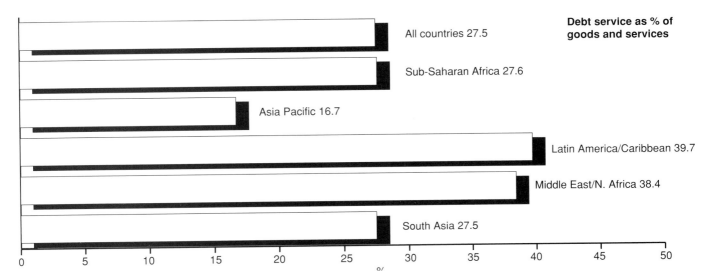

Debt service as % of goods and services

All countries 27.5

Sub-Saharan Africa 27.6

Asia Pacific 16.7

Latin America/Caribbean 39.7

Middle East/N. Africa 38.4

South Asia 27.5

%

Fig. 6.23 Debt service ratios 1989

for instance. The difference has to be made up in other ways, one of which is to borrow money. In doing so, they have to pay interest to meet the difference between what they sell and what they need to buy. This money comes from foreign governments, from international banks and even from commercial banks. Countries have to 'service' their debts (pay back capital and interest). One measure of the indebtedness of a country is its *debt service ratio*. This measures the relationship between interest and capital repayments and earnings from exports of goods and services that year. Figure 6.23 shows the debt service ratios for six world areas in 1989.

The present state of affairs with extremely high debt service ratios in some of the world's poorest countries, began to take shape in the 1970s. At that time, there was a major crisis in world oil production. The OPEC countries (Organisation of Petroleum Exporting Countries) raised the price of oil many times over in the early 1970s, partly by cutting back on production and partly by agreeing prices amongst themselves (a cartel agreement). This led to huge amounts of money suddenly finding its way into the world banking system as it was deposited by the oil producers. They spent a lot of this wealth on the building of new roads, buildings and industries in their countries, but to make the 'spare' money work for them, they also lent some to other countries. Many of the borrowing countries were developing nations which needed finance partly to pay their increased oil bills and partly to pay for expensive development schemes. If a person over-borrows and cannot repay the money, then that person can be declared bankrupt. The same could theoretically apply to a country, but if an entire nation were to be declared bankrupt, the world banking system would be called into question and massive instability would arise. Safe in this knowledge, the major banks often lent money unwisely, without ensuring that the recipient would be able to repay it. The aid receivers all too often spent this 'easy' money on huge and unwise 'development' programmes, new capital cities or major hydro-electric power schemes.

Interest rates rose sharply at the end of the 1970s and countries which had borrowed large amounts found the debt repayments rising. They often did not earn enough from exports to service their debts. Mexico was one of the first countries to face collapse because of this vicious spiral of debt (Fig. 6.24) and Jamaica was another (see p. 191). In the end, neither was allowed to collapse. Their debt was rescheduled, meaning that they were given longer to pay it off. Other ways in which the same problem has been solved in the past have included partial write-offs, exchanging debt for a 'share' in the country's wealth and selling the debt at a lower rate on the banking market. Since the 1980s, much greater care has been taken with borrowing and running up debts.

Trade is essential to the world economy. On the other hand, the above examples give a picture of why it can also be a very dangerous thing. It is not only the developing countries which face a trading problem. The United States of America, for example, had a trade deficit of minus $126 780 million in 1987–88, largely because its population insisted on buying imported consumer goods.

207

Trade

Source: The Economist: Vital World Statistics, 1990.

Agriculture	% of total exports	Textiles and clothing	% of total exports	Mining and quarrying	% of total exports	Manufacturing	% of total exports
1 Somalia	98.4	1 Macao	71.5	1 Libya	99.6	1 Bermuda	100.0
2 Mali	88.7	2 Bangladesh	70.8	2 Brunei	97.0	2 Japan	99.5
3 Burkina Faso	85.1	3 Pakistan	58.3	3 Saudi Arabia	96.0	3 Barbados	99.2
4 Sudan	83.6	4 Nepal	53.6	4 Congo	91.1	4 Macao	98.5
5 Madagascar	82.4	5 Benin	41.2	5 Angola	84.5	5 Austria	98.4
6 Burundi	81.5	6 Portugal	40.8	6 Gabon	83.1	6 Neth Antilles	98.2
7 Malawi	80.1	7 Malta	38.1	7 Niger	79.7	7 Malta	98.0
8 Tanzania	77.2	8 Hong Kong	37.5	8 Algeria	73.8	8 West Germany	98.0
9 Honduras	77.1	9 Uruguay	37.3	9 Bolivia	73.6	9 Sweden	97.7
10 Nicaragua	76.3	10 Greece	35.7	10 Bahamas	68.8	10 Italy	97.1

Most dependent on:

Source:
New Internationalist,
February 1990.

Largest deficits ($m)		Largest surpluses ($m)	
1 US	−126 180	1 Japan	79 590
2 UK	−26 015	2 West Germany	48 640
3 Australia	−11 218	3 Taiwan	17 925
4 Saudi Arabia	−9 583	4 South Korea	14 161
5 Canada	−8 330	5 Switzerland	8 326
6 Italy	−5 446	6 Netherlands	5 310
7 India	−5 192	7 Kuwait	4 713
8 Venezuela	−4 692	8 Belgium	3 379
9 China	−3 934	9 UAE	2 805
10 Spain	−3 783	10 Yugoslavia	2 489
11 Norway	−3 678	11 Hong Kong	1 890
12 France	−3 547	12 Malaysia	1 802
13 Finland	−2 998	13 Singapore	1 660
14 Mexico	−2 905	14 Turkey	1 500
15 Sweden	−2 549	15 Romania	1 408
16 Denmark	−1 828	16 East Germany	1 400
17 Thailand	−1 671	17 South Africa	1 272
18 Argentina	−1 615	18 Oman	851
19 Cuba	−1 588	19 Puerto Rico	751
20 USSR	−1 500	20 Panama	737

Source: The Economist: Vital World Statistics, 1990

WHERE IT GOES

Developed countries still have a virtual monopoly on world trade – a great deal of their wealth depends on it. The value of their manufactured exports is seven times greater than that of developing countries. The Eastern trading area includes all centrally planned economies – thus it includes countries like China and Vietnam which are more normally grouped with developing countries.

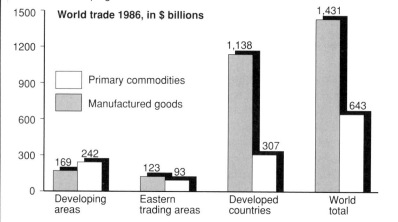

World trade 1986, in $ billions

WHO IT BENEFITS

The world divides clearly between countries that have got richer during the 1980s and those that have got poorer (measured by increases or falls in GDP). A total of 48 countries have been getting poorer during the 1980s – almost as many as those that have got richer.

The countries that have got richer, like South Korea or Malaysia, increasingly export manufactured goods for world markets, not primary commodities. Those that have got poorer, like Ethiopia and Zaire, are almost all totally dependent on the export of primary commodities.

	Number of countries with rising GDP per capita 1980–7	% of primary commodities to total exports 1987	Country examples
High-income countries	22	28	US, EC, Singapore
Upper-income countries	9	50	S. Korea, Brazil
Lower-income countries	14	50	Mauritius, Malaysia
Low-income countries	9	52	China, India, Pakistan
Total	54	42	

... and falling GDP

High-income countries	3	87	Saudi Arabia, Kuwait
Upper-income countries	5	76	Trinidad, Argentina
Lower-income countries	18	55	Guatemala, Chile
Low-income countries	22	86	Zaire, Mozambique
Total	48	74	

HOW IT GROWS

International trade has grown almost without interruption since the eighteenth century at least. Nearly always it grows faster than production. This is why it is sometimes called the 'engine of growth'. Only between the two World Wars, a period dominated by the Great Depression of the 1930s, did trade grow less fast than production. Rates of growth in trade today are much less spectacular than they were in the 1950s and 1960s, but trade still grows faster than production. This offers scope for new exporters to produce for world markets.

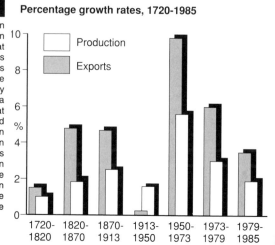

Percentage growth rates, 1720-1985

Aid

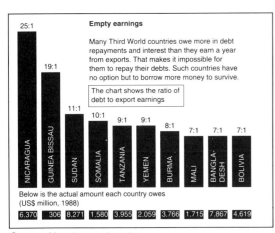

Empty earnings

Many Third World countries owe more in debt repayments and interest than they earn a year from exports. That makes it impossible for them to repay their debts. Such countries have no option but to borrow more money to survive.

The chart shows the ratio of debt to export earnings

Below is the actual amount each country owes (US$ million, 1988)

NICARAGUA	GUINEA BISSAU	SUDAN	SOMALIA	TANZANIA	YEMEN	BURMA	MALI	BANGLA-DESH	BOLIVIA
25:1	19:1	11:1	10:1	9:1	9:1	8:1	7:1	7:1	7:1
6,370	306	8,271	1,580	3,955	2,059	3,766	1,715	7,867	4,619

Source: New Internationalist

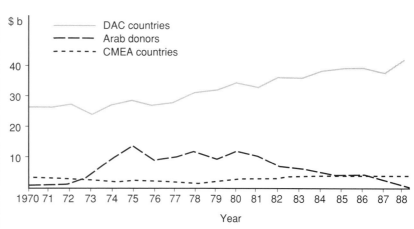

Aid by major donors ($bn, 1987 prices and exchange rates)

DAC = Development Assistance Committee, a group of OECD countries

CMEA = Council for Mutual Economic Assistance (mainly CIS)

(*Source*: The Economist: *Vital World Statistics*, 1990)

Western bonanza

	1982	1983	1984	1985	1986	Cumulative Totals (US$ billions) 5 years
Net total resource flows – official development finance, total export credits and private investments – from rich to poor countries	117.8	97.7	86.1	82.3	84.7	468.6
Total annual debt service bill – the amount of GNP spent on debt repayments – of developing countries	131.6	131.5	131.7	140.7	152.8	688.3
Net flows of money from poor to rich countries	13.8	33.8	45.6	58.4	68.1	219.7

Source: New Internationalist/OECD: Financing and External Debt of Developing countries, 1986 survey.

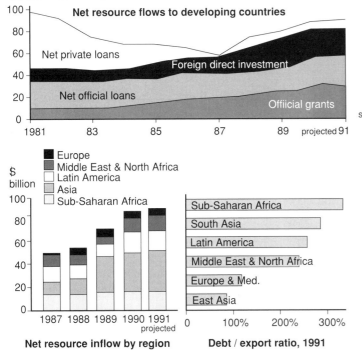

$ billion in constant prices

Net resource flows to developing countries

Net private loans

Foreign direct investment

Net official loans

Official grants

1981 83 85 87 89 projected 91

- Europe
- Middle East & North Africa
- Latin America
- Asia
- Sub-Saharan Africa

Net resource inflow by region

Sub-Saharan Africa
South Asia
Latin America
Middle East & North Africa
Europe & Med.
East Asia

Debt / export ratio, 1991

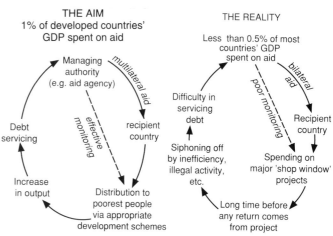

THE AIM
1% of developed countries' GDP spent on aid

Managing authority (e.g. aid agency) — multilateral aid — recipient country — Distribution to poorest people via appropriate development schemes — Increase in output — Debt servicing — effective monitoring

THE REALITY

Less than 0.5% of most countries' GDP spent on aid — bilateral aid — Recipient country — Spending on major 'shop window' projects — Long time before any return comes from project — Siphoning off by inefficiency, illegal activity, etc. — Difficulty in servicing debt — poor monitoring

Source: The *Economist: Vital World Statistics, 1990.*

EXERCISE
Write an essay entitled 'Critically evaluate the statement that Trade, not Aid, will lead to true development'.

On the other hand, aid can also be dangerous. It was aid which helped to place Mexico and Jamaica in such repayment problems. Food aid, which can flood a market with cheap grain, for example, can lead to the collapse of local farming, as has been the case following natural disasters in Ethiopia and Bangladesh. The people can come to rely solely on aid unless it is planned carefully. The right development path must therefore balance a sustainable trading

policy with a prudent aid programme. Some of the factors which govern trade and aid and the results springing from them are shown on pp. 208–9.

Oil price rise (early 1970s)
OPEC countries earn vast amounts of money
Money paid into banks
Banks lend to developing countries
Huge development schemes financed
Debt repayments increase
Developing countries cannot service debt
Rescheduling, or futher loans taken out
Crop failure or fall in commodity prices mean debt cannot be repaid
Further indebtedness

Fig. 6.24 The vicious spiral of debt

QUESTIONS

6.12 **(a)** What is meant by the term 'debt service'?

(b) Where are the debt service ratios worst? Why do you think this is the case?

(c) In what ways can debt repayment be relaxed?

6.13 To what extent do you think that fairer trading conditions would enable more rapid growth in the economies of the developing countries?

6.14 Read pp. 208–9 on Trade and Aid and collect further information on:
- GATT (the General Agreement on Tariff and Trade)
- trading blocs (e.g. the European Community, EFTA – European Free Trade Area)
- import tariffs
- contra-deals (including bartering).

Choose one of the subjects you have researched and
(a) explain the term;
(b) show why it is important to any one country or area.

Problem-Solving Exercises

A. Aluminium recycling

The information provided in Figs. 6.25 to 6.34 should be read before attempting the following exercise.

Figure 6.25 presents data on the conservative assumption that a quarter of what is currently thrown away by households in the UK is easily recoverable. At present rates of usage, this would mean that 175 kg per household per year could be recovered with some ease. Nationally, this would mean that 3.5 million tonnes of waste would no longer be buried or incinerated. It would be used

instead as raw material for industry, cutting down on excessive dumping and incineration. It would benefit the UK financially and the world from the point of view of resource conservation. Further study of one constituent of the waste, however, reveals many more issues associated with recycling.

Aluminium recycling
Aluminium is produced by refining bauxite, a material found in soils developed in hot climates with alternate wet and dry periods. One of the largest deposits currently being worked is in Amazonia, around the Trombetas

A

Weight of UK household dustbin waste (excl. civic amenity waste)	14 million tonnes/yr
No. of households in UK	20 million
Wt. of waste per house per year	700 kg
If just 25% potentially recoverable	175 kg/house/yr

B Estimated weight contribution of recyclables

	kg/household/yr
Paper and board	90
Plastics (bottles)	12
Plastics (film)	5
Glass	40
Ferrous metals	20
Aluminium metal	2
Textiles/rags	6
TOTAL	175

Fig. 6.25 Waste in the UK

Fig. 6.26 Current production of bauxite

Country	Bauxite production* (000 t)		
	1988	1989	1990
France	978	720	560
Greece	2 533	2 576	2 610
Yugoslavia	3 034	3 252	2 950
Other Europe	20	12	10
Total Europe	**6 565**	**6 560**	**6 130**
Guinea	16 800	17 500	18 000
Sierra Leone	1 403	1 548	1 450
Other Africa	291	387	390
Total Europe	**18 494**	**19 435**	**19 840**
Total North America	**588**	**670**	**500**
Brazil	7 728	7 894	8500
Guyana	1 774	1 340	1 600
Jamaica	7 408	9 395	10 940
Surinam	3 434	3 530	3 300
Other Latin America	718	866	980
Total Latin America	**21 062**	**23 025**	**25 320**
India	3 829	4 345	4 900
Other Asia	1 239	1 881	1 820
Total Asia	**5 068**	**6 226**	**6 720**
Total Oceania	**36 370**	**38 583**	**40 260**
Total World	**88 147**	**94 499**	**98 770**

* World excluding Soviet Bloc (CMEA) and China (PRC)

river. As Fig. 6.26 demonstrates, much of the current production of bauxite is in developing countries. Since the production of aluminium involves large amounts of electrical energy (Fig. 6.27), relatively cheap and reliable sources of power are sought. It was for aluminium smelting that the dams and hydroelectric power schemes at Kitimat in British Columbia, Canada and Akosombo, Ghana were principally designed. In the latter case, although Ghana does have some bauxite, most of the raw material needed was imported from Jamaica before being refined and re-exported as aluminium ingots to the United States of America. Consequently, little value was added to the economy in Ghana from mining or manufacturing.

Although the input of energy to produce alumina from bauxite is very high (150 million kilowatt hours per 900 tonnes of alumina), it may not be as expensive as it seems in the first place. The energy used is usually renewable (HEP), which is cheap and environmentally friendly (if the effects of the dam and the lake are ignored for the time being). The conversion factor of energy to power is 90% for HEP, whereas fossil fuels convert to energy at a factor of about 35%. It is even cheaper if the costs of re-smelting scrap are considered. Based on a cradle-to-grave analysis of costs, aluminium is a very cost-effective material for packaging, or would be if it were recycled more efficiently. It takes only 5% of the energy required to turn bauxite into aluminium, to turn used beverage cans (UBCs) into aluminium, and there is no limit to the number of times recycling can take place.

Stage	Process	Product	Location
Bauxite mining	Open-cast mining	BAUXITE	Largely tropical countries
Refining	Chemical process using coke, starch, caustic soda, water, limestone and power	ALUMINA	Coastal, often in cooler areas
Smelting	Electrolysis	ALUMINIUM	Near sources of cheap power
Fabrication	Manufacture	ALUMINIUM ARTICLES	Developed world

Fig. 6.27 Stages in the production of aluminium

Fig. 6.28 Recycling depends on consumers putting their waste in separate bins

Fig. 6.29 Aluminium cans – the facts

1. It takes the equivalent of two and a half litres of petrol to manufacture one aluminium can (starting from raw materials).
2. Currently, less than one-third of the world production of aluminium comes from scrap.
3. Since aluminium recycling began in the USA 20 years ago, 415 billion cans weighing 190 million tonnes have been recycled, earning collectors about $5 billion.
4. The UK aluminium beverage can market exceeded 125 000 tonnes in 1990 (4230 million cans, up 10.4% on 1989).
5. The USA aluminium beverage can market exceeded 86 billion cans in 1990.
6. More than 60% of the UBCs in the USA were recycled in 1990.
7. USA recycling centres employed some 30 000 people in 1990.
9. Over half the beverage cans sold in the UK are made of aluminium (56.4%).
10. In 1990, there were 1200 aluminium can recovery centres in the UK and 19 000 registered aluminium can recycling groups.

Fig. 6.30 The position of aluminium in packaging according to Alcoa (Reuters, 11.3.91)

The position of aluminium in packaging

Aluminium in packaging has a wide range of applications, for example foil-wrap, TV dinner plates, drinks cans, bottle closures and aerosols. The advantages of using aluminium are equally wide-ranging such as excellent barrier features against light, air and water for sensitive food and medical products, light-weight, easily decorated, quick chilling and strong for many food and drinks applications. Manufacturers shipping their products over long distances certainly benefit from energy and cost savings.

The use of aluminium in modern packaging, to facilitate the use of modern distribution and retail systems and to satisfy the demands of today's discriminating consumer is essential and indispensable. It is furthermore increasingly being recognised that the convenience benefits which aluminium offers do not have to be paid for by the environment. Far from being an environmental problem, recyclable aluminium is recognised as being part of the solution.

The essential good waste management components of reduction and recycling have been practised and developed by the aluminium industry for many more years than the 'green' organisations have been fashionable. When full, objective 'cradle to grave' ecological evaluations of products for suitability for packaging are carried out, it must be recognised that aluminium offers many environmental benefits.

British Alcan Aluminium will have to import large quantities of scrap aluminium cans from around the world to meet a shortage in domestic supplies for its new recycling works being built near Warrington.

The 50 000 tonne per year plant, being built at a cost of £28 million at Latchford Locks, is expected to come on stream in October next year. But the total quantity of aluminium cans recycled in the UK each year is only sufficient to keep this plant operating at one-tenth of its full capacity.

Just 5000 tonnes of the 50 000 tonnes of aluminium cans used in the UK each year are currently recycled.

Aluminium collection schemes supported by British Alcan around the country have so far been slow to take off. Until the tonnages collected are significantly increased it will be necessary to import large quantities of scrap to keep the furnaces operating at full tilt, says British Alcan's chief executive Doug Ritchie.

As a whole, the UK imports around 250 000 tonnes of aluminium a year.

Ritchie hopes the new plant will provide an incentive for can producers to install more aluminium rather than steel can-making facilities. But it will also save British Alcan money since recycling uses only 5% of the energy required to produce aluminium originally.

Aluminium – Europe follows US lead on can recycling

by Stephen Hays

London, March 13, Reuter – The recycling of aluminium drink cans is increasing rapidly in Western Europe. But Europeans still lag far behind the US.

A recycling trade group said Americans consumed more drink cans than the rest of the world put together in 1990 and a record 55 billion used beverage cans (UBCs), or over 60% of all cans used, were recycled, saving a huge amount of energy. This equals about 900 000 tonnes of aluminium, dwarfing the 'green' effort in Western Europe, where it is said 26 000 to 27 000 tonnes of aluminium were recycled from drink cans last year.

But the recycling rate in Western Europe rose to 20% of all aluminium UBCs in 1990, from 16% in 1989 and less than 10% in 1987, said Alexander Wirtz, general manager of the Aluminium Can Recycling Association (ACRA). The association was formed in the early 1980s from five leading aluminium groups – Alcan Aluminium Ltd, Aluminium Co of America (ALCOA), Reynolds Metals Co, Pechiney and Vaw Vereinigte Aluminium-Werke AG (VAW).

'The US has had more than 20 years to achieve its current level of recycling. We have been around for a far shorter period,' Wirtz said. 'But (we) believe that a 50% recycling rate in Western Europe is feasible,' Wirtz added.

The production of aluminium is extremely energy intensive. To produce one tonne from scrap requires only 5% of the energy needed to produce a tonne of primary aluminium. Some analysts estimate energy saved in the US in 1990 from aluminium recycling represented more than 20 million barrels of oil. About 96% of US beverage cans are made of aluminium and more than a third of all US aluminium scrap is now recovered in UBC form under a 'buy back' system, metal broker Billiton-Enthoven said in its latest aluminium market report.

The structure of the West European market means that it is unlikely that UBCs will become as prominent in secondary aluminium supply. But the ACRA said there is potential for a large rise in recovered metal from this source.

For example, in Britain, which accounts for over 40% of all drink cans consumed in the region, the ACRA began promoting aluminium recycling only 18 months ago. During the fourth quarter of 1990 the rate of aluminium UBC recycling broke through the 10% barrier, realising some 4000 tonnes of metal for the year. Recycling rose as aluminium overtook its rival tinplate in drink can production and achieved a 56.4% share of the UK's 7.5 billion UBC market in 1990 against 41.4% in 1989. The sharp increase in aluminium's use in UBCs in Britain occurred as the total drink can market expanded by over 10% last year, and is due mainly to the start-up of new large aluminium can-filling facilities at Wakefield (1.2 billions cans a year) and Rugby (1.5 billion cans) by two of the UK's largest drink firms, Coca Cola and Britvic. Spokesmen from both companies said that they had no preference for either aluminium or tinplate. But one can-filler said that his company had weight limitations on his 700 trucks and that by reducing the proportion of steel tinplate in exchange for lighter aluminium cans, he could take 50 trucks off the road and avoid putting 11.600 tonnes of carbon dioxide into the air a year.

(continued)

Fig. 6.32

Fig. 6.32 (*cont*)

ACRA has informed the UK's Department of Trade and Industry that it aims for a 50% recycling rate by 1995. In anticipation of this growth in supply, British Alcan Aluminium has invested £28 million in a 50 000-tonne-a-year capacity UBC recycling plant at Warrington. It is due to start up in October.

If this rate of increase is maintained, Britain will soon pass Sweden, which, based on ACRA data, now recovers the largest quantity of aluminium from UBCs in Western Europe. It has an extremely high recycling rate of 82% though its total drink can market is around one eighth of Britain's. All UBCs in Sweden are fabricated from aluminium and the Swedes recovered 12 900 tonnes of the metal from the cans in 1989 through their successful voluntary deposit system.

In the UK some 19 000 registered aluminium can recycling groups receive payment for cans recovered.

It is the relatively high inherent value of the aluminium can metal – more than 20 times higher than some competing materials – that makes it pay to divert it from other waste. But in Germany, the second largest UBC market in Western Europe after Britain (about 3.8 billion cans a year), the aluminium industry finds it extremely difficult to achieve market penetration and a critical mass for recycling because of the emphasis on refillable glass bottles, Wirtz said. In 1990 the German government issued a directive that the market share for refillable drink containers must be held stable at 72% versus 28% for 'one-way' or recyclable packages. Furthermore, aluminium in Germany has only a 15% market share in drink cans compared to tinplate – which despite its low scrap value is generally recycled because of the German authorities' insistence on integrated waste management.

The recycling ethic looks set to spread further in Western Europe in future, through EC commission backing. The commission has put its weight behind a new draft proposal for member states to increase their recycling of total packaging waste from the current 20% to 60% and reduce the total volume of packaging by 10%. The timeframe for this has yet to be decided.

Fig. 6.33 Aluminium can recycling in Europe

Country	Annual growth (tonnes)			
	1987	1988	1989	1990
United Kingdom	290	500	1 200	4000 min.
Ireland	—	10	65	NA
Austria	—	45	440	NA
Switzerland	300	350	500	NA
Italy	230	660	1 980	NA
Greece	650	1 000	1 500	NA
Sweden	11 000	11 700	12 900	NA
Others	300	535	695	NA
Total	12 800	14 800	19 280	26 000 /27 000
% of consumption	<10	13	16	20

Fig. 6.34 *Financial Times,* 11.9.91

Aluminium gets top marks for publicity

Kenneth Gooding looks at Greek ideas on recycling

Beaming bright-eyed children are talking about the environment. The captivating moment is captured by cameras from three television channels.

The children explain how they collect and sell used aluminium cans, not only to reduce waste and litter but also for the money which buys extra equipment for their school.

The setting is the island of Skyros where the mayor is hosting celebrations to mark Greece's National Aluminium Recycling Day.

It is one more coup in the aluminium industry's campaign to promote the idea that it produces "green" or environmentally friendly packaging. In the propaganda war the aluminium companies are leaving the steel can makers, their main rivals in the fizzy drinks packaging business, well behind.

Later in the day the children play and distribute leaflets about aluminium can recycling as Skyros' mayor makes a speech and introduces 11 other people, mainly local politicians, who also want to have their say.

Like the 17 mayors from other municipalities who have travelled to the island, half an hour's flight north of Athens, the politicians have had to do their homework. By now they are fully aware of the benefits claimed for aluminium cans: that aluminium is particularly suitable for recycling because it can be melted down into new metal again and again without loss of quality; that up to 95 per cent of the energy used in the production of primary aluminium is saved during the remelting process because the original energy invested is

preserved in the metal; and so on.

The idea of linking pictures of happy children with a product or campaign is not original. But the Aluminium Association of Greece also used its national aluminium recycling day for an innovation: it gathered top executives from the aluminium industry and senior members of the European Commission for a colloquium and exchange of ideas. The industry put its point of view, the Brussels bureaucrats explained EC ideas about such matters as recycling, packaging, waste management, education, energy and taxation – all topics in which the aluminium industry has a vested interest. The Greek Aluminium Association started its can recycling campaign as recently as 1986. In that year 22m cans were recycled. In 1990 the total was up to 110m. Today 24 municipalities in Greece and four communities are running aluminium recycling projects. The association also gained Ministry of Education approval to take the campaign into the schools and now has more than 400 elementary and high schools on its list. It provides information material and technical equipment and keeps in constant touch with teachers and parents associations.

The Greek armed forces also have aluminium can recycling programmes. For example, special containers for collecting cans have been placed on all the Greek Navy's vessels and in Navy training camps.

The Greek association has been able to draw heavily on the experience of the Aluminium Can Recycling Association (Acra), set up to promote the concept

Europe's recycling rate lags that in China, Hong Kong and Korea, where 90 per cent of used beverage cans are collected and re-used

throughout Europe by some of the world's biggest producers: Alcan of Canada, two US groups, Alcoa and Reynolds, Pechiney of France and VAW of Germany.

These producers are providing money not only to promote aluminium can recycling but also to help put the necessary collection infrastructure in place.

They have good commercial reasons for doing so. Not only does recycling cut their costs, Europe needs the metal. What used to be called western Europe consumed

4.6m tonnes of primary aluminium in various products last year while production in the region provided only 3.6m tonnes.

Because it takes so much energy to produce primary aluminium, output of the metal in Europe is expected, at best, to stabilise and might even fall even though consumption is showing a healthy rate of growth. The industry is putting its new production plants in areas outside Europe where energy is cheap. Already 61 per cent of the energy needed to make primary aluminium in the western world comes from hydro-electric power – which the industry constantly reminds customers is an inexhaustible and environmentally acceptable type of power.

Aluminium recycling is already well-established in Europe. About 80 per cent of aluminium used in building and more than 90 per cent used in transport components is recycled. By these standards the can business is not doing particularly well because the industry estimates that by the end of last year its

recycling rate was running at about 20 per cent. However, this brought in 25 000 tonnes of used aluminium cans.

Europe's recycling rate lags that in China, where 90 per cent of used beverage cans are collected and re-used. Hong Kong and South Korea also achieve 90 per cent, and more than 60 per cent of aluminium cans are recycled in the US and Australia.

Europe is doing its best to catch up. Recycling rates are growing by 25 per cent a year and events like Greece's recycling day should increase public awareness. The industry is certain that by 1995 at least half of all aluminium cans sold in Europe will be recycled.

It also expects that the efforts to promote recycling will have another spin-off – aluminium's share of the beverage can market will increase even further and that Europe might even follow the US example. More than 95 per cent of the 90bn cans of beers and soft drinks sold in the US each year are made of aluminium – and that uses a lot of metal.

QUESTIONS

6.15 Why might aluminium be preferred to steel as a material for making cans?

6.16 Why is recycling aluminium a better use of energy than producing it from bauxite?

6.17 What would be the consequences for a country such as Jamaica if user countries all introduced efficient recycling programmes?

6.18 Why is recycling currently not carried out to any great extent in the United Kingdom?

6.19 What role have the following played in the promotion of greater recycling of aluminium?

  (a) the producers (Alcan, Alcoa, etc.)

  (b) governments

  (c) consumer pressure

  (d) financial incentives?

6.20 How might an efficient aluminium recycling programme be organised? Try to think how the following might play a part in such a programme:

  education, organisation of refuse collection, encouragement of industry,

informing consumers of the results.

6.21 Write an article for a packaging industry magazine, making the case for better recycling of aluminium, and UBCs in particular, in the UK. You could offer suggestions about how industry and households could be supported by government and business in their desire to recycle more cans.

6.22 How would an increase in world recycling of aluminium affect countries such as Ghana? Do developed countries which increase their recycling capacity have any obligations to help with economic problems caused by the drop in demand for either raw materials or smelting expertise in the developing world?

6.23 Collect information about other recycling schemes and look out for any good ideas that could be applied to such large-scale schemes as national aluminium recycling projects.

B. Eco-tourism

The previous items under the heading 'A global action plan' may seem to concern large bodies of people or decisions that will be made without reference to individuals. Is there anything that the *individual* can do to contribute to the more sustainable use of the world's resources?

One of the fastest growing industries throughout the world, and one which provides a large part of the income for many developing countries, is tourism. There are two faces to the tourist industry, however. On one side, it generates much needed capital and improves living standards. On the other, it threatens the environment by which people have been attracted in the first place. The following information presents a glimpse of the two faces of tourism.

Fig. 6.35 The influence of tourism on a Third World location

THE GOOD SIDE	THE BAD SIDE
1. INFRASTRUCTURE IMPROVED Airport, main roads, water supply, electricity supply improved.	DISPARITIES CREATED Tourist areas tend to have better infrastructure than rest of country.
2. INCOME FROM TOURISM Fed into local economy, boosting agriculture and cottage industry.	MUCH OF VALUE DIVERTED The organising company (and country) derives much of the real profit.
3. INCREASE IN EMPLOYMENT Training is introduced especially in hotel and catering work and industries such as those producing tourist items increase.	LOW-LEVEL EMPLOYMENT Many of the jobs created are in serving capacities.
4. EXPOSURE TO DIFFERENT IDEAS Tourists bring with them different ideas and ways of doing things.	RESENTMENT Locals may resent the wealth of the tourists.
5. TOURISM ACTS AS 'GROWTH POLE' New hotel complexes, etc., act as stimuli for improving infrastructure, agriculture, industry, education, etc., improving the standard of living.	ENVIRONMENTAL PROBLEMS Tourists arrive expecting unspoilt beaches, natural vegetation, rich fauna, clean air, etc. If too many tourists arrive, all these are degraded.

Fig. 6.36 People of a hill tribe in northern Thailand selling tourist items

The World of Tourists

The unattractive side of tourism is more than just a nuisance: the implications are very serious, especially when you bear in mind that international tourism is still only at the fledgling stage. The British are actually some of the world's most enthusiastic travellers, with 60 per cent or more of the population enjoying at least one holiday a year and with a third of these holidays being spent abroad. Perhaps the fact that we live on an island has something to do with it. At any rate some of our more land-locked European neighbours are much more content to stay at home. Fewer than 50 per cent of Austrians take any holiday at all and only one in five travel abroad. The French take only one-third as many foreign holidays as the British and, surprisingly, only 6 per cent of North Americans travel abroad; even then half of these trips are to neighbouring Mexico or Canada. Japan, too, has great potential for a future massive contribution to the tourist population. At the moment there are around nine million Japanese tourist trips abroad each year compared with thirty million British tourist trips. If the Japanese travelled in the same proportion as we do there would be over sixty million trips abroad each year. It is only a matter of time before the Chinese and Eastern Europeans start travelling. Think of the problems then! If we have a tourist problem now, what will happen when these major nations begin to realise their full tourist potential?

Of course it is not simply a question of numbers but more a question of the demands which large numbers of tourists from developed economies in North America, Europe, Japan and Australasia place on locations and countries incapable of sustaining or carrying such volume. All of us expect a reasonable standard of accommodation: good food, fresh and clean water, plenty of things to do and the opportunity to move around a bit in a quick and comfortable manner. And all this at a reasonably affordable cost. The most economical way of doing this – and very successful it is too in terms of stimulating the business – is to employ the methods common to all big business. Market the product, advertise, create a demand and attract sufficient numbers of people so that the economies of scale make the whole thing reasonably affordable. Aim for quantity and the rest will follow.

The Good Tourist

To define what makes a 'good tourist' …
The most common simile used in this context is that of the 'host' and 'guest'. Giving the tourist the status of a guest is useful in that it puts the onus for good manners and assimilation with the norm squarely on the tourist. Specifically then, a 'good tourist', like a 'good guest in your home' will:

– respond and adapt to the ways of life and customs of the other environment or country. Put simply, 'when in Rome, do as the Romans do'.
– act in a responsible and sensitive manner towards the people, culture and physical environment.
– not seek to exploit any economic advantage he or she has which diminishes the standing of the host.
– leave any place visited in at least as healthy a state as when he or she first arrived and, if possible when visiting an area of deprivation, leave a practical thank you as a lasting memento of your visit.

Unless tourists behave responsibly and use their enormous economic influence to encourage the tourist industry to do likewise, then in time, inevitably, the quality of the tourist experience will be diminished for all.

The Environmental Issue

The strains of such development can be great. Not only do cultural values become undermined but the physical environment also suffers abuse as short-term economic goals, whether of governments or private investors, overrides the long-term best interests or air, land and water. Many Mediterranean resorts have such a major sewage disposal problem that beach pollution defies even international sanitation schemes, resulting in incidents such as the 1988 typhoid scare in the Spanish resort of Salou. Constant demand can

Fig. 6.37 The good tourist: extracts from *The Good Tourist* by Katie Wood and Syd House (Mandarin, 1991)

Fig. 6.38 Silk weaving in Chieng Mai, N. Thailand

217

Fig. 6.38 (*cont*)

place an intolerable strain on natural resources if resorts try to develop beyond their environmental carrying capacity. The ever-increasing popularity and availability of skiing holidays has damaged large parts of the Alps through inappropriate development and has exacerbated the damage to Alpine forests attributed to acid rain as trees are cleared to make way for extended ski-runs. The Lake District, one of Britain's most outstanding areas of natural beauty and a tourist attraction that draws many overseas visitors to this country, is now suffering considerable erosion as the soil and natural vegetation is walked away by thousands of feet every year. Such examples underline the complicated nature of many of these issues.

Is all tourist development bad? Should international tourism be restricted? Can we, or should we interfere in areas where people's livelihood is dependent upon tourists and visitors? Is it fair that in order to create a high material standard of living we in the developed world, having exploited our environment and resources, should say to 'underdeveloped' countries such as the Caribbean nations, Thailand and Indonesia, that they should not follow our example but should 'enjoy' only small-scale development without the benefits of large gains in economic growth? The answers are not easy to find and they may change over time. Nevertheless it is essential to seek a balance between enjoyment of the natural and cultural resources of any area, town or country, and the protection and conservation of those very resources for future generations to enjoy.

The other side of the equation contains those positive elements of tourism so eloquently pushed by the proponents of the industry in the early days of mass tourism. Travel 'broadened the mind', 'broke down frontiers' between previously hostile and suspicious neighbouring countries and 'provided jobs and economic growth' in a variety of areas and business sectors. And why not? 'Tourism has become the noblest instrument of this century for achieving international understanding' commented one writer in the early 1960s.

Austria	100.3	Italy	212.1
Belgium	301.9	Netherlands	182.1
Denmark	433.4	Norway	296.9
Finland	160.4	Portugal	209.5
France	215.9	Spain	380.0
W. Germany	126.1	Sweden	241.7
Greece	219.4	Switzerland	810.9
Ireland	231.7	UK	179.7

Fig. 6.39 Tourism receipts per head in Europe, 1987 ($US)

Fig. 6.40 Some of the most sensitive environments in Europe

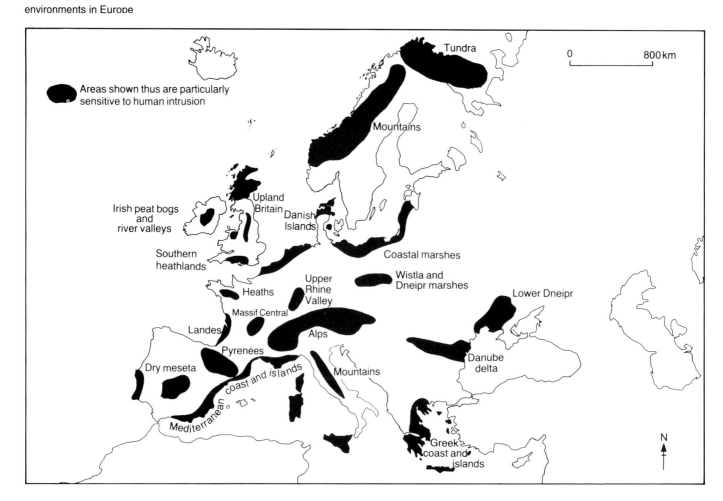

Fig. 6.41

A Traveller's Guide to Green Tourism

Introduction

This pocket-sized guide is intended to help the traveller to take account of a whole range of environmental issues in the planning, travelling and enjoyment of a holiday.

It is a guide of good practice which should enable the visitor to make an effective contribution to the goal of a more sustainable and environmentally friendly holiday. Above all remember when you visit a foreign country to act as a guest not a customer. By respecting local customs and cultures and showing friendship to local people you will be helping to forge lasting harmony between peoples.

Dick Sisman
Chairman GREEN FLAG INTERNATIONAL

Holiday Preparation and Planning

- Take time to learn in advance about the places you intend to visit. Learn a few words and phrases of the language – if only "please" and "thank you". You will find that even the smallest of pleasantries receives a generous response and a little knowledge of culture and natural history will enhance your experience. Find out about the food of the area – try to cook some local dishes yourself before you go!

- Consider what to take with you. There are some simple tips which make an enormous difference to the effect you have whilst abroad. For example, remove the wrapping of packaged goods and new clothes before you leave. Waste disposal in many countries is far less effective than ours. Unwrap soaps, take bottles out of boxes and where possible substitute paper for plastic.

- Only take environmentally friendly detergents and shampoos for hand washing and hair washing. This will help to keep water supplies, rivers, streams and the sea free from pollution. Ensure that sun creams and lotions are environmentally friendly – have you seen the awful film of sun oils on some swimming pools?

- Choose natural oils and other skin preparations for body protection, buying natural products can help a third world economy.

- Take a camera to record plants and animals seen. Never be tempted to bring back living material.

- Take time to think about your holiday plans. Why am I taking this particular holiday? Are there ways in which I can make some contribution to the environment when I am abroad? What new experiences and skills will my holiday give me? Holiday planning should include the consideration of the effect of your visit, especially in the world's most beautiful places.

- Look at the environmental content of brochures. Try to travel with a company that shows that it has taken account of environmental issues in putting together holiday programmes. A number of companies now assist conservation projects at destinations. Seek these out and let the company know that you have chosen to travel with them because of their environmental policies. This will encourage more companies to follow suit.

- Take a few small gifts from your home country; if you then find yourself receiving local hospitality you will be able to reciprocate.

QUESTIONS

6.24 Using the examples given, or others known to you, write a list of the possible advantages and disadvantages of developing tourism in a Third World country which has a sensitive evironment.

6.25 Use the statistics on tourist receipts per head in Europe, 1987 (Fig. 6.39) to construct a suitable map to show the relative development of the industry throughout the continent.

6.26 Describe the patterns revealed by your map.

6.27 Explain any concentrations of tourist receipts you have found.

6.28 Referring to Fig. 6.40, describe the areas of Europe that are most threatened by tourist development by comparing the map drawn in answer to question 6.25 with the location of sensitive environments.

6.29 Green Flag International is a body which promotes 'good tourism'. In particular, it establishes and helps conservation projects at tourist destinations. In 1990, it produced a leaflet entitled *A Traveller's Guide to Green Tourism*. This set out a number of points about Holiday Preparation and Planning, On Holiday, Travelling and Arriving Home. The leaflet was intended to help tourists adapt to their holiday destination and do as little damage as possible whilst there. Figure 6.41 gives an idea of some of the points it made. Study the data in Figs. 6.35 to 6.41 and produce your own 'Traveller's Guide to Good Tourism', making at least four suggestions under each of the headings mentioned.

 Whilst on holiday, tourists usually take a large number of photographs. This is so that they can report back to their friends at a later date, but it can have a very intrusive effect on the people being photographed.

QUESTIONS

6.30 Look at the cartoons (Fig. 6.42) and comment on the intrusive effects photography can have.

6.31 Make six suggestions about how photography in tourist areas could be more sensitive than it is at the moment.

The blatantly 'stolen' photograh.

The photograph 'stolen' at long distance.

How would I feel if she took a photograph of me in a demeaning situation?

Fig. 6.42 The intrusive effects of photography

Fig. 6.43 Should this photograph have been taken?

Appendix

This section briefly outlines various techniques that can be used to tackle the questions in this book. To provide as comprehensive a coverage as possible, any relevant formulae are first provided, followed by an explanation of terms, together with hints on their application.

1. The data set

Analysing the data set is an important element in this book. There are various relevant techniques, some of which are described here.

Measures of central tendency

Mean   the 'average' of everyday speech. To compute it, add the values of readings (T) and divide by the number of readings (n). Therefore,

$$\text{Mean} = \frac{T}{n}$$

Median   the middle reading of a set. To find it, draw a dispersion graph of the values. If you have seven readings, the median is the fourth from either extreme. If you have six readings, it is the mid-point between the third and fourth readings.

Mode   the most commonly occurring reading (e.g. see Fig. A.1).

You can observe from Fig. A.1 that the mean sometimes signifies little since, in this case, no actual readings are found at that value. Measures of the 'spread' of data are therefore important in describing the set.

Measures of the spread of data

Variance   Having established the mean, it would be useful to know the variation of each of the members of the data set from this figure. To find this, the variance is computed. The

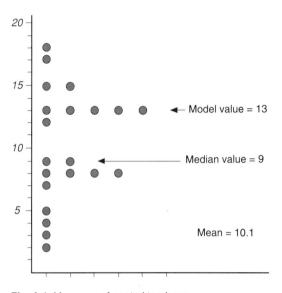

Fig. A.1 Measures of central tendency

formula for this is:

$$\frac{\Sigma(x - \bar{x})^2}{N}$$

where Σ = the sum of
x = the value of the reading
$\bar{x}$ = the mean value
N = the number of readings

In other words, the variance is the mean of the squared deviations from the mean. The square is used because some of the deviations would be positive and some negative. When either of these values is squared, it gives a positive figure.

Standard deviation   If you were dealing with degrees Celsius as your data, the variance would be expressed in terms of, for example, two squared degrees Celsius. This is obviously meaningless, so a further step would be to find the square root of the variance. In other words,

$$\sigma = \sqrt{\frac{\Sigma(x - \bar{x})^2}{N}}$$

where σ = the standard deviation (also written as s; other terms as in variance).

The normal distribution   Many statistical tests rely on the observation that, given a large enough number of readings, a histogram of the frequency of those readings would resemble a bell ('the bell-shaped curve') as in Fig. A.2. If this is the case, then certain important mathematical properties of the data can be inferred.

68% of all data in this set would fall between the mean ± one standard deviation. 95% would fall between ± 1.96 standard deviations and 99% would fall between ± 2.56 standard deviations of the mean.

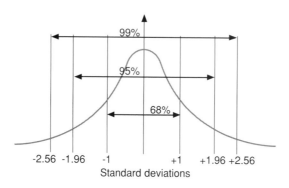

Fig. A.2 The normal distribution

Standard scores (or z scores)
In any data set, the values of the data may have changed over time (e.g. one set of readings may be in Fahrenheit and one in Celsius). In order to compare the distributions of two different sets of data, or where units are unknown, z scores are computed. To do this, subtract the mean from the value of the reading, then divide by the standard deviation. In other words,

$$z = \frac{x - \bar{x}}{\sigma}$$

All the foregoing measures of dispersion are for distributions which have a range of values. Sometimes, as in market research data when people are asked to respond either 'Yes' or 'No', there are only two choices. The resulting distribution is called a **binomial distribution** and the formulae used for variance and standard deviation are slightly different.

For a binomial distribution:

$$\text{variance} = p(100 - p)$$

$$\text{standard deviation} = \sqrt{p(100 - p)}$$

where p is the % saying 'yes'.
$(100 - p)$ is the % saying 'no'.

Implications
Standard errors   If we use sampling techniques, as we do very frequently in geography (see p. 223), we need to know how close to the real situation our estimate of the mean lies. To do this, we use the standard deviation for the *sample*, which, to separate it from the standard deviation (see above) is known as the standard error of the mean

$$\text{Standard error of the mean} = \frac{\sigma}{\sqrt{n}}$$

where n = the number of readings in the sample.

As an example, a sample of $n = 200$ men in the UK report their weekly beer consumption as follows:

$$\text{Mean} = \bar{x} = 5.6 \text{ pints}$$

$$\text{Standard deviation} = \sigma = 2.1 \text{ pints}$$

$$\text{Sample size} = n = 200$$

$$\therefore \text{Standard error of the mean}$$

$$= \frac{2.1}{\sqrt{200}} = 0.148 \text{ pints}$$

You will remember from the work on standard deviations that 95% of the readings will lie between plus or minus 1.96 standard deviations of the mean. Applying this to the beer consumption statistics, we can say that the true mean of the population will have a 95% chance of falling in the range: sample mean (5.6 pints) ± 1.96 standard errors of the mean

i.e. $x \pm 1.96s$

At the 99% confidence level, it would be $x \pm 2.58s$.

For the example quoted, the 95% confidence limits for the mean $x = 5.6$ are given by

$$5.6 \pm 1.96 \times \frac{2.1}{\sqrt{200}}$$

$$= 5.6 \pm 1.96 \times 0.148$$

$$= 5.6 \pm 0.29$$

In other words, there is a 95% probability that the true mean of the population is between 5.31 and 5.89 pints.

Significance testing A survey of 2000 people in 1991 showed that 30% would like to see a new restaurant located near Reading Station. A similar survey in 1992 showed that 28.2% would support such a venture. Was there a significant change between the two dates?

The sampling error on a response of 30% in a survey of 2000 is plus or minus 2% (see Fig. A.3). To find whether a change of 1.8% ($30\% - 28.2\%$) between the two dates is significant, work out the standard error for the difference between the two percentages.

$$\text{Standard error } (p_1 - p_2) = \sqrt{xy\left(\frac{1}{n_1} + \frac{1}{n_2}\right)}$$

where p_1 is the first percentage,

p_2 is the second percentage,

n_1 and n_2 are the respective sample sizes

$$x = \frac{n_1 p_1 + n_2 p_2}{n_1 + n_2}$$

$$y = 100 - x$$

The significance is worked out by comparing the actual difference in the percentages with the standard error, i.e.

$$z = \frac{p_1 - p_2}{\text{standard error } (p_1 - p_2)}$$

If z is equal to or greater than 1.96, we say that the difference is significant at the 5% level. In this case,

$$x = \frac{(2000 \times 30) + (2000 \times 28.2)}{2000 + 2000} = 29.1$$

$$y = 100 - 29.1 = 70.9$$

Standard error $(p_1 - p_2)$

$$= \sqrt{(29.1)(70.9)\left(\frac{1}{2000} + \frac{1}{2000}\right)}$$

$$= \sqrt{2.063}$$

$$= 1.44$$

$$z = \frac{30 - 28.2}{1.44}$$

$$= 1.25$$

The value of z is less than the critical value of 1.96, so we cannot say that there has been a significant change (at the 95% confidence level) between the two dates.

Confidence limits

If 68% of people in a sample said that they ate takeaway food regularly and 40% said they ate out at restaurants regularly, can we be sure that there was a real difference between these two figures? In order to find out, we need to know the size of the sample. If it were 300, then we have all the figures to substitute into the standard error formula, which is

$$\text{S.E.} = \sqrt{\frac{p\% (100 - p\%)}{n}}$$

where p was the percentage responding affirmatively and n was the sample size.

For the above example, the first S.E. would be

$$\sqrt{\frac{68(32)}{300}} = 2.69$$

The second would be

$$\sqrt{\frac{40(60)}{300}} = 2.83$$

The standard error figure is then multiplied by 1.96 to say that, at the 95% confidence level, the actual confidence limits for those eating takeaways regularly were

$$68\% \pm (2.69 \times 1.96) = 68\% \pm 5.27\%$$
$$= \text{from } 62.73\% \text{ to } 73.27\%$$

For those who ate out, the limits were

$$40\% \pm (2.83 \times 1.96) = 40\% \pm 5.55\%$$
$$= \text{from } 34.45\% \text{ to } 45.55\%$$

Because the two ranges do not overlap, you can confidently say that there is a real difference between the numbers who eat takeaway meals and those who eat out.

2. Other techniques

Sample size
There are formulae for deciding the sample size required for a particular survey, but the easiest way to decide on both the size and what it means for the confidence limits is to use the table (Fig. A.3). For example, reading from this table, if a sample of 200 people were used and 98% of them said they used a particular shopping centre, the real figure (at the 95% confidence level) actually lies between 100% (i.e. 98% + 2%) and 96% (98% − 2%). The decision on sample size should in fact be

Fig. A.3 Sample size calculator – range of error of estimates of population with one characteristic at 95% confidence limits (percentage plus or minus)

Percentage affirmative	Sample sizes												
	25	50	100	200	300	400	500	800	1000	2000	5000	25 000	50 000
98% or 2%	5.6	4.0	2.8	2.0	1.6	1.4	1.3	0.98	0.9	0.61	0.4	0.18	0.11
97% or 3%	6.8	4.9	3.4	2.4	2.0	1.7	1.5	1.2	1.1	0.75	0.49	0.22	0.14
96% or 4%	7.8	5.6	3.9	2.8	2.3	2.0	1.8	1.4	1.3	0.86	0.56	0.25	0.16
95% or 5%	8.7	6.2	4.4	3.1	2.5	2.2	2.0	1.5	1.4	0.96	0.62	0.27	0.17
94% or 6%	9.5	6.8	4.8	3.4	2.8	2.4	2.1	1.7	1.5	1.0	0.68	0.3	0.19
92% or 8%	10.8	7.7	5.4	3.8	3.1	2.7	2.4	1.9	1.7	1.2	0.77	0.34	0.22
90% or 10%	12.0	8.5	6.0	4.3	3.5	3.0	2.7	2.1	1.9	1.3	0.85	0.38	0.24
88% or 12%	13.0	9.2	6.5	4.6	3.8	3.3	2.9	2.3	2.1	1.4	0.92	0.41	0.26
85% or 15%	14.3	10.1	7.1	5.1	4.1	3.6	3.2	2.5	2.3	1.6	1.0	0.45	0.29
80% or 20%	16.0	11.4	8.0	5.7	4.6	4.0	3.6	2.8	2.5	1.8	1.1	0.5	0.32
75% or 25%	17.3	12.3	8.7	6.1	5.0	4.3	3.9	3.0	2.8	1.9	1.2	0.55	0.35
70% or 30%	18.3	13.0	9.2	6.5	5.3	4.6	4.1	3.2	2.9	2.0	1.3	0.58	0.37
65% or 35%	19.1	13.5	9.5	6.8	5.5	4.8	4.3	3.3	3.1	2.1	1.4	0.6	0.38
60% or 40%	19.6	13.9	9.8	7.0	5.7	4.9	4.4	3.4	3.1	2.2	1.4	0.62	0.39
55% or 45%	19.8	14.1	9.9	7.0	5.8	5.0	4.5	3.5	3.2	2.2	1.4	0.62	0.4
50%	20.0	14.2	10.0	7.1	5.8	5.0	4.5	3.5	3.2	2.2	1.4	0.63	0.4

made by reading across the 50% row (the 'worst case'). If you would be satisfied with a maximum margin of error of plus or minus 7.1% on any survey, a sample of 200 would be acceptable. Note that predictions from a small sample are unreliable and should be used with great care.

Moving means
Moving means are used to even out the fluctuations in a pattern and therefore show a trend in data. They are plotted on a graph using the average (mean) of three or more records. If five-year moving means are used, the sum of the data for the five years is computed, divided by five and the resultant figure plotted for the third year (the central

point). The first record is then dropped from the data, the sixth added, the computation repeated and the result plotted for the fourth year, and so on.

Chi squared test
The chi squared test is used to compare observed data with theory (expected data). It is a 'goodness of fit' test which uses frequency figures arranged in 'cells' as in Fig. A.4. The top figure in each 'cell' is the one which has been observed. The lower one is the 'expected' value. This is found by using the following formula:

$$\text{Expected frequency} = \frac{\text{row total} \times \text{column total}}{\text{overall total}}$$

Age group	HANDICAPS AT EARLEY GOLF CLUB			
	0 - 5	6 - 12	13 - 20	Total
15-25	2 / 8	16 / 9	10 / 11	28
26-35	20 / 16	16 / 18	20 / 22	56
36+	25 / 23	20 / 25	35 / 32	80
Total	47	52	65	164

Observed value – this means that, at Earley Golf Club, 25 people over the age of 36 had a handicap of between 0 and 5.

Expected value – this is computed by the raw total (80) multiplied by the column total (47) divided by the grand total (164).

Fig. A.4 A chi squared table

The expected frequencies represent the 'null hypothesis'.

The expected frequencies represent the 'null hypothesis': this is what the figures would be like if there was nothing influencing them to create an unexpectedly uneven distribution. Once the table has been completed, the value of the chi squared (χ^2) statistic is found by using the formula

$$\chi^2 = \sum \frac{(O - E - 0.5)^2}{E}$$

where E = the expected frequencies

O = the observed frequencies

Σ = the sum of

To use this formula, follow these steps:

(i) Complete a table of observed and expected frequencies.

(ii) Find the difference between the observed and expected frequencies in each cell, always taking the smaller number from the larger. Take 0.5 from each answer (Yates' correction) – this will give you a more conservative estimate of chi squared.

(iii) Square each cell value.

(iv) Divide the cell total by the frequency expected for that particular cell.

(v) Add the cell values to obtain a total.

(vi) Assess the value of chi squared by comparing the computed value with the critical values in Fig. A.5. The degrees of freedom (*df*) are found by using the formula:

$$df = (\text{no. of rows} - 1)(\text{no. of columns} - 1)$$

(vii) State the conclusion. If the value of chi squared equals or exceeds the value shown in Fig. A.5, the null hypothesis can be rejected.

Spearman's rank correlation

When two sets of data are compared, it may be found that one *correlates* well with the other, i.e. as one set changes, so does the other. Three possible correlations are shown as scattergraphs in Fig. A.6.

df	Level of significance			
	0.05	0.025	0.005	0.0005
1	2.706	3.841	6.635	10.83
2	4.605	5.991	9.210	13.82
3	6.251	7.815	11.34	16.27
4	7.779	9.488	13.28	18.47
5	9.236	11.07	15.09	20.52
6	10.64	12.59	16.81	22.46
7	12.02	14.07	18.48	24.32
8	13.36	15.51	20.09	26.12
9	14.68	16.92	21.67	27.88
10	15.99	18.31	23.21	29.59
11	17.28	19.68	24.73	31.26
12	18.55	21.03	26.22	32.91
13	19.81	22.36	27.69	34.53
14	21.06	23.68	29.14	36.12
15	22.31	25.00	30.58	37.70
16	23.54	26.30	32.00	39.25
17	24.77	27.59	33.41	40.79
18	25.99	28.87	34.81	42.31
19	27.20	30.14	36.19	43.82
20	28.41	31.41	37.57	45.31

Fig. A.5 Critical values of χ^2. χ^2 must be equal to or more than the stated value to be significant

The degree of association between the two sets of data can also be assessed by computing a correlation coefficient, which gives a mathematical measure of how much one set of figures changes in line with changes in the other set. Figure A.7 shows the possible range of figures for this correlation coefficient.

One measure of correlation is achieved by the Spearman's rank correlation. To use this, rank the figures in the two data sets. Rank 1 is the highest figure, rank 2 the second highest and so on.

Then substitute into the formula:

$$R_s = 1 - \frac{6\Sigma d^2}{n(n^2 - 1)}$$

where d = the squared values of the differences between the ranked scores added together

n = the number of paired ranks

Fig. A.6 Three possible correlations

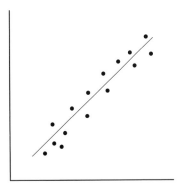

Good positive correlation

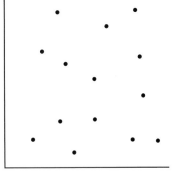

No correlation

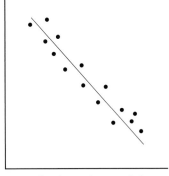

Good negative correlation

225

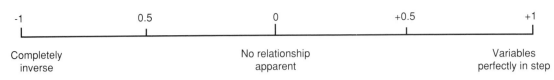

Fig. A.7 Correlation coefficient scale

Label	Score of one variable (A)	Score of second variable (B)	Ranked scores of A	Ranked scores of B	A − B	(A − B)²
a						
b						
c						
d						
						Sum of (A − B)²

Fig. A.8 A framework for computing Spearman's rank correlation coefficient

Computation will be facilitated by drawing up a table as in Fig. A.8. The significance of the statistic should then be found by comparing the answer with the values in Fig. A.9 to see how well they relate to one another.

Scattergraphs

Scattergraphs are useful for setting up certain statistical tests and assessing the relevance of their results. They are graphs showing how two sets of data relate to one another. Figure A.10 gives an example.

Spearman's rank correlation could be used to assess the degree of relationship between the two sets of data in this case. If, however, a scattergraph shows a change in direction of association between the two sets, as in Fig. A.11, Spearman's rank should *not* be used but another technique, such as Pearson's product-moment correlation, used instead.

Once such a technique has been used, an idea of the type of association that exists between the data sets can be given. There may well be 'residuals' shown up by the scatter-graph which make the statistical relationship between the two sets less impressive than it might otherwise be. A scattergraph can be used to identify these residuals and attempt an explanation of their existence, as in Fig. A.12.

Indices

Another method of tracking changes over time whilst suppressing major fluctuations is to use indices. For a certain date, one key figure in the data is given the index of 100 and all the other figures are expressed as a percentage of this. For example:

Production of A, 1990 = 220 tonnes
Production of B, 1990 = 160 tonnes
Production of C, 1990 = 260 tonnes

Let A, 1990 = index 100

	Level of significance			
N	0.05	0.025	0.01	0.005
5	0.900	1.000	1.00	—
6	0.829	0.886	0.943	1.000
7	0.714	0.786	0.893	0.929
8	0.643	0.738	0.833	0.881
9	0.600	0.683	0.783	0.833
10	0.564	0.648	0.746	0.794
12	0.506	0.591	0.712	0.777
14	0.456	0.544	0.645	0.715
16	0.425	0.506	0.601	0.665
18	0.399	0.475	0.564	0.625
20	0.377	0.450	0.534	0.591
22	0.359	0.428	0.508	0.562
24	0.343	0.409	0.485	0.537
26	0.329	0.392	0.465	0.515
28	0.317	0.377	0.448	0.496
30	0.306	0.364	0.432	0.478

Fig. A.9 Critical values of Spearman's rank correlation coefficient, rho. Rho must be equal to or more than the stated value to be significant

N = the number of paired scores used.
Treat a negative value of rho as if it were positive, when using the table, but when interpreting it don't forget that it will indicate an inverse relationship.

Therefore

$$B = \frac{160 \times 100}{220}$$

$$= 72.7$$

$$C = \frac{260 \times 100}{220}$$

$$= 118.2$$

Indices are usually used to track change over time, but sometimes figures get very large, or very small, depending on the factor being tracked. In this case, re-indexing usually occurs. The figure reached by the factor that was originally index 100 is re-indexed to 100 and all the others are dealt with in the way outlined above. This has occurred several times with the production figures reported by the FAO.

Lorenz curves

Lorenz curves show how evenly distributed a particular item is. The line of even distribution, where each area in a country, for example, has an equal share of wealth, is the diagonal (d) in Fig. A.13. The more the cumulative percentage graph of the distribution of a particular item diverges from this, the less equal is the distribution.

Topological maps

A map can be drawn to represent the data for any geographical area, displaying the density or distribution data in a form which also represents the rough shape of the areas concerned. To construct such a map, use squared paper as a base. Compute the number of units to be represented, then use a scale to enable you to represent the largest and smallest on the same map. Shade in the required number of squares to represent both the shape of the area concerned and the relative size of the data. The completed map looks like a pixel map (see the section on remote sensing in Chapter 1) where one pixel represents one unit. An example is given in Fig. A.14.

Map distortions

Maps are usually drawn using a distance scale. For example, the O.S. 1:50 000 map uses a scale of 1 cm = 50 000 cm, or 2 cm = 1 km. An idea of how an area is 'viewed' under certain other circumstances can be achieved by using not a distance scale, but some other measurement such as time or cost. The following example (Fig. A.15) is of an island,

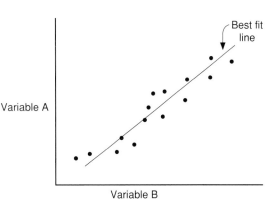

Fig. A.10 A scattergraph

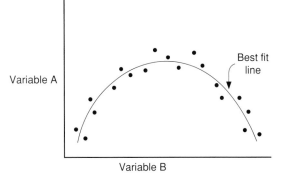

Fig. A.11 A scattergraph with a best fit line that necessitates use of a different correlation technique

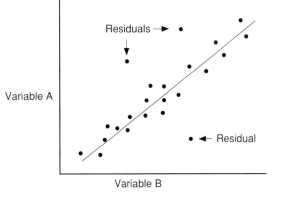

Fig. A.12 A scattergraph showing residuals

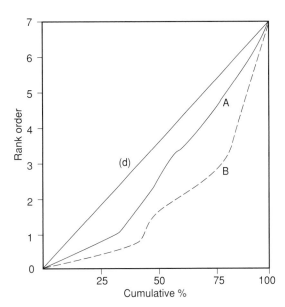

Fig. A.13 Lorenz curves – B is less evenly distributed than A

227

Fig. A.14 A topological map of population by standard region

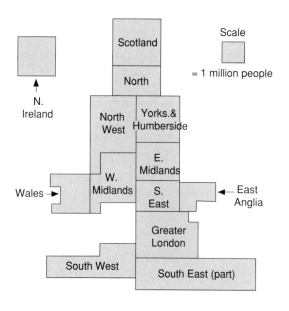

drawn to scale and then 'transformed' by using the travelling time data instead of distance. Such maps are useful to track changes in communications networks over time and to explain people's perceptions of an area.

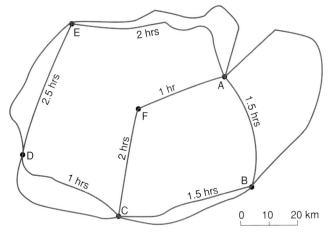

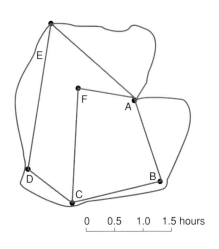

Fig. A.15 An island – reality and time-distortion

The times are the average time by public transport between towns in hours

A time–distance distortion of the island

Index